MECHANICS

MECHANICS

by
KEITH R. SYMON
University of Wisconsin

ADDISON—WESLEY PUBLISHING COMPANY, Inc.

READING, MASSACHUSETTS

To my Father

PREFACE

This text is intended as the basis for an intermediate course in mechanics at the undergraduate level. Such a course, as essential preparation for advanced work in physics, has several major objectives. It must develop in the student a thorough understanding of the fundamental principles of mechanics. It should treat in detail certain specific problems of primary importance in physics; for example, the harmonic oscillator, and the motion of a particle under a central force. The problems suggested and those worked out in the text have been chosen with regard to their interest and importance in physics, as well as to their instructive value. This book contains sufficient material for a two-semester course, and is arranged in such a way that, with appropriate omissions, it can be used for a single three- or four-hour course for one semester. The author has used this material, with the omission of Chapters 8 and 9, and of a number of sections from earlier chapters, in a four-hour course in mechanics.

The choice of topics and their treatment throughout the book are intended to emphasize the modern point of view. Applications to atomic physics are made wherever possible, with an indication as to the extent of the validity of the results of classical mechanics. The inadequacies in classical mechanics are carefully pointed out, and the points of departure for quantum mechanics and for relativistic mechanics are indicated. The development, except for the last chapter, proceeds directly from Newton's laws of motion, which form a suitable basis from which to attack most mechanical problems. Some problems which are most easily treated by more advanced methods have been omitted; for example, the motion of a rigid body in space, which is most elegantly treated with the use of tensor algebra.

An important objective of a first course in mechanics is to train the student to think about physical phenomena in mathematical terms. Most students have a fairly good intuitive feeling for mechanical phenomena in a qualitative way. The study of mechanics should aim at developing an almost equally intuitive feeling for the precise mathematical formulation of physical problems, and for the physical interpretation of the mathematical solutions. The examples treated in the text have been worked out so as to integrate, as far as possible, the mathematical treatment with the physical interpretation. After working an assigned problem, the student should study it until he is sure he understands the physical interpretation of every feature of the mathematical treatment. He should decide whether the result agrees with his physical intuition about the problem. If the answer is fairly complicated, he should try to see whether it can be simplified in certain special or limiting cases. He should try to formulate and solve similar problems on his own.

Only a knowledge of differential and integral calculus has been presupposed. Mathematical concepts beyond those treated in the first year of calculus are introduced and explained as needed. A previous course in elementary differential equations or vector analysis may be helpful, but it is the author's experience that students with an adequate preparation in algebra and calculus are able to handle the elementary vector analysis and differential equations needed for this course with the explanations provided herein. A physics student is likely to get more out of his advanced courses in mathematics if he has previously encountered these concepts in physics.

The text has been written so as to afford maximum flexibility in the selection and arrangement of topics to be covered. With the exception of Chapter 1, the first five sections of Chapter 2, Sections 1, 3, 4, 5, 7, 8, 9, and 12 of Chapter 3, and Sections 1 through 3 of Chapter 4, almost any section or group of sections can be postponed or omitted without prejudice to the understanding of the remaining material.

In the first chapter, the basic concepts of mechanics are reviewed, and the laws of mechanics and of gravitation are formulated and applied to a few simple examples. The second chapter undertakes a fairly thorough study of the problem of one-dimensional motion. The chapter concludes with a study of the harmonic oscillator, as probably the most important example of one-dimensional motion. Use is made of complex numbers to represent oscillating quantities. The last section, on the principle of superposition, makes some use of Fourier series, and may be omitted or, better, passed over with a brief indication of the significance of the principle of superposition and the way in which Fourier series are used to treat the problem of an arbitrary applied force function.

Chapter 3 begins with a development of vector algebra and its use in describing motions in a plane or in space. Bold-face letters are used for vectors. Section 3–6 is a brief introduction to vector analysis, which is used very little in this book except in Chapter 8, and it may be omitted or skimmed rapidly if Chapter 8 and one or two proofs in Chapters 3 and 6 are omitted. The author feels there is some advantage in introducing the student to the concepts and notation of vector analysis at this stage, where the level of treatment is fairly easy; in later courses where the physical concepts and mathematical treatment become more difficult, it will be well if the notations are already familiar. The theorems stating the time rates of change of momentum, energy, and angular momentum are derived for a moving particle, and several problems are discussed, of which motion under central forces receives major attention. Examples are taken from astronomical and from atomic problems.

In Chapter 4, the conservation laws of energy, momentum, and angular momentum are derived, with emphasis on their position as cornerstones of present-day physics. They are then applied to typical problems, particularly collision problems. The two-body problem is solved, and the motion of two coupled harmonic oscillators is worked out. The general theory of coupled oscillations is best treated by means of linear transformations in vector spaces, but the behavior of coupled oscillating systems is too important to be omitted altogether from an intermediate course. The rigid body is discussed in Chapter 5 as a special kind of system of particles. Only rotation about a fixed axis is treated; the more general study of the motion of a rigid body is left to a later course, where more advanced methods are used. The section on statics treats the problem of the reduction of a system of forces to an equivalent simpler system. Elementary treatments of the equilibrium of beams, flexible strings, and of fluids are given in Sections 5-9, 5-10, and 5-11.

The theory of gravitation is studied in some detail in Chapter 6. The last section, on the gravitational field equations, may be omitted without disturbing the continuity of the remaining material. The laws of motion in moving coordinate systems are worked out in Chapter 7, and applied to motion on the rotating earth and to the motion of a system of charged particles in a magnetic field. Particular attention is paid to the status in Newtonian mechanics of the "fictitious forces" which appear when moving coordinate systems are introduced, and to the role to be played by such forces in the general theory of relativity.

In Chapter 8, an introductory treatment of vibrating strings and of the motion of fluids is presented, with emphasis on the fundamental concepts and mathematical methods which are used in treating the mechanics of continuous media. The last chapter, on Lagrange's equations, is included as an introduction to the methods of advanced dynamics. In a shorter course, either or both of the last two chapters may be omitted without destroying the unity of the course.

The problems at the end of each chapter are arranged in the order in which the material is covered in the chapter, for convenience in assignment. They vary considerably in difficulty. Some are fairly easy; a few are probably too difficult for the average college junior or senior to solve without some assistance.

Grateful acknowledgment is made to Professor Francis W. Sears of M.I.T. and to Professor George H. Vineyard of Brookhaven National Laboratory for their many helpful suggestions.

K. R. S.

February 1953

CONTENTS

CONTENTS xiii

CHAPTER 1

ELEMENTS OF NEWTONIAN MECHANICS

1-1 Mechanics, an exact science. When we say that physics is an exact science, we mean that its laws are expressed in the form of mathematical equations which describe and predict the results of precise quantitative measurements. The advantage in a quantitative physical theory is not alone the practical one that it gives us the power accurately to predict and to control natural phenomena. By a comparison of the results of accurate measurements with the numerical predictions of the theory, we can gain considerable confidence that the theory is correct, and we can determine in what respects it needs to be modified. It is often possible to explain a given phenomenon in several rough qualitative ways, and if we are content with that, it may be impossible to decide which theory is correct. But if a theory can be given which predicts correctly the results of measurements to four or five (or even two or three) significant figures, the theory can hardly be very far wrong. Rough agreement might be a coincidence, but close agreement is unlikely to be. Furthermore, there have been many cases in the history of science when small but significant discrepancies between theory and accurate measurements have led to the development of new and more far-reaching theories. Such slight discrepancies would not even have been detected if we had been content with a merely qualitative explanation of the phenomena.

The symbols which are to appear in the equations that express the laws of a science must represent quantities which can be expressed in numerical terms. Hence the concepts in terms of which an exact science is to be developed must be given precise numerical meanings. If a definition of a quantity (mass, for example) is to be given, the definition must be such as to specify precisely how the value of the quantity is to be determined in any given case. A qualitative remark about its meaning may be helpful, but is not sufficient as a definition. As a matter of fact, it is probably not possible to give an ideally precise definition of every concept appearing in a physical theory. Nevertheless, when we write down a mathematical equation, the presumption is that the symbols appearing in it have precise meanings, and we should strive to make our ideas as clear and precise as possible, and to recognize at what points there is a lack of precision or clarity. Sometimes a new concept can be defined in terms of others whose meanings are known, in which case there is no problem. For example,

$$\text{momentum} = \text{mass} \times \text{velocity}$$

1

gives a perfectly precise definition of "momentum" provided "mass" and "velocity" are assumed to be precisely defined already. But this kind of definition will not do for all terms in a theory, since we must start somewhere with a set of basic concepts or "primitive" terms whose meanings are assumed known. The first concepts to be introduced in a theory cannot be defined in the above way, since at first we have nothing to put on the right side of the equation. The meanings of these primitive terms must be made clear by some means that lies outside of the physical theories being set up. We might, for example, simply use the terms over and over until their meanings become clear. This is the way babies learn a language and probably, to some extent, freshman physics students learn the same way. We might define all primitive terms by stating their meaning in terms of observation and experiment. In particular, nouns designating measurable quantities, like force, mass, etc., may be defined by specifying the operational process for measuring them. One school of thought holds that all physical terms should be defined in this way. Or we might simply state what the primitive terms are, with a rough indication of their physical meaning, and then let the meaning be determined more precisely by the laws and postulates we lay down and the rules that we give for interpreting theoretical results in terms of experimental situations. This is the most convenient and flexible way, and is the way physical theories are usually set up. It has the disadvantage that we are never sure that our concepts have been given a precise meaning. It is left to experience to decide not only whether our laws are correct, but even whether the concepts we use have a precise meaning. The modern theories of relativity and quanta arise as much from fuzziness in classical concepts as from inaccuracies in classical laws.

Historically, mechanics is the earliest branch of physics to be developed as an exact science. The laws of levers and of fluids in static equilibrium were known to Greek scientists in the third century B.C. The tremendous development of physics in the last three centuries began with the discovery of the laws of mechanics by Galileo and Newton. The laws of mechanics as formulated by Isaac Newton in the middle of the seventeenth century and the laws of electricity and magnetism as formulated by James Clerk Maxwell about two hundred years later are the two basic theories of classical physics. Relativistic physics, which began with the work of Einstein in 1905, and quantum physics, as based upon the work of Heisenberg and Schroedinger in 1925–1926, require a modification and reformulation of mechanics and electrodynamics in terms of new physical concepts. Nevertheless, modern physics builds on the foundations laid by classical physics, and a clear understanding of the principles of classical mechanics and electrodynamics is still essential in the study of relativistic and quantum physics. Furthermore, in the vast majority of practical applications of mechanics to the various branches of engineering and to astronomy, the laws of classical mechanics can still be applied.   Except when bodies travel at speeds approaching the speed of light, or when enormous masses or enormous distances are involved, relativistic mechanics gives the same results as classical mechanics; indeed, it must, since we know from experience that classical mechanics gives correct results in ordinary applications. Similarly, quantum mechanics should and does agree with classical mechanics except when applied to physical systems of molecular size or smaller. Indeed, one of the chief guiding principles in formulating new physical theories is the requirement that they must agree with the older theories when applied to those phenomena where the older theories are known to be correct.

Mechanics is the study of the motions of material bodies.   Mechanics may be divided into three subdisciplines, *kinematics*, *dynamics*, and *statics*. Kinematics is the study and description of the possible motions of material bodies.   Dynamics is the study of the laws which determine, among all possible motions, which motion will actually take place in any given case.   In dynamics we introduce the concept of force.   The central problem of dynamics is to determine for any physical system the motions which will take place under the action of given forces.   Statics is the study of forces and systems of forces, with particular reference to systems of forces which act on bodies at rest.

We may also subdivide the study of mechanics according to the kind of physical system to be studied.   This is, in general, the basis for the outline of the present book.   The simplest physical system, and the one we shall study first, is a single particle.   Next we shall study the motion of a system of particles.   A rigid body may be treated as a special kind of system of particles.   Finally, we shall study the motions of continuous media, elastic and plastic substances, solids, liquids, and gases.

A great many of the applications of classical mechanics may be based directly on Newton's laws of motion.   All of the problems studied in this book, except in the last chapter, are treated in this way.   There are, however, a number of other ways of formulating the principles of classical mechanics.   The equations of Lagrange and of Hamilton are examples. They are not new physical theories, for they may be derived from Newton's laws, but they are different ways of expressing the same physical theory. They use more advanced mathematical concepts, they are in some respects more elegant than Newton's formulation, and they are in some cases more powerful in that they allow the solutions of some problems whose solution based directly on Newton's laws would be very difficult.   The more different ways we know to formulate a physical theory, the better chance we have of learning how to modify it to fit new kinds of phenomena as they are discovered.   This is one of the main reasons for the importance of the more advanced formulations of mechanics.   They are a starting point for the newer theories of relativity and quanta.

1–2 Kinematics, the description of motion. Mechanics is the science which studies the motions of physical bodies. We must first describe motions. Easiest to describe are the motions of a particle, which is an object whose size and internal structure are negligible for the problem with which we are concerned. The earth, for example, could be regarded as a particle for most problems in planetary motion, but certainly not for terrestrial problems. We can describe the position of a particle by specifying a point in space. This may be done by giving three coordinates. Usually, rectangular coordinates are used. For a particle moving along a straight line (Chapter 2) only one coordinate need be given. To describe the motion of a particle, we specify the coordinates as functions of time:

$$\text{one dimension: } x(t),$$
$$\text{three dimensions: } x(t), y(t), z(t). \tag{1-1}$$

The basic problem of classical mechanics is to find ways to determine functions like these which specify the positions of objects as functions of time, for any mechanical situation. The physical meaning of the function $x(t)$ is contained in the rules which tell us how to measure the coordinate x of a particle at a time t. Assuming we know the meaning of $x(t)$, or at least that it has a meaning (this assumption, which we make in classical mechanics, is not quite correct according to quantum mechanics), we can define the x-component of velocity v_x at time t as*

$$v_x = \dot{x} = \frac{dx}{dt}, \tag{1-2}$$

and, similarly,

$$v_y = \dot{y} = \frac{dy}{dt}, \quad v_z = \dot{z} = \frac{dz}{dt}.$$

We now define the components of acceleration a_x, a_y, a_z as the derivatives of the velocity components with respect to time (we list several equivalent notations which may be used):

$$a_x = \dot{v}_x = \frac{dv_x}{dt} = \ddot{x} = \frac{d^2x}{dt^2},$$
$$a_y = \dot{v}_y = \frac{dv_y}{dt} = \ddot{y} = \frac{d^2y}{dt^2}, \tag{1-3}$$
$$a_z = \dot{v}_z = \frac{dv_z}{dt} = \ddot{z} = \frac{d^2z}{dt^2}.$$

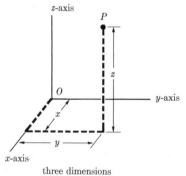

three dimensions

one dimension

Fig. 1–1. Rectangular coordinates specifying the position of a particle P relative to an origin O.

---

* We shall denote a time derivative either by d/dt or by a dot. Both notations are given in Eqs. (1–2).

For many purposes some other system of coordinates may be more convenient for specifying the position of a particle. When other coordinate systems are used, appropriate formulas for components of velocity and acceleration must be worked out. Spherical, cylindrical, and plane polar coordinates will be discussed in Chapter 3. For problems in two and three dimensions, the concept of a vector is very useful as a means of representing positions, velocities, and accelerations. A systematic development of vector algebra will be given in Section 3–1.

To describe a system of particles, we may specify the coordinates of each particle in any convenient coordinate system. Or we may introduce other kinds of coordinates, for example, the coordinates of the center of mass, or the distance between two particles. If the particles form a rigid body, the three coordinates of its center of mass and three angular coordinates specifying its orientation in space are sufficient to specify its position. To describe the motion of continuous matter, for example a fluid, we would need to specify the density $\rho(x,y,z,t)$ at any point (x,y,z) in space at each instant t in time, and the velocity vector $v(x,y,z,t)$ with which the matter at the point (x,y,z) is moving at time t. Appropriate devices for describing the motion of physical systems will be introduced as needed.

1–3 Dynamics. Mass and force. Experience leads us to believe that the motions of physical bodies are controlled by interactions between them and their surroundings. Observations of the behavior of projectiles and of objects sliding across smooth, well-lubricated surfaces suggest the idea that changes in the velocity of a body are produced by interaction with its surroundings. A body isolated from all interactions would have a constant velocity. Hence, in formulating the laws of dynamics, we focus our attention on accelerations.

Let us imagine two bodies interacting with each other and otherwise isolated from interaction with their surroundings. As a rough approximation to this situation, imagine two boys, not necessarily of equal size, engaged in a tug of war over a rigid pole on smooth ice. Although no two actual bodies can ever be isolated completely from interactions with all other bodies, this is the simplest kind of situation to think about and one for which we expect the simplest mathematical laws. Careful experiments with actual bodies lead us to conclusions as to what we should observe if we could achieve ideal isolation of two bodies. We should observe that the two bodies are always accelerated in opposite directions, and that the ratio of their accelerations is constant for any particular pair of bodies no matter how strongly they may be pushing or pulling each other. If we measure the coordinates x_1 and x_2 of the two bodies along the line of their accelerations, then

$$\ddot{x}_1/\ddot{x}_2 = -k_{12}, \qquad (1\text{–}4)$$

where k_{12} is a positive constant characteristic of the two bodies concerned. The negative sign expresses the fact that the accelerations are in opposite directions.

Furthermore, we find that in general the larger or heavier or more massive body is accelerated the least. We find, in fact, that the ratio k_{12} is proportional to the ratio of the weight of body 2 to that of body 1. The accelerations of two interacting bodies are inversely proportional to their weights. This suggests the possibility of a dynamical definition of what we shall call the *masses* of bodies in terms of their mutual accelerations. We choose a standard body as a unit mass. The mass of any other body is defined as the ratio of the acceleration of the unit mass to the acceleration of the other body when the two are in interaction:

$$m_i = k_{1i} = -\ddot{x}_1/\ddot{x}_i, \tag{1-5}$$

where m_i is the mass of body i, and body 1 is the standard unit mass.

In order that Eq. (1-5) may be a useful definition, the ratio k_{12} of the mutual accelerations of two bodies must satisfy certain requirements. If the mass defined by Eq. (1-5) is to be a measure of what we vaguely call the amount of matter in a body, then the mass of a body should be the sum of the masses of its parts, and this turns out to be the case to a very high degree of precision. It is not essential, in order to be useful in scientific theories, that physical concepts for which we give precise definitions should correspond closely to any previously held common-sense ideas. However, most precise physical concepts have originated from more or less vague common-sense ideas, and mass is a good example. Later, in the theory of relativity, the concept of mass is somewhat modified, and it is no longer exactly true that the mass of a body is the sum of the masses of its parts.

One requirement which is certainly essential is that the concept of mass be independent of the particular body which happens to be chosen as having unit mass, in the sense that the ratio of two masses will be the same no matter what unit of mass may be chosen. This will be true because of the following relation, which is found experimentally, between the mutual acceleration ratios defined by Eq. (1-4) of any three bodies:

$$k_{12}k_{23}k_{31} = 1. \tag{1-6}$$

Suppose that body 1 is the unit mass. Then if bodies 2 and 3 interact with each other, we find, using Eqs. (1-4), (1-6), and (1-5),

$$\begin{aligned}
\ddot{x}_2/\ddot{x}_3 &= -k_{23} \\
&= -\frac{1}{k_{12}k_{31}} \\
&= -k_{13}/k_{12} \\
&= -m_3/m_2.
\end{aligned} \tag{1-7}$$

The final result contains no explicit reference to body 1, which was taken to be the standard unit mass. Thus the ratio of the masses of any two bodies is the negative inverse of the ratio of their mutual accelerations, independently of the unit of mass chosen.

By Eq. (1–7), we have, for two interacting bodies,

$$m_2\ddot{x}_2 = -m_1\ddot{x}_1. \tag{1–8}$$

This suggests that the quantity (*mass* $\times$ *acceleration*) will be important, and we call this quantity the *force* acting on a body. The acceleration of a body in space has three components, and the three components of force acting on the body are

$$F_x = m\ddot{x}, \quad F_y = m\ddot{y}, \quad F_z = m\ddot{z}. \tag{1–9}$$

The forces which act on a body are of various kinds, electric, magnetic, gravitational, etc., and depend on the behavior of other bodies. In general, forces due to several sources may act on a given body, and it is found that the total force given by Eq. (1–9) is the vector sum of the forces which would be present if each source were present alone.

The theory of electromagnetism is concerned with the problem of determining the electric and magnetic forces exerted by electrical charges and currents upon one another. The theory of gravitation is concerned with the problem of determining the gravitational forces exerted by masses upon one another. The fundamental problem of mechanics is to determine the motions of any mechanical system, given the forces acting on the bodies which make up the system.

1–4 Newton's laws of motion. Isaac Newton was the first to give a complete formulation of the laws of mechanics. Newton stated his famous three laws as follows:*

(1) Every body continues in its state of rest or of uniform motion in a straight line unless it is compelled to change that state by forces impressed upon it.

(2) Rate of change of momentum is proportional to the impressed force, and is in the direction in which the force acts.

(3) To every action there is always opposed an equal reaction.

In the second law, momentum is to be defined as the product of the mass and the velocity of the particle. Momentum, for which we use the symbol p, has three components, defined along x-, y-, and z-axes by the equations

$$p_x = mv_x, \quad p_y = mv_y, \quad p_z = mv_z. \tag{1–10}$$

---

* Isaac Newton, *Mathematical Principles of Natural Philosophy* and his *System of the World*, tr. by F. Cajori (p. 13). Berkeley: University of California Press, 1934.

The first two laws, together with the definition of momentum, Eq. (1–10), and the fact that the mass is constant by Eq. (1–4),* are equivalent to Eqs. (1–9), which express them in mathematical form. The third law states that when two bodies interact, the force exerted on body 1 by body 2 is equal and opposite in direction to that exerted on body 2 by body 1. This law expresses the experimental fact given by Eq. (1–4), and can easily be derived from Eq. (1–4) and from Eqs. (1–5) and (1–9).

The status of Newton's first two laws, or of Eqs. (1–9), is often the subject of dispute. We may regard Eqs. (1–9) as defining force in terms of mass and acceleration. In this case, Newton's first two laws are not laws at all but merely definitions of a new concept to be introduced in the theory. The physical laws are then the laws of gravitation, electromagnetism, etc., which tell us what the forces are in any particular situation. Newton's discovery was not that force equals mass times acceleration, for this is merely a definition of "force." What Newton discovered was that the laws of physics are most easily expressed in terms of the concept of force defined in this way. Newton's third law is still a legitimate physical law expressing the experimental result given by Eq. (1–4) in terms of the concept of force. This point of view toward Newton's first two laws is convenient for many purposes and is often adopted. Its chief disadvantage is that Eqs. (1–9) define only the total force acting on a body, whereas we often wish to speak of the total force as a (vector) sum of component forces of various kinds due to various sources. The whole science of statics, which deals with the forces acting in structures at rest, would be unintelligible if we took Eqs. (1–9) as our definition of force, for all accelerations are zero in a structure at rest.

We may also take the laws of electromagnetism, gravitation, etc., together with the parallelogram law of addition, as defining "force." Equation (1–9) then becomes a law connecting previously defined quantities. This has the disadvantage that the definition of force changes whenever a new kind of force (e.g., nuclear force) is discovered, or whenever modifications are made in electromagnetism or in gravitation. Probably the best plan, the most flexible at least, is to take force as a primitive concept of our theory, perhaps defined operationally in terms of measurements with a spring balance. Then Newton's laws are laws, and so are the laws of theories of special forces like gravitation and electromagnetism.

---

* In the theory of relativity, the mass of a body is not constant, but depends on its velocity. In this case, law (2) and Eqs. (1–9) are not equivalent, and it turns out that law (2) is the correct formulation. Force should then be equated to time rate of change of momentum. The simple definition (1–5) of mass is not correct according to the theory of relativity unless the particles being accelerated move at low velocities.

Aside from the question of procedure in regard to the definition of force, there are other difficulties in Newton's mechanics. The third law is not always true. It fails to hold for electromagnetic forces, for example, when the interacting bodies are far apart or rapidly accelerated and, in fact, it fails for any forces which propagate from one body to another with finite velocities. Fortunately, most of our development is based on the first two laws. Whenever the third law is used, its use will be explicitly noted and the results obtained will be valid only to the extent that the third law holds.

Another difficulty is that the concepts of Newtonian mechanics are not perfectly clear and precise, as indeed no concepts can probably ever be for any theory, although we must develop the theory as if they were. An outstanding example is the fact that no specification is made of the coordinate system with respect to which the accelerations mentioned in the first two laws are to be measured. Newton himself recognized this difficulty but found no very satisfactory way of specifying the correct coordinate system to use. Perhaps the best way to formulate these laws is to say that there is a coordinate system with respect to which they hold, leaving it to experiment to determine the correct coordinate system. It can be shown that if these laws hold in any coordinate system, they hold also in any coordinate system moving uniformly with respect to the first. This is called the principle of Newtonian relativity, and will be proved in Section 7–1, although the reader should find little difficulty in proving it for himself.

Two assumptions which are made throughout classical physics are that the behavior of measuring instruments is unaffected by their state of motion so long as they are not rapidly accelerated, and that it is possible, in principle at least, to devise instruments to measure any quantity with as small an error as we please. These two assumptions fail in extreme cases, the first at very high velocities, the second when very small magnitudes are to be measured. The failure of these assumptions forms the basis of the theory of relativity and the theory of quantum mechanics, respectively. However, for a very wide range of phenomena, Newton's mechanics is correct to a very high degree of accuracy, and forms the starting point at which the modern theories begin. Not only the laws but also the concepts of classical physics must be modified according to the modern theories. However, an understanding of the concepts of modern physics is made easier by a clear understanding of the concepts of classical physics. These difficulties are pointed out here in order that the reader may be prepared to accept later modifications in the theory. This is not to say that Newton himself (or the reader either at this stage) ought to have worried about these matters before setting up his laws of motion. Had he done so, he probably never would have developed his theory at all. It was necessary to make whatever assumptions seemed reasonable in order to get started. Which assumptions needed to be altered, and when, and in what way, could only be determined later by the successes and failures of the theory in predicting experimental results.

1–5 Gravitation. Although there had been previous suggestions that the motions of the planets and of falling bodies on earth might be due to a property of physical bodies by which they attract one another, the first to formulate a mathematical theory of this phenomenon was Isaac Newton. Newton showed, by methods to be considered later, that the motions of the planets could be quantitatively accounted for if he assumed that with every pair of bodies is associated a force of attraction proportional to their masses and inversely proportional to the square of the distance between them. In symbols,

$$F = \frac{Gm_1m_2}{r^2},$$ (1–11)

where m_1, m_2 are the masses of the attracting bodies, r is the distance between them, and G is a universal constant whose value according to experiment is

$$G = 6.66 \times 10^{-8} \text{ cm}^3\text{-sec}^{-2}\text{-gm}^{-1}.$$ (1–12)

For a spherically symmetrical body, we shall show later (Section 6–2) that the force can be computed as if all the mass were at the center. For a small body of mass m at the surface of the earth, the force of gravitation is therefore

$$F = mg,$$ (1–13)

where

$$g = \frac{GM}{R^2} = 980.2 \text{ cm-sec}^{-2},$$ (1–14)

and M is the mass of the earth and R its radius. The quantity g has the dimensions of an acceleration, and we can readily show by Eqs. (1–9) and (1–13) that any freely falling body at the surface of the earth is accelerated downward with an acceleration g.

The fact that the gravitational force on a body is proportional to its mass, rather than to some other constant characterizing the body (e.g., its electric charge), is more or less accidental from the point of view of Newton's theory. This fact is fundamental in the general theory of relativity. The proportionality between gravitational force and mass is probably the reason why the theory of gravitation is ordinarily considered a branch of mechanics, while theories of other kinds of force are not.

Equation (1–13) gives us a more convenient practical way of measuring mass than that contemplated in the original definition (1–5). We may measure a mass by measuring the gravitational force on it, as in a spring balance, or by comparing the gravitational force on it with that on a standard mass, as in the beam or platform balance; in other words, by weighing it.

1-6 Units and dimensions. In setting up a system of units in terms of which to express physical measurements, we first choose arbitrary standard units for a certain set of "fundamental" physical quantities (e.g., mass, length, and time) and then define further derived units in terms of the fundamental units (e.g., the unit of velocity is one unit length per unit of time). It is customary to choose mass, length, and time as the fundamental quantities in mechanics, although there is nothing sacred in this choice. We could equally well choose some other three quantities, or even more or fewer than three quantities, as fundamental.

There are three systems of units in common use, the centimeter-gram-second or cgs system, the meter-kilogram-second or mks system, and the foot-pound-second or English system, the names corresponding to the names of the three fundamental units in each system.* Units for other kinds of physical quantities are obtained from their defining equations by substituting the units for the fundamental quantities which occur. For example, velocity, by Eq. (1–2),

$$v_x = \frac{dx}{dt},$$

is defined as a distance divided by a time. Hence the units of velocity are cm/sec, m/sec, and ft/sec in the three above-mentioned systems, respectively.

Similarly, the reader can show that the units of force in the three systems as given by Eq. (1–9) are gm-cm-sec^{-2}, kgm-m-sec^{-2}, lb-ft-sec^{-2}. These units happen to have the special names dyne, newton, and poundal, respectively. *Gravitational units* of force are sometimes defined by replacing Eqs. (1–9) by the equations

$$F_x = m\ddot{x}/g, \quad F_y = m\ddot{y}/g, \quad F_z = m\ddot{z}/g, \qquad (1\text{--}15)$$

where $g = 980.2$ cm-sec$^{-2} = 9.802$ m-sec$^{-2} = 32.16$ ft-sec^{-2} is the standard acceleration of gravity at the earth's surface. Unit force is then that force exerted by the standard gravitational field on unit mass. The names gram-weight, kilogram-weight, pound-weight are given to the gravitational units of force in the three systems. In the present text, we shall write the fundamental law of mechanics in the form (1–9) rather than (1–15); hence we shall be using the *absolute* units for force and not the gravitational units.

Henceforth the question of units will rarely arise, since nearly all our examples will be worked out in algebraic form. It is assumed that the reader is sufficiently familiar with the units of measurement and their

---

* In the mks system, there is a fourth fundamental unit, the coulomb of electrical charge, which enters into the definitions of electrical units. Electrical units in the cgs system are all defined in terms of centimeters, grams, and seconds. Electrical units in the English system are practically never used.

manipulation to be able to work out numerical examples in any system of units should the need arise.

In any physical equation, the dimensions or units of all additive terms on both sides of the equation must agree when reduced to fundamental units. As an example, we may check that the dimensions of the gravitational constant in Eq. (1–11) are correctly given in the value quoted in Eq. (1–12):

$$F = \frac{Gm_1m_2}{r^2}. \tag{1–11}$$

We substitute for each quantity the units in which it is expressed:

$$(\text{gm-cm-sec}^{-2}) = \frac{(\text{cm}^3\text{-sec}^{-2}\text{-gm}^{-1})(\text{gm})(\text{gm})}{(\text{cm}^2)} = (\text{gm-cm-sec}^{-2}). \tag{1–16}$$

The check does not depend on which system of units we use so long as we use absolute units of force, and we may check dimensions without any reference to units, using symbols l, m, t for length, mass, time:

$$(mlt^{-2}) = \frac{(l^3t^{-2}m^{-1})(m)(m)}{(l^2)} = (mlt^{-2}). \tag{1–17}$$

When constant factors like G are introduced, we can, of course, always make the dimensions agree in any particular equation by choosing appropriate dimensions for the constant. If the units in the terms of an equation do not agree, the equation is certainly wrong. If they do agree, this does not guarantee that the equation is right. However, a check on dimensions in a result will reveal most of the mistakes that result from algebraic errors. The reader should form the habit of mentally checking the dimensions of his formulas at every step in a derivation. When constants are introduced in a problem, their dimensions should be worked out from the first equation in which they appear, and used in checking subsequent steps.

1–7 Some elementary problems in mechanics. Before beginning a systematic development of mechanics based on the laws introduced in this chapter, we shall review a few problems from elementary mechanics in order to fix these laws clearly in mind.

One of the simplest mechanical problems is that of finding the motion of a body moving in a straight line, and acted upon by a constant force. If the mass of the body is m and the force is F, we have, by Newton's second law,

$$F = ma. \tag{1–18}$$

The acceleration is then constant:

$$a = \frac{dv}{dt} = \frac{F}{m}. \tag{1–19}$$

If we multiply Eq. (1–19) by dt, we obtain an expression for the change in velocity dv occurring during the short time dt:

$$dv = \frac{F}{m} dt. \tag{1–20}$$

Integrating, we find the total change in velocity during the time t:

$$\int_{v_0}^{v} dv = \int_{0}^{t} \frac{F}{m} dt, \tag{1–21}$$

$$v - v_0 = \frac{F}{m} t, \tag{1–22}$$

where v_0 is the velocity at $t = 0$. If x is the distance of the body from a fixed origin, measured along its line of travel, then

$$v = \frac{dx}{dt} = v_0 + \frac{F}{m} t. \tag{1–23}$$

We again multiply by dt and integrate to find x:

$$\int_{x_0}^{x} dx = \int_{0}^{t} \left(v_0 + \frac{F}{m} t \right) dt, \tag{1–24}$$

$$x = x_0 + v_0 t + \tfrac{1}{2} \frac{F}{m} t^2, \tag{1–25}$$

where x_0 represents the position of the body at $t = 0$. We now have a complete description of the motion. We can calculate from Eqs. (1–25) and (1–22) the velocity of the body at any time t, and the distance it has traveled. A body falling freely near the surface of the earth is acted upon by a constant force given by Eq. (1–13), and by no other force if air resistance is negligible. In this case, if x is the height of the body above some reference point, we have

$$F = -mg. \tag{1–26}$$

The negative sign appears because the force is downward and the positive direction of x is upward. Substituting in Eqs. (1–19), (1–22), and (1–25), we have the familiar equations

$$a = -g, \tag{1–27}$$
$$v = v_0 - gt, \tag{1–28}$$
$$x = x_0 + v_0 t - \tfrac{1}{2} g t^2. \tag{1–29}$$

In applying Newton's law of motion, Eq. (1–18), it is essential to decide first to what body the law is to be applied, then to insert the mass m of that body and the total force F acting on it. Failure to keep in mind this rather obvious point is the source of many difficulties, one of which is illustrated by the horse-and-wagon dilemma. A horse pulls upon a wagon, but according to Newton's third law the wagon pulls back with an equal and opposite force upon the horse. How then can either the wagon or the horse move? The reader who can solve problem 4 at the end of this chapter will have no difficulty answering this question.

Consider the motion of the system illustrated in Fig. 1–2. Two masses m_1 and m_2 hang from the ends of a rope over a pulley, and we will suppose that m_2 is greater than m_1. We take x as the distance from the pulley to

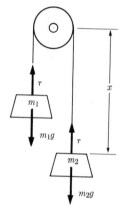

m_2. Since the length of the rope is constant, the coordinate x fixes the positions of both m_1 and m_2. Both move with the same velocity

$$v = \frac{dx}{dt}, \qquad (1\text{–}30)$$

the velocity being positive when m_1 is moving upward and m_2 is moving downward. If we neglect friction and air resistance, the forces on m_1 and m_2 are

FIG. 1–2. Atwood's machine.

$$F_1 = -m_1g + \tau, \qquad (1\text{–}31)$$
$$F_2 = m_2g - \tau, \qquad (1\text{–}32)$$

where τ is the tension in the rope. The forces are taken as positive when they tend to produce a positive velocity dx/dt. Note that the terms involving τ in these equations satisfy Newton's third law. The equations of motion of the two masses are

$$-m_1g + \tau = m_1a, \qquad (1\text{–}33)$$
$$m_2g - \tau = m_2a, \qquad (1\text{–}34)$$

where a is the acceleration dv/dt, and is the same for both masses. By adding Eqs. (1–33) and (1–34), we can eliminate τ and solve for the acceleration:

$$a = \frac{d^2x}{dt^2} = \frac{(m_2 - m_1)}{(m_1 + m_2)}\, g. \qquad (1\text{–}35)$$

The acceleration is constant and the velocity v and position x can be found at any time t as in the preceding example. We can substitute for a from Eq. (1–35) in either Eq. (1–33) or (1–34) and solve for the tension:

$$\tau = \frac{2m_1m_2}{m_1 + m_2}\, g. \qquad (1\text{–}36)$$

As a check, we note that if $m_1 = m_2$, then $a = 0$ and

$$\tau = m_1g = m_2g, \qquad (1\text{–}37)$$

as it should if the masses are in static equilibrium. As a matter of interest, note that if $m_2 \gg m_1$, then

$$a \doteq g, \qquad (1\text{–}38)$$
$$\tau \doteq 2m_1 g. \qquad (1\text{–}39)$$

The reader should convince himself that these two results are to be expected in this case.

When several forces act on a body, its acceleration is determined by the vector sum of the forces which act. Conversely, any force can be resolved in any convenient manner into vector components whose vector sum is the given force, and these components can be treated as separate forces acting on the body.* As an example, we consider

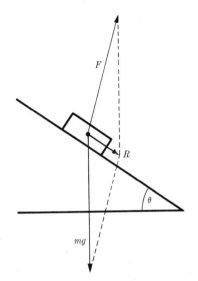

FIG. 1–3. Forces acting on a brick sliding down an incline.

a brick of mass m sliding down an incline, as shown in Fig. 1–3. The two forces which act on the brick are the weight mg and the force F with which the plane acts on the brick. These two forces are added according to the parallelogram law to give a resultant R which acts on the brick:

$$R = ma. \qquad (1\text{–}40)$$

Since the brick is accelerated in the direction of the resultant force, it is evident that if the brick slides down the incline without jumping off or penetrating into the inclined plane, the resultant force R must be directed along the incline. In order to find R, we resolve each force into components parallel and perpendicular to the incline, as in Fig. 1–4. The force F exerted on the brick by the plane is resolved in Fig. 1–4 into two components, a force N normal to the plane preventing the brick from penetrating the plane, and a force f parallel to the plane, and opposed to the motion of the brick, arising from the friction between the brick and the plane. Adding parallel components, we obtain

$$R = mg \sin \theta - f, \qquad (1\text{–}41)$$

and

$$0 = N - mg \cos \theta. \qquad (1\text{–}42)$$

---

* A systematic development of vector algebra will be given in Chapter 3. Only an understanding of the parallelogram law for vector addition is needed for the present discussion.

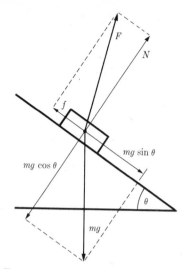

FIG. 1–4. Resolution of forces into components parallel and perpendicular to the incline.

If the frictional force f is proportional to the normal force N, as is approximately true for most dry sliding surfaces, then

$$f = \mu N = \mu mg \cos \theta, \quad (1\text{–}43)$$

where μ is the coefficient of friction. Using Eqs. (1–43), (1–41), and (1–40), we can calculate the acceleration:

$$a = g(\sin \theta - \mu \cos \theta). \quad (1\text{–}44)$$

The velocity and position can now be found as functions of the time t, as in the first example. Equation (1–44) holds only when the brick is sliding down the incline. If it is sliding up the incline, the force f will oppose the motion, and the second term in Eq. (1-44) will be positive. This could only happen if the brick were given an initial velocity up the incline. If the brick is at rest, the frictional force f may have any value up to a maximum $\mu_s N$:

$$f \leq \mu_s N, \quad (1\text{–}45)$$

where μ_s, the coefficient of static friction, is usually greater than μ. In this case R is zero, and

$$f = mg \sin \theta \leq \mu_s mg \cos \theta. \quad (1\text{–}46)$$

According to Eq. (1–46), the angle θ of the incline must not be greater than a limiting value θ_r, the *angle of repose*:

$$\tan \theta \leq \tan \theta_r = \mu_s. \quad (1\text{–}47)$$

If θ is greater than θ_r, the brick cannot remain at rest.

If a body moves with constant speed v around a circle of radius r, its acceleration is toward the center of the circle, as we shall prove in Chapter 3, and is of magnitude

$$a = \frac{v^2}{r}. \quad (1\text{–}48)$$

Such a body must be acted on by a constant force toward the center. This centripetal force is given by

$$F = ma = \frac{mv^2}{r}. \quad (1\text{–}49)$$

Note that mv^2/r is not a "centrifugal force" directed away from the center, but is mass times acceleration and is directed toward the center, as is the centripetal force F. As an example, the moon's orbit around the earth is nearly circular, and if we assume that the earth is at rest at the center, then, by Eq. (1–11), the force on the moon is

$$F = \frac{GMm}{r^2}, \tag{1–50}$$

where M is the mass of the earth and m that of the moon. We can express this force in terms of the radius R of the earth and the acceleration g of gravity at the earth's surface by substituting for GM from Eq. (1–14):

$$F = \frac{mgR^2}{r^2}. \tag{1–51}$$

The speed v of the moon is

$$v = \frac{2\pi r}{T}, \tag{1–52}$$

where T is the period of revolution. Substituting Eqs. (1–51) and (1–52) in Eq. (1–49), we can find r:

$$r^3 = \frac{gR^2T^2}{4\pi^2}. \tag{1–53}$$

This equation was first worked out by Isaac Newton in order to check his inverse square law of gravitation.* It will not be quite accurate because the moon's orbit is not quite circular, and also because the earth does not remain at rest at the center of the moon's orbit, but instead wobbles slightly due to the attraction of the moon. By Newton's third law, this attractive force is also given by Eq. (1–51). Since the earth is much heavier than the moon, its acceleration is much smaller, and Eq. (1–53) will not be far wrong. The exact treatment of this problem is given in Section 4–7. Another small error is introduced by the fact that g, as determined experimentally, includes a small effect due to the earth's rotation. (See Section 7–3.) If we insert the measured values,

$$g = 980.2 \text{ cm-sec}^{-2},$$
$$R = 6,368 \text{ kilometers},$$
$$T = 27\tfrac{1}{3} \text{ days},$$

we obtain, from Eq. (1–53),

$$r = 383,000 \text{ kilometers}.$$

The mean distance to the moon according to modern measurements is

$$r = 385,000 \text{ kilometers}.$$

The values of r and R available to Newton would not have given such close agreement.

---

* Isaac Newton, *op. cit.*, p. 407.

PROBLEMS

1. Compute the gravitational force of attraction between an electron and a proton at a separation of 0.5A (1A = 10^{-8} cm). Compare with the electrostatic force of attraction at the same distance.

2. The coefficient of viscosity η is defined by the equation

$$\frac{F}{A} = \eta \frac{dv}{ds},$$

where F is the frictional force acting across an area A in a moving fluid, and dv is the difference in velocity parallel to A between two layers of fluid a distance ds apart, ds being measured perpendicular to A. Find the units in which the viscosity η would be expressed in the foot-pound-second, cgs, and mks systems. Find the three conversion factors for converting coefficients of viscosity from one of these systems to another.

3. A motorist is approaching a green traffic light with a speed v_0, when the light turns to amber. (a) If his reaction time is τ, during which he makes his decision to stop and applies his foot to the brake, and if his maximum braking deceleration is a, what is the minimum distance s_{min} from the intersection at the moment the light turns to amber in which he can bring his car to a stop? (b) If the amber light remains on for a time t before turning red, what is the maximum distance s_{max} from the intersection at the moment the light turns to amber such that he can continue into the intersetion at speed v_0 without running the red light? (c) Show that if his initial speed v_0 is greater than

$$v_{0\ max} = 2a(t - \tau),$$

there will be a range of distances from the intersection such that he can neither stop in time nor continue through without running the red light. (d) Make some reasonable estimates of τ, t, and a, and calculate $v_{0\ max}$ in miles per hour. If $v_0 = \frac{2}{3}v_{0\ max}$, calculate s_{min} and s_{max}.

4. A boy of mass m pulls (horizontally) a sled of mass M. The coefficient of friction between sled and snow is μ. (a) Draw a diagram showing all forces acting on the boy and on the sled. (b) Find the horizontal and vertical components of each force at a moment when boy and sled each have an acceleration a. (c) If the coefficient of static friction between the boy's feet and the ground is μ_s, what is the maximum acceleration he can give to himself and the sled, assuming traction to be the limiting factor?

5. A floor mop of mass m is pushed with a force F directed along the handle, which makes an angle θ with the vertical. The coefficient of friction with the floor is μ. (a) Draw a diagram showing all forces acting on the mop. (b) For a given θ,μ, find the force F required to slide the mop with uniform velocity across the floor. (c) Show that if θ is less than the angle of repose, the mop cannot be started across the floor by pushing along the handle. Neglect the mass of the mop handle.

6. A box of mass m slides across a horizontal table with coefficient of friction μ. The box is connected by a rope which passes over a pulley to a body of mass M hanging alongside the table. Find the acceleration of the system and the tension in the rope.

7. The brick shown in Figs. 1–3 and 1–4 is given an initial velocity v_0 up the incline. The angle θ is greater than the angle of repose. Find the distance the brick moves up the incline, and the time required for it to slide up and back to its original position.

8. A curve in a highway of radius of curvature r is banked at an angle θ with the horizontal. If the coefficient of friction is μ_s, what is the maximum speed with which a car can round the curve without skidding?

9. Assuming the earth moves in a circle of radius 93,000,000 miles, with a period of revolution of one year, find the mass of the sun in tons.

10. (a) Compute the mass of the earth from its radius and the values of g and G. (b) Look up the masses and distances of the sun and moon and compute the force of attraction between earth and sun and between earth and moon. Check your results by making a rough estimate of the ratio of these two forces from a consideration of the fact that the former causes the earth to revolve about the sun once a year, whereas the latter causes the earth to wobble in a small circle, approximately once a month, about the common center of gravity of the earth-moon system.

11. The sun is about 25,000 light years from the center of the galaxy, and travels approximately in a circle at a speed of 175 mi/sec. Find the approximate mass of the galaxy by assuming that the gravitational force on the sun can be calculated as if all the mass of the galaxy were at its center. Express the result as a ratio of the galactic mass to the sun's mass. (You do not need to look up either G or the sun's mass to do this problem, if you compare the revolution of the sun around the galactic center with the revolution of the earth about the sun.)

CHAPTER 2

MOTION OF A PARTICLE IN ONE DIMENSION

2–1 Momentum and energy theorems. In this chapter, we study the motion of a particle of mass m along a straight line, which we will take to be the x-axis, under the action of a force F directed along the x-axis. The discussion will be applicable, as we shall see, to other cases where the motion of a mechanical system depends on only one coordinate, or where all but one coordinate can be eliminated from the problem.

The motion of the particle is governed, according to Eq. (1–9), by the equation

$$m \frac{d^2x}{dt^2} = F. \tag{2–1}$$

Before considering the solution of Eq. (2–1), we shall define some concepts which are useful in discussing mechanical problems, and prove some simple general theorems about one-dimensional motion. The linear momentum p, according to Eq. (1–10), is defined as

$$p = mv = m \frac{dx}{dt}. \tag{2–2}$$

From Eq. (2–1), using Eq. (2–2) and the fact that m is constant, we obtain

$$\frac{dp}{dt} = F. \tag{2–3}$$

This equation states that the time rate of change of momentum is equal to the applied force, and is, of course, just Newton's second law. We may call it the (differential) momentum theorem. If we multiply Eq. (2–3) by dt and integrate from t_1 to t_2, we obtain an integrated form of the momentum theorem:

$$p_2 - p_1 = \int_{t_1}^{t_2} F \, dt. \tag{2–4}$$

Equation (2–4) gives the change in momentum due to the action of the force F between the times t_1 and t_2. The integral on the right is called the *impulse* delivered by the force F during this time; F must be known as a function of t alone in order to evaluate the integral. If F is given as $F(x,v,t)$, then the impulse can be computed for any particular given motion $x(t),v(t)$.

A quantity which will turn out to be of considerable importance is the *kinetic energy*, defined by the equation

$$T = \tfrac{1}{2}mv^2. \tag{2–5}$$

If we multiply Eq. (2–1) by v, we obtain

$$mv \frac{dv}{dt} = Fv,$$

or

$$\frac{d}{dt}(\tfrac{1}{2}mv^2) = \frac{dT}{dt} = Fv. \tag{2–6}$$

Equation (2–6) gives the rate of change of kinetic energy, and may be called the (differential) energy theorem. If we multiply by dt and integrate from t_1 to t_2, we obtain the integrated form of the energy theorem:

$$T_2 - T_1 = \int_{t_1}^{t_2} Fv \, dt. \tag{2–7}$$

Equation (2–7) gives the change in energy due to the action of the force F between the times t_1 and t_2. The integral on the right is called the *work* done by the force during this time. The integrand Fv on the right is the time rate of doing work, and is called the *power* supplied by the force F. In general, when F is given as $F(x,v,t)$, the work can only be computed for a particular specified motion $x(t),v(t)$. Since $v = dx/dt$, we can rewrite the work integral in a form which is convenient when F is known as a function of x:

$$T_2 - T_1 = \int_{x_1}^{x_2} F \, dx. \tag{2–8}$$

2–2 Discussion of the general problem of one-dimensional motion. If the force F is known, the equation of motion (2–1) becomes a second order ordinary differential equation for the unknown function $x(t)$. The force F may be known as a function of any or all of the variables t, x, and v. For any given motion of a dynamical system, all dynamical variables $(x,v,F,p,T,$ etc.) associated with the system are, of course, functions of the time t, that is, each has a definite value at any particular time t. However, in many cases a dynamical variable such as the force may be known to bear a certain functional relation to x, or to v, or to any combination of x, v, and t. As an example, the gravitational force acting on a body falling from a great height above the earth is known as a function of the height above the earth. The frictional drag on such a body would depend on its speed and on the density of the air and hence on the height above the earth; if atmospheric conditions are changing, it would also depend on t. If F is given as $F(x,v,t)$, then when $x(t)$ and $v(t)$ are known, these functions can be substituted to give F as a function of the time t alone; however, in general, this cannot be done until after Eq. (2–1) has been solved, and even then the function $F(t)$ may be different for different possible motions of the particle. In any case, if F is given as $F(x,v,t)$ (where F may depend on any or all of these variables), then Eq. (2–1) becomes a definite differential equation to be solved:

$$\frac{d^2x}{dt^2} = \frac{1}{m} F(x,\dot{x},t).$$ (2–9)

This is the most general type of second order ordinary differential equation, and we shall be concerned in this chapter with studying its solutions and their applications to mechanical problems.

Equation (2–9) applies to all possible motions of the particle under the action of the specified force. In general, there will be many such motions, for Eq. (2–9) prescribes only the acceleration of the particle at every instant in terms of its position and velocity at that instant. If we know the position and velocity of a particle at a certain time, we can determine its position a short time later (or earlier). Knowing also its acceleration, we can find its velocity a short time later. Equation (2–9) then gives the acceleration a short time later. In this manner, we can trace out the past or subsequent positions and velocities of a particle if its position x_0 and velocity v_0 are known at any one time t_0. Any pair of values of x_0 and v_0 will lead to a possible motion of the particle. We call t_0 the *initial instant*, although it may be any moment in the history of the particle, and the values of x_0 and v_0 at t_0 we call the *initial conditions*. Instead of specifying initial values for x and v, we could specify initial values of any two quantities from which x and v can be determined; for example, we may specify x_0 and the initial momentum $p_0 = mv_0$. These initial conditions, together with equation (2–9), then represent a perfectly definite problem whose solution should be a unique function $x(t)$ representing the motion of the particle under the specified conditions.

The mathematical theory of second order ordinary differential equations leads to results in agreement with what we expect from the nature of the physical problem in which the equation arises. The theory asserts that, ordinarily, an equation of the form (2–9) has a unique continuous solution $x(t)$ which takes on given values x_0 and v_0 of x and $\dot{x}$ at any chosen initial value t_0 of t. "Ordinarily" here means, as far as the beginning mechanics student is concerned, "in all cases of physical interest."* The properties of differential equations like Eq. (2–9) are derived in most treatises on differential equations. We know that any physical problem must always have a unique solution, and therefore any force function $F(x,\dot{x},t)$ which can occur in a physical problem will necessarily satisfy the required conditions for those values of $x,\dot{x},t$ of physical interest. Thus ordinarily we do not need to worry about whether a solution exists. However, most mechanical problems involve some simplification of the actual

---

* For a rigorous mathematical statement of the conditions for the existence of a solution of Eq. (2–9), see W. Leighton, *An Introduction to the Theory of Differential Equations.* New York: McGraw-Hill, 1952. (Appendix 1.)

consider the three cases

physical situation, and it is possible to oversimplify or otherwise distort a physical problem in such a way that the resulting mathematical problem no longer possesses a unique solution.   The general practice of physicists in mechanics and elsewhere is to proceed, ignoring questions of mathe·· matical rigor.   On those fortunately rare occasions when we run into difficulty, we then consult our physical intuition, or check our lapses of rigor, until the source of the difficulty is discovered.   Such a procedure may bring shudders to the mathematician, but it is the most convenient and rapid way to apply mathematics to the solution of physical problems. The physicist, while he may proceed in a nonrigorous fashion, should nevertheless be acquainted with the rigorous treatment of the mathematical methods which he uses.

The existence theorem for Eq. (2–9) guarantees that there is a unique mathematical solution to this equation for all cases which will arise in practice.   In some cases the exact solution can be found· by elementary methods.   Most of the problems considered in this text will be of this nature. Fortunately, many of the most important mechanical problems in physics can be solved without too much difficulty.   In fact, one of the reasons why certain problems are considered important is that they can be easily solved. The physicist is concerned with discovering and verifying the laws of physics.   In checking these laws experimentally, he is free, to a large extent, to choose those cases where the mathematical analysis is not too difficult to carry out.   The engineer is not so fortunate, since his problems are selected not because they are easy to solve, but because they are of practical importance.   In engineering, and often also in physics, many cases arise where the exact solution of Eq. (2–9) is difficult or impossible to obtain.   In such cases various methods are available for obtaining at least approximate answers.   The reader is referred to courses and texts on differential equations for a discussion of such methods.*   From the point of view of theoretical mechanics, the important point is that a solution always does exist and can be found, as accurately as desired.   We shall restrict our attention to examples which can be treated by simple methods.

2–3 Applied force depending on the time.   If the force F is given as a function of the time, then the equation of motion (2–9) can be solved in the following manner.   Multiplying Eq. (2–9) by dt and integrating from an initial instant t_0 to any later (or earlier) instant t, we obtain Eq. (2–4), which in this case we write in the form

$$mv - mv_0 = \int_{t_0}^{t} F(t) \, dt. \tag{2–10}$$

---

* W. E. Milne, *Numerical Calculus*.   Princeton: Princeton University Press, 1949.   (Chapter 5.)

H. Levy and E. A. Baggott, *Numerical Solutions of Differential Equations*. New York: Dover Publications, 1950.

Since $F(t)$ is a known function of t, the integral on the right can, at least in principle, be evaluated and the right member is then a function of t (and t_0). We solve for v:

$$v = \frac{dx}{dt} = v_0 + \frac{1}{m} \int_{t_0}^{t} F(t)\, dt. \tag{2-11}$$

Now multiply by dt and integrate again from t_0 to t:

$$x - x_0 = v_0(t - t_0) + \frac{1}{m} \int_{t_0}^{t} \left[\int_{t_0}^{t} F(t)\, dt \right] dt. \tag{2-12}$$

To avoid confusion, we may rewrite the variable of integration as t' in the first integral and t'' in the second:

$$x = x_0 + v_0(t - t_0) + \frac{1}{m} \int_{t_0}^{t} dt'' \int_{t_0}^{t''} F(t')\, dt'. \tag{2-13}$$

This gives the required solution $x(t)$ in terms of two integrals which can be evaluated when $F(t)$ is given. A definite integral can always be evaluated. If an explicit formula for the integral cannot be found, then at least it can always be computed as accurately as we please by numerical methods. For this reason, in the discussion of a general type of problem such as the one above, we ordinarily consider the problem solved when the solution has been expressed in terms of one or more definite integrals. In a practical problem, the integrals would have to be evaluated to obtain the final solution in usable form.*

Problems in which F is given as a function of t usually arise when we seek to find the behavior of a mechanical system under the action of some external influence. As an example, we consider the motion of a free electron of charge $-e$ when subject to an oscillating electric field along the x-axis:

$$E_x = E_0 \cos (\omega t + \theta). \tag{2-14}$$

The force on the electron is

$$F = -eE_x = -eE_0 \cos (\omega t + \theta). \tag{2-15}$$

---

* The reader who has studied differential equations may be disturbed by the appearance of three constants, t_0, v_0, and x_0, in the solution (2–13), whereas the general solution of a second order differential equation should contain only two arbitrary constants. Mathematically, there are only two independent constants in Eq. (2–13), an additive constant containing the terms $x_0 - v_0 t_0$ plus a term from the lower limit of the last integral, and a constant multiplying t containing the term v_0 plus a term from the lower limit of the first integral. Physically, we can take any initial instant t_0, and then just two parameters x_0 and v_0 are required to specify one out of all possible motions subject to the given force.

The equation of motion is

$$m \frac{dv}{dt} = -eE_0 \cos (\omega t + \theta). \qquad (2\text{–}16)$$

We multiply by dt and integrate, taking $t_0 = 0$:

$$v = \frac{dx}{dt} = v_0 + \frac{eE_0 \sin \theta}{m\omega} - \frac{eE_0}{m\omega} \sin (\omega t + \theta). \qquad (2\text{–}17)$$

Integrating again, we obtain

$$x = x_0 - \frac{eE_0 \cos \theta}{m\omega^2} + \left[v_0 + \frac{eE_0 \sin \theta}{m\omega} \right] t + \frac{eE_0}{m\omega^2} \cos (\omega t + \theta). \quad (2\text{–}18)$$

If the electron is initially at rest at $x_0 = 0$, this becomes

$$x = - \frac{eE_0 \cos \theta}{m\omega^2} + \frac{eE_0 \sin \theta}{m\omega} t + \frac{eE_0}{m\omega^2} \cos (\omega t + \theta). \qquad (2\text{–}19)$$

The problem considered here is of interest in connection with the propagation of radio waves through the ionosphere, which contains a high density of free electrons. The oscillating term is of chief interest, since the other terms would average out over a large number of electrons. (Since the wave arrives at different electrons at different times, θ would have different values for different electrons. The average values of $\sin \theta$ and $\cos \theta$ are zero.) We see that the oscillatory part of the displacement x is 180° out of phase with the applied force due to the electric field. Since the electron has a negative charge, the resulting electric polarization is 180° out of phase with the electric field. The result is that the dielectric constant of the ionosphere is less than one. (In an ordinary dielectric at low frequencies, the charges are displaced in the direction of the electric force on them, and the dielectric constant is greater than one.) Since the velocity of light is

$$v = c(\mu\epsilon)^{-\frac{1}{2}}, \qquad (2\text{–}20)$$

where $c = 3 \times 10^{10}$ cm/sec and ϵ and μ are the dielectric constant and magnetic permeability respectively, and since $\mu = 1$ here, the (phase) velocity v of radio waves in the ionosphere is greater than the velocity c of electromagnetic waves in empty space. Thus waves entering the ionosphere at an angle are bent back toward the earth. The effect is seen to be inversely proportional to ω^2, so that for high enough frequencies, the waves do not return to the earth but pass out through the ionosphere.

Only a slight knowledge of electromagnetic theory is required to carry this discussion through mathematically.* The dipole moment of the electron displaced from its equilibrium position is

---

* See, e.g., G. P. Harnwell, *Principles of Electricity and Electromagnetism,* 2nd ed. New York: McGraw-Hill, 1949. (Section 2.4.)

$$-ex = -\frac{e^2}{m\omega^2} E_0 \cos(\omega t + \theta) = -\frac{e^2}{m\omega^2} E_x,$$ (2–21)

if we consider only the oscillating term. If there are N electrons per cm³, the total dipole moment per unit volume is (here the other terms in x would cancel out on the average)

$$P_x = -\frac{Ne^2}{m\omega^2} E_x.$$ (2–22)

The electric displacement is

$$D_x = E_x + 4\pi P_x = \left(1 - \frac{4\pi Ne^2}{m\omega^2}\right) E_x.$$ (2–23)

Since the dielectric constant is defined by

$$D_x = \epsilon E_x,$$ (2–24)

we conclude that

$$\epsilon = 1 - \frac{4\pi Ne^2}{m\omega^2},$$ (2–25)

and since $\mu = 1$,

$$v = c\left(1 - \frac{4\pi Ne^2}{m\omega^2}\right)^{-\frac{1}{2}}.$$ (2–26)

It is left to the reader to explain physically the origin of the constant term and the term linear in t in Eq. (2–19) in terms of the phase of the electric field at the initial instant. How do the terms in Eq. (2–19) depend on e, m, E_0, and ω? Explain physically. Why does the oscillatory term turn out to be out of phase with the applied force?

2–4 Damping force depending on the velocity. Another type of force which allows an easy solution of Eq. (2–9) is the case when F is a function of v alone:

$$m\frac{dv}{dt} = F(v).$$ (2–27)

To solve, we multiply by $[mF(v)]^{-1} dt$ and integrate from t_0 to t:

$$\int_{v_0}^{v} \frac{dv}{F(v)} = \frac{t - t_0}{m}.$$ (2–28)

The integral on the left can be evaluated, in principle at least, when $F(v)$ is given, and an equation containing the unknown v results. If this equation is solved for v (we assume in general discussions that this can always be done), we will have an equation of the form

$$v = \frac{dx}{dt} = \varphi\left(v_0, \frac{t - t_0}{m}\right).$$ (2–29)

The solution for x is then

$$x = x_0 + \int_{t_0}^{t} \varphi\left(v_0, \frac{t - t_0}{m}\right) dt. \tag{2-30}$$

In the case of one-dimensional motion, the only important kinds of forces which depend on the velocity are frictional forces. The force of sliding or rolling friction between dry solid surfaces is nearly constant for a given pair of surfaces with a given normal force between them, and depends on the velocity only in that its direction is always opposed to the velocity. The force of friction between lubricated surfaces or between a solid body and a liquid or gaseous medium depends on the velocity in a complicated way, and the function $F(v)$ can usually be given only in the form of a tabulated summary of experimental data. In certain cases and over certain ranges of velocity, the frictional force is proportional to some fixed power of the velocity:

$$F = (\mp)bv^n. \tag{2-31}$$

If n is an odd integer, the negative sign should be chosen in the above equation. Otherwise the sign must be chosen so that the force has the opposite sign to the velocity v. The frictional force is always opposed to the velocity, and therefore does negative work, i.e., absorbs energy from the moving body. A velocity dependent force in the same direction as the velocity would represent a source of energy; such cases do not often occur.

As an example, we consider the problem of a boat traveling with initial velocity v_0, which shuts off its engines at $t_0 = 0$ when it is at the position $x_0 = 0$. We assume the force of friction given by Eq. (2-31) with $n = 1$:

$$m \frac{dv}{dt} = -bv. \tag{2-32}$$

We solve equation (2-32), following the steps outlined above [Eqs. (2-27) to (2-30)]:

$$\int_{v_0}^{v} \frac{dv}{v} = -\frac{b}{m} t,$$

$$\ln \frac{v}{v_0} = -\frac{b}{m} t,$$

$$v = v_0 e^{-bt/m}. \tag{2-33}$$

We see that as $t \to \infty$, $v \to 0$, as it should, but that the boat never comes completely to rest in any finite time. The solution for x is

$$x = \int_0^t v_0 e^{-bt/m} dt$$

$$= \frac{mv_0}{b}(1 - e^{-bt/m}). \tag{2-34}$$

As $t \rightarrow \infty$, x approaches the limiting value

$$x_s = \frac{mv_0}{b}. \tag{2-35}$$

Thus we can specify a definite distance that the boat travels in stopping. Although according to the above result, Eq. (2–33), the velocity never becomes exactly zero, when t is sufficiently large the velocity becomes so small that the boat is practically stopped. Let us choose some small velocity v_s such that when $v < v_s$ we are willing to regard the boat as stopped (say, for example, the average random speed given to an anchored boat by the waves passing by it). Then we can define the time t_s required for the boat to stop by

$$v_s = v_0 e^{-bt_s/m}, \quad t_s = \frac{m}{b} \ln \frac{v_0}{v_s}. \tag{2-36}$$

Since the logarithm is a slowly changing function, the stopping time t_s will not depend to any great extent on precisely what value of v_s we choose so long as it is much smaller than v_0. It is often instructive to expand solutions in a Taylor series in t. If we expand the right side of Eqs. (2–33) and (2–34) in power series in t, we obtain*

$$v = v_0 - \frac{bv_0}{m} t + \cdots, \tag{2-37}$$

$$x = v_0 t - \frac{1}{2} \frac{bv_0}{m} t^2 + \cdots. \tag{2-38}$$

Note that the first two terms in the series for v and x are just the formulas for a particle acted on by a constant force $-bv_0$, which is the initial value of the frictional force in Eq. (2–32). This is to be expected, and affords a fairly good check on the algebra which led to the solution (2–34). Series expansions are a very useful means of obtaining simple approximate formulas valid for a short range of time.

The characteristics of the motion of a body under the action of a frictional force as given by Eq. (2–31) depend on the exponent n. In general,

---

* The reader who has not already done so should memorize the Taylor series for a few simple functions like

$$e^x = 1 + x + \frac{x^2}{2} + \frac{x^3}{2 \cdot 3} + \frac{x^4}{2 \cdot 3 \cdot 4} + \cdots,$$

$$\ln (1 + x) = x - \frac{x^2}{2} + \frac{x^3}{3} - \frac{x^4}{4} + \cdots,$$

$$(1 + x)^n = 1 + nx + \frac{n(n - 1)}{2} x^2 + \frac{n(n - 1)(n - 2)}{2 \cdot 3} x^3 + \cdots.$$

These three series are extremely useful in obtaining approximations to complicated formulas, valid when x is small.

a large exponent n will result in rapid initial slowing but slow final stopping, and vice versa, as one can see by sketching graphs of F vs. v for various values of n. For small enough values of n, the velocity comes to zero in a finite time. For large values of n, the body not only requires an infinite time, but travels an infinite distance before stopping. This disagrees with ordinary experience, an indication that while the exponent n may be large at high velocities, it must become smaller at low velocities. The exponent $n = 1$ is often assumed in problems involving friction, particularly when friction is only a small effect to be taken into account approximately. The reason for taking $n = 1$ is that this gives easy equations to solve, and is often a fairly good approximation when the frictional force is small, provided b is properly chosen.

2–5 Conservative force depending on position. Potential energy. One of the most important types of motion occurs when the force F is a function of the coordinate x alone:

$$m \frac{dv}{dt} = F(x). \tag{2–39}$$

We have then, by the energy theorem (2–8),

$$\tfrac{1}{2}mv^2 - \tfrac{1}{2}mv_0^2 = \int_{x_0}^{x} F(x)\,dx. \tag{2–40}$$

The integral on the right is the work done by the force when the particle goes from x_0 to x. We now define the *potential energy* $V(x)$ as the work done by the force when the particle goes from x to some chosen standard point x_s:

$$V(x) = \int_{x}^{x_s} F(x)\,dx = -\int_{x_s}^{x} F(x)\cdot dx. \tag{2–41}$$

The reason for calling this quantity potential energy will appear shortly. In terms of $V(x)$, we can write the integral in Eq. (2–40) as follows:

$$\int_{x_0}^{x} F(x)\,dx = -V(x) + V(x_0). \tag{2–42}$$

With the help of Eq. (2–42), Eq. (2–40) can be written

$$\tfrac{1}{2}mv^2 + V(x) = \tfrac{1}{2}mv_0^2 + V(x_0). \tag{2–43}$$

The quantity on the right depends only on the initial conditions and is therefore constant during the motion. It is called the total energy E, and we have the law of conservation of kinetic plus potential energy, which holds, as we can see, only when the force is a function of position alone:

$$\tfrac{1}{2}mv^2 + V(x) = T + V = E. \tag{2–44}$$

Solving for v, we obtain

$$v = \frac{dx}{dt} = \sqrt{\frac{2}{m}} [E - V(x)]^{\frac{1}{2}}. \tag{2-45}$$

The function $x(t)$ is to be found by solving for x the equation

$$\sqrt{\frac{m}{2}} \int_{x_0}^{x} [E - V(x)]^{-\frac{1}{2}} \, dx = t - t_0. \tag{2-46}$$

In this case, the initial conditions are expressed in terms of the constants E and x_0.

In applying Eq. (2–46), and in taking the indicated square root in the integrand, care must be taken to use the proper sign, depending on whether the velocity v given by Eq. (2–45) is positive or negative. In cases where v is positive during some parts of the motion and negative during other parts, it may be necessary to carry out the integration in Eq. (2–46) separately for each part of the motion.

From the definition (2–41) we can express the force in terms of the potential energy:

$$F = -\frac{dV}{dx}. \tag{2-47}$$

This equation can be taken as expressing the physical meaning of the potential energy. The potential energy is a function whose negative derivative gives the force. The effect of changing the coordinate of the standard point x_s is to add a constant to $V(x)$. Since it is the derivative of V which enters into the dynamical equations as the force, the choice of standard point x_s is immaterial. A constant can always be added to the potential $V(x)$ without affecting the physical results. (The same constant must, of course, be added to E.)

As an example, we consider the problem of a particle subject to a linear restoring force, for example, a mass fastened to a spring:

$$F = -kx. \tag{2-48}$$

The potential energy, if we take $x_s = 0$, is

$$V(x) = -\int_{0}^{x} -kx \, dx$$
$$= \tfrac{1}{2}kx^2. \tag{2-49}$$

Equation (2–46) becomes, for this case, with $t_0 = 0$,

$$\sqrt{\frac{m}{2}} \int_{x_0}^{x} (E - \tfrac{1}{2}kx^2)^{-\frac{1}{2}} \, dx = t. \tag{2-50}$$

Now make the substitutions

$$\sin \theta = x \sqrt{\frac{k}{2E}}, \tag{2-51}$$

$$\omega = \sqrt{\frac{k}{m}}, \tag{2-52}$$

so that

$$\sqrt{\frac{m}{2}} \int_{x_0}^{x} (E - \tfrac{1}{2}kx^2)^{-\frac{1}{2}} \, dx = \frac{1}{\omega} \int_{\theta_0}^{\theta} d\theta = \frac{1}{\omega} (\theta - \theta_0),$$

and, by Eq. (2–50),

$$\theta = \omega t + \theta_0.$$

We can now solve for x in Eq. (2–51):

$$x = \sqrt{\frac{2E}{k}} \sin \theta = A \sin (\omega t + \theta_0), \tag{2-53}$$

where

$$A = \sqrt{\frac{2E}{k}}. \tag{2-54}$$

Thus the coordinate x oscillates harmonically in time, with amplitude A and frequency $\omega/2\pi$. The initial conditions are here determined by the constants A and θ_0, which are related to E and x_0 by

$$E = \tfrac{1}{2}kA^2, \tag{2-55}$$
$$x_0 = A \sin \theta_0. \tag{2-56}$$

Notice that in this example we meet the sign difficulty in taking the square root in Eq. (2–50) by replacing $(1 - \sin^2 \theta)^{-\frac{1}{2}}$ by $(\cos \theta)^{-1}$, a quantity which can be made either positive or negative as required by choosing θ in the proper quadrant.

A function of the dependent variable and its first derivative, which is constant for all solutions of a second order differential equation, is called a *first integral* of the equation. The function $\tfrac{1}{2}m\dot{x}^2 + V(x)$ is called the *energy integral* of Eq. (2–39). An integral of the equations of motion of a mechanical system is also called a *constant of the motion*. In general, any mechanical problem can be solved if we can find enough first integrals, or constants of the motion.

Even in cases where the integral in Eq. (2–46) cannot easily be evaluated or the resulting equation solved to give an explicit solution for $x(t)$, the energy integral, Eq. (2–44), gives us useful information about the solution. For a given energy E, we see from Eq. (2–45) that the particle is confined to those regions on the x-axis where $V(x) \leq E$. Furthermore, the velocity is proportional to the square root of the difference between E and $V(x)$. Hence, if we plot $V(x)$ versus x, we can give a good qualitative description of the kinds of motion that are possible. For the potential energy func-

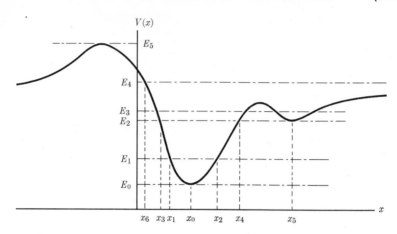

FIG. 2–1. A potential energy function for one-dimensional motion.

tion shown in Fig. 2–1 we note that the least energy possible is E_0. At this energy, the particle can only be at rest at x_0. With a slightly higher energy E_1, the particle can move between x_1 and x_2; its velocity decreases as it approaches x_1 or x_2, and it stops and reverses its direction when it reaches either x_1 or x_2, which are called *turning points* of the motion. With energy E_2, the particle may oscillate between turning points x_3 and x_4, or remain at rest at x_5. With energy E_3, there are four turning points and the particle may oscillate in either of the two potential valleys. With energy E_4, there is only one turning point; if the particle is initially travel-ing to the left, it will turn at x_6 and return to the right, speeding up over the valleys at x_0 and x_5, and slowing down over the hill between. At energies above E_5, there are no turning points and the particle will move in one direction only, varying its speed according to the depth of the potential at each point.

A point where $V(x)$ has a minimum is called a point of *stable equilibrium*. A particle at rest at such a point will remain at rest. If displaced a slight distance, it will experience a restoring force tending to return it, and it will oscillate about the equilibrium point. A point where $V(x)$ has a maxi-mum is called a point of *unstable* equilibrium. In theory, a particle at rest there can remain at rest, since the force is zero, but if it is displaced the slightest distance, the force acting on it will push it farther away from the unstable equilibrium position. A region where $V(x)$ is constant is called a region of *neutral* equilibrium, since a particle can be displaced slightly without suffering either a restoring or a repelling force.

This kind of qualitative discussion, based on the energy integral, is simple and very useful. Study this example until you understand it well enough to be able to see at a glance, for any potential energy curve, the types of motion that are possible.

It may be that only part of the force on a particle is derivable from a potential function $V(x)$. Let F' be the remainder of the force:

$$F = -\frac{dV}{dx} + F'. \tag{2–57}$$

In this case the energy $(T + V)$ is no longer constant. If we substitute F from Eq. (2–57) in Eq. (2–1), and multiply by dx/dt, we have, after rearranging terms,

$$\frac{d}{dt}(T + V) = F'v. \tag{2–58}$$

The time rate of change of kinetic plus potential energy is equal to the power delivered by the additional force F'.

2–6 Falling bodies. One of the simplest and most commonly occurring types of one-dimensional motion is that of falling bodies. We take up this type of motion here as an illustration of the principles discussed in the preceding sections.

A body falling near the surface of the earth, if we neglect air resistance, is subject to a constant force

$$F = -mg, \tag{2–59}$$

where we have taken the positive direction as upward. The equation of motion is

$$m\frac{d^2x}{dt^2} = -mg. \tag{2–60}$$

The solution may be obtained by any of the three methods discussed in Sections 2–3, 2–4, and 2–5, since a constant force may be considered as a function of either t, v, or x. The reader will find it instructive to solve the problem by all three methods. We have already obtained the result in Chapter 1 [Eqs. (1–28), (1–29)].

In order to include the effect of air resistance, we may assume a frictional force proportional to v, so that the total force is

$$F = -mg - bv. \tag{2–61}$$

The constant b will depend on the size and shape of the falling body, as well as on the viscosity of the air. The problem must now be treated as a case of $F(v)$:

$$m\frac{dv}{dt} = -mg - bv. \tag{2–62}$$

Taking $v_0 = 0$ at $t = 0$, we proceed as in Section 2–4 [Eq. (2–28)]:

$$\int_0^v \frac{dv}{v + (mg/b)} = -\frac{bt}{m}. \tag{2–63}$$

We integrate and solve for v:

$$v = -\frac{mg}{b}(1 - e^{-bt/m}).\tag{2-64}$$

We may obtain a formula useful for short times of fall by expanding the exponential function in a power series:

$$v = -gt + \tfrac{1}{2}\frac{bg}{m}t^2 + \cdots.\tag{2-65}$$

Thus for a short time ($t \ll m/b$), $v = -gt$, approximately, and the effect of air resistance can be neglected. After a long time, we see from Eq. (2–64) that

$$v \doteq -\frac{mg}{b}, \quad \text{if} \quad t \gg \frac{m}{b}.$$

The velocity mg/b is called the *terminal velocity* of the falling body in question. The body reaches within $1/e$ of its terminal velocity in a time $t = m/b$. We could use the experimentally determined terminal velocity to find the constant b. We now integrate Eq. (2–64), taking $x_0 = 0$:

$$x = \frac{m^2 g}{b^2}\left(1 - \frac{bt}{m} - e^{-bt/m}\right).\tag{2-66}$$

By expanding the exponential function in a power series, we obtain

$$x = -\tfrac{1}{2}gt^2 + \tfrac{1}{6}\frac{bg}{m}t^3 + \cdots.\tag{2-67}$$

If $t \ll m/b$, $x \doteq -\tfrac{1}{2}gt^2$, as in Eq. (1–29). When $t \gg m/b$,

$$x \doteq \left(\frac{m^2 g}{b^2} - \frac{mg}{b}t\right).$$

This result is easily interpreted in terms of terminal velocity. Why is the positive constant present?

For small heavy bodies with large terminal velocities, a better approximation may be

$$F = bv^2.\tag{2-68}$$

upward $-mg + bv$

The reader should be able to show that with the frictional force given by Eq. (2–68), the result (taking $x_0 = v_0 = 0$ at $t_0 = 0$) is

$$v = -\sqrt{\frac{mg}{b}}\tanh\left(\sqrt{\frac{bg}{m}}\,t\right)\tag{2-69}$$

$$\doteq \begin{cases} -gt, & \text{if } t \ll \sqrt{\dfrac{m}{bg}}, \\[2ex] -\sqrt{\dfrac{mg}{b}}, & \text{if } t \gg \sqrt{\dfrac{m}{bg}}, \end{cases}$$

2-67

verify (2-69) and (2-70)

$$x = -\frac{m}{b}\ln\cosh\left(\sqrt{\frac{bg}{m}}\,t\right)$$

(2–70)

$$\doteq \begin{cases} -\tfrac{1}{2}gt^2, & \text{if } t \ll \sqrt{\dfrac{m}{bg}}, \\[2mm] \dfrac{m}{b}\ln 2 - \sqrt{\dfrac{mg}{b}}\,t, & \text{if } t \gg \sqrt{\dfrac{m}{bg}}. \end{cases}$$

Again there is a terminal velocity, given this time by $(mg/b)^{\frac{1}{2}}$. The terminal velocity can always be found as the velocity at which the frictional force equals the gravitational force, and will exist whenever the frictional force becomes sufficiently large at high velocities.

In the case of bodies falling from a great height, the variation of the gravitational force with height should be taken into account. In this case, we neglect air resistance, and measure x from the center of the earth. Then if M is the mass of the earth and m the mass of the falling body,

$$F = -\frac{mMG}{x^2},$$

(2–71)

and

$$V(x) = -\int_\infty^x F\,dx = -\frac{mMG}{x},$$

(2–72)

where we have taken $x_s = \infty$ in order to avoid a constant term in $V(x)$. Equation (2–45) becomes

$$v = \frac{dx}{dt} = \pm\sqrt{\frac{2}{m}\left(E + \frac{mMG}{x}\right)^{\frac{1}{2}}}.$$

(2–73)

The plus sign refers to ascending motion, the minus sign to descending motion.

The function $V(x)$ is plotted in Fig. 2–2. We see that there are two types of motion, depending on whether E is positive or negative. When E is positive, there is no turning point, and if the body is initially moving upward, it will continue to move upward forever, with decreasing velocity, approaching the limiting velocity

$$v_l = \sqrt{\frac{2E}{m}}.$$

(2–74)

When E is negative, there is a turning point at a height

$$x_T = \frac{mMG}{-E}.$$

(2–75)

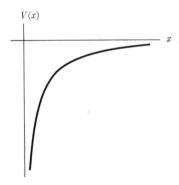

Fig. 2–2. Plot of $V(x) = -(mMG/x)$.

If the body is initially moving upward, it will come to a stop at x_T, and fall back to the earth. The dividing case between these two types of motion occurs when the initial position and velocity are such that $E = 0$. The turning point is then at infinity, and the body moves upward forever, approaching the limiting velocity $v_l = 0$. If $E = 0$, then at any height x, the velocity will be

$$v_e = \sqrt{\frac{2MG}{x}}. \tag{2-76}$$

This is called the *escape velocity* for a body at distance x from the center of the earth, because a body moving upward at height x with velocity v_e will just have sufficient energy to travel upward indefinitely (if there is no air resistance).

To find $x(t)$, we must evaluate the integral

$$\int_{x_0}^{x} \frac{dx}{\pm \left(E + \frac{mMG}{x}\right)^{\frac{1}{2}}} = \sqrt{\frac{2}{m}}\, t, \tag{2-77}$$

where x_0 is the height at $t = 0$. To solve for the case when E is negative, we substitute

$$\cos \theta = \sqrt{\frac{-Ex}{mMG}}. \tag{2-78}$$

Equation (2-77) then becomes

$$\frac{mMG}{(-E)^{\frac{3}{2}}} \int_{\theta_0}^{\theta} 2 \cos^2 \theta \, d\theta = \sqrt{\frac{2}{m}}\, t. \tag{2-79}$$

(We choose a positive sign for the integrand so that θ will increase when t increases.) We can, without loss of generality, take x_0 to be at the turning point x_T, since the body will at some time in its past or future career pass through x_T if no force except gravity acts upon it, provided $E < 0$. Then $\theta_0 = 0$, and

$$\frac{mMG}{(-E)^{\frac{3}{2}}} (\theta + \sin \theta \cos \theta) = \sqrt{\frac{2}{m}}\, t,$$

or

$$\theta + \tfrac{1}{2} \sin 2\theta = \sqrt{\frac{2MG}{x_T^3}}\, t, \tag{2-80}$$

and

$$x = x_T \cos^2 \theta. \tag{2-81}$$

This pair of equations cannot be solved explicitly for $x(t)$. A numerical solution can be obtained by choosing a sequence of values of θ and finding the corresponding values of x and t from Eqs. (2-80) and (2-81). That part of the motion for which x is less than the radius of the earth will, of course, not be correctly given, since Eq. (2-71) assumes all the mass of the earth concentrated at $x = 0$ (not to mention the fact that we have omitted from our equation of motion the forces which would act on the body when it collides with the earth).

The solution can be obtained in a similar way for the cases when E is positive or zero.

2–7 The simple harmonic oscillator. The most important problem in one-dimensional motion, and fortunately one of the easiest to solve, is the harmonic or linear oscillator. The simplest example is that of a mass m fastened to a spring whose constant is k. If we measure x from the relaxed position of the spring, then the spring exerts a restoring force

$$F = -kx. \qquad (2\text{--}82)$$

The potential energy associated with this force is

$$V(x) = \tfrac{1}{2}kx^2. \qquad (2\text{--}83)$$

The equation of motion, if we assume no other force acts, is

$$m\frac{d^2x}{dt^2} + kx = 0. \qquad (2\text{--}84)$$

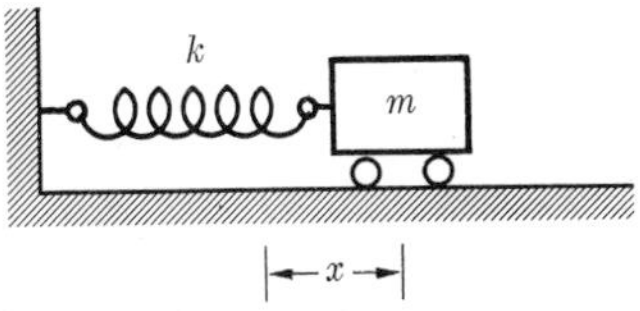

Fig. 2–3. Model simple harmonic oscillator.

Equation (2–84) describes the free harmonic oscillator. Its solution was obtained in Section 2–5. The motion is a simple sinusoidal oscillation about the point of equilibrium. In all physical cases, there will be some frictional force acting, though it may often be very small. As a good approximation in most cases, particularly when the friction is small, we can assume that the frictional force is proportional to the velocity. Since this is the only kind of frictional force for which the problem can easily be solved, we shall restrict our attention to this case. If we use Eq. (2–31) for the frictional force with $n = 1$, the equation of motion then becomes

$$m\frac{d^2x}{dt^2} + b\frac{dx}{dt} + kx = 0. \qquad (2\text{--}85)$$

This equation describes the damped harmonic oscillator. Its motion, at least for small damping, consists of a sinusoidal oscillation of gradually decreasing amplitude, as we shall show later. If the oscillator is subject to an additional impressed force $F(t)$, its motion will be given by

$$m\frac{d^2x}{dt^2} + b\frac{dx}{dt} + kx = F(t). \qquad (2\text{--}86)$$

If $F(t)$ is a sinusoidally varying force, Eq. (2–86) leads to the phenomenon of resonance, where the amplitude of oscillation becomes very large when the frequency of the impressed force equals the natural frequency of the free oscillator.

The importance of the harmonic oscillator problem lies in the fact that equations of the same form as Eqs. (2–84)–(2–86) turn up in a wide variety of physical problems. In almost every case of one-dimensional motion where the potential energy function $V(x)$ has one or more minima, the motion of the particle for small oscillations about the minimum point follows equation (2–84). To show this, let $V(x)$ have a minimum at $x = x_0$, and expand the function $V(x)$ in a Taylor series about this point:

$$V(x) = V(x_0) + \left(\frac{dV}{dx}\right)_{x_0} (x - x_0) + \tfrac{1}{2} \left(\frac{d^2V}{dx^2}\right)_{x_0} (x - x_0)^2$$

$$+ \tfrac{1}{6} \left(\frac{d^3V}{dx^3}\right)_{x_0} (x - x_0)^3 + \cdots . \quad (2\text{–}87)$$

The constant $V(x_0)$ can be dropped without affecting the physical results. Since x_0 is a minimum point,

$$\left(\frac{dV}{dx}\right)_{x_0} = 0, \quad \left(\frac{d^2V}{dx^2}\right)_{x_0} \geq 0. \quad (2\text{–}88)$$

Making the abbreviations

$$k = \left(\frac{d^2V}{dx^2}\right)_{x_0}, \quad (2\text{–}89)$$

$$x' = x - x_0, \quad (2\text{–}90)$$

we can write the potential function in the form

$$V(x') = \tfrac{1}{2}kx'^2 + \cdots . \quad (2\text{–}91)$$

For sufficiently small values of x', provided $k \neq 0$, we can neglect the terms represented by dots, and Eq. (2–91) becomes identical with Eq. (2–83). Hence, for small oscillations about any potential minimum, except in the exceptional case $k = 0$, the motion is that of a harmonic oscillator.

When a solid is deformed, it resists the deformation with a force proportional to the amount of deformation, provided the deformation is not too great. This statement is called *Hooke's law*. It follows from the fact that the undeformed solid is at a potential energy minimum and that the potential energy may be expanded in a Taylor series in the coordinate describing the deformation. If a solid is deformed beyond a certain point, called its *elastic limit*, it will remain permanently deformed; that is, its structure is altered so that its undeformed shape for minimum potential energy is changed. It turns out in most cases that the higher order terms in the series (2–91) are negligible almost up to the elastic limit, so that Hooke's law holds almost up to the elastic limit. When the elastic limit is exceeded and plastic flow takes place, the forces depend in a complicated way not only on the shape of the material, but also on the velocity of deformation and even on its previous history, so that the forces can no longer be specified in terms of a potential energy function.

Thus practically any problem involving mechanical vibrations reduces to that of the harmonic oscillator at small amplitudes of vibration, that is, so long as the elastic limits of the materials involved are not exceeded. The motions of stretched strings and membranes, and of sound vibrations in an enclosed gas or in a solid, result in a number of so-called normal modes of vibration, each mode behaving in many ways like an independent harmonic oscillator. An electric circuit containing inductance L, resistance R, and capacitance C in series, and subject to an applied electromotive force $E(t)$, satisfies the equation

$$L \frac{d^2q}{dt^2} + R \frac{dq}{dt} + \frac{q}{C} = E(t), \tag{2-92}$$

where q is the charge on the condenser and dq/dt is the current. This equation is identical in form with Eq. (2–86). Early work on electrical circuits was often carried out by analogy with the corresponding mechanical problem. Today the situation is often reversed, and the mechanical and acoustical engineers are able to make use of the simple and effective methods developed by electrical engineers for handling vibration problems. The theory of electrical oscillations in a transmission line or in a cavity is similar mathematically to the problem of the vibrating string or resonating air cavity. The quantum mechanical theory of an atom can be put in a form which is identical mathematically with the theory of a system of harmonic oscillators.

2–8 Linear differential equations with constant coefficients. Equations (2–84)–(2–86) are examples of second order linear differential equations. The *order* of a differential equation is the order of the highest derivative that occurs in it. Most equations of mechanics are of second order. (Why?) A *linear* differential equation is one in which there are no terms of higher than first degree in the dependent variable (in this case x) and its derivatives. Thus the most general type of linear differential equation of order n would be

$$a_n(t) \frac{d^nx}{dt^n} + a_{n-1}(t) \frac{d^{n-1}x}{dt^{n-1}} + \cdots + a_1(t) \frac{dx}{dt} + a_0(t)x = b(t). \tag{2-93}$$

If $b(t) = 0$, the equation is said to be *homogeneous;* otherwise it is *inhomogeneous.* Linear equations are important because there are simple general methods for solving them, particularly when the coefficients $a_0, a_1, \ldots, a_n$ are constants, as in Eqs. (2–84)–(2–86). In the present section, we shall solve the problem of the free harmonic oscillator [Eq. (2–84)], and at the same time develop a general method of solving any linear homogeneous differential equation with constant coefficients. This method is applied in Section 2–9 to the damped harmonic oscillator equation (2–85). In Section 2–10 we shall study the behavior of a harmonic oscillator under a sinusoidally oscillating impressed force. In Section 2–11 a theorem is developed which forms the basis for attacking Eq. (2–86) with any impressed force $F(t)$, and the methods of attack are discussed briefly.

The solution of Eq. (2–84), which we obtained in Section 2–5, we now write in the form

$$x = A \sin (\omega_0 t + \theta), \quad \omega_0 = \sqrt{\frac{k}{m}}. \tag{2–94}$$

This solution depends on two "arbitrary" constants A and θ. They are called arbitrary because no matter what values are given to them, the solution (2–94) will satisfy Eq. (2–84). They are not arbitrary in a physical problem, but depend on the initial conditions. It can be shown that the general solution of any second order differential equation depends on two arbitrary constants. By this we mean that we can write the solution in the form

$$x = x(t;C_1,C_2), \tag{2–95}$$

such that for every value of C_1 and C_2, or every value within a certain range, $x(t;C_1,C_2)$ satisfies the equation and, furthermore, practically every solution of the equation is included in the function $x(t;C_1,C_2)$ for some value of C_1 and C_2.* If we can find a solution containing two arbitrary constants which satisfies a second order differential equation, then we can be sure that practically every solution will be included in it. The methods of solution of the differential equations studied in previous sections have all been such as to lead directly to a solution corresponding to the initial conditions of the physical problem. In the present and subsequent sections of this chapter, we shall consider methods which lead to a general solution containing two arbitrary constants. These constants must then be given the proper values to fit the initial conditions of the physical problem; the fact that a solution with two arbitrary constants is the general solution guarantees that we can always satisfy the initial conditions by proper choice of the constants.

We now state two theorems regarding linear homogeneous differential equations:

THEOREM I. *If $x = x_1(t)$ is any solution of a linear homogeneous differential equation, and C is any constant, then $x = Cx_1(t)$ is also a solution.*

THEOREM II. *If $x = x_1(t)$ and $x = x_2(t)$ are solutions of a linear homogeneous differential equation, then $x = x_1(t) + x_2(t)$ is also a solution.*

We prove these theorems only for the case of a second order equation, since mechanical equations are generally of this type:

---

* The only exceptions are certain "singular" solutions which may occur in regions where the mathematical conditions for a unique solution (Section 2–2) are not satisfied.

$$a_2(t) \frac{d^2x}{dt^2} + a_1(t) \frac{dx}{dt} + a_0(t)x = 0. \tag{2-96}$$

Assume that $x = x_1(t)$ satisfies Eq. (2-96). Then

$$a_2(t) \frac{d^2(Cx_1)}{dt^2} + a_1(t) \frac{d(Cx_1)}{dt} + a_0(t)(Cx_1) =$$

$$C \left[a_2(t) \frac{d^2x_1}{dt^2} + a_1(t) \frac{dx_1}{dt} + a_0(t)x_1 \right] = 0.$$

Hence $x = Cx_1(t)$ also satisfies Eq. (2-96). If $x_1(t)$ and $x_2(t)$ both satisfy Eq. (2-96), then

$$a_2(t) \frac{d^2(x_1 + x_2)}{dt^2} + a_1(t) \frac{d(x_1 + x_2)}{dt} + a_0(t)(x_1 + x_2)$$

$$= \left[a_2(t) \frac{d^2x_1}{dt^2} + a_1(t) \frac{dx_1}{dt} + a_0(t)x_1 \right] + \left[a_2(t) \frac{d^2x_2}{dt^2} + a_1(t) \frac{dx_2}{dt} + a_0(t)x_2 \right] = 0.$$

Hence $x = x_1(t) + x_2(t)$ also satisfies Eq. (2-96). The problem of finding the general solution of Eq. (2-96) thus reduces to that of finding any two independent "particular" solutions $x_1(t)$ and $x_2(t)$, for then Theorems I and II guarantee that

$$x = C_1x_1(t) + C_2x_2(t) \tag{2-97}$$

is also a solution. Since this solution contains two arbitrary constants, it must be the general solution. The requirement that $x_1(t)$ and $x_2(t)$ be independent means in this case that one is not a multiple of the other. If $x_1(t)$ were a constant multiple of $x_2(t)$, then Eq. (2-97) would really contain only one arbitrary constant. The right member of Eq. (2-97) is called a *linear combination* of x_1 and x_2.

In the case of equations like (2-84) and (2-85), where the coefficients are constant, a solution of the form $x = e^{pt}$ always exists. For, assume that a_0, a_1, and a_2 are all constant in Eq. (2-96) and substitute

$$x = e^{pt}, \quad \frac{dx}{dt} = pe^{pt}, \quad \frac{d^2x}{dt^2} = p^2e^{pt}. \tag{2-98}$$

We then have

$$(a_2p^2 + a_1p + a_0)e^{pt} = 0. \tag{2-99}$$

Cancelling out e^{pt}, we have an algebraic equation of second degree in p. Such an equation has, in general, two roots. If they are different, this gives two independent functions e^{pt} satisfying Eq. (2-96) and our problem is solved. If the two roots for p should be equal, we have found only one solution, but then, as we shall show in the next section, the function

$$x = te^{pt} \tag{2-100}$$

also satisfies the differential equation. The linear homogeneous equation of nth order with constant coefficients can also be solved by this method.

Let us apply the method to Eq. (2–84). Making the substitution (2–98), we have

$$mp^2 + k = 0, \tag{2–101}$$

whose solution is

$$p = \pm \sqrt{-\frac{k}{m}} = \pm i\omega_0, \quad \omega_0 = \sqrt{\frac{k}{m}}. \tag{2–102}$$

This gives, as the general solution,

$$x = C_1 e^{i\omega_0 t} + C_2 e^{-i\omega_0 t}. \tag{2–103}$$

In order to interpret this result, we remember that

$$e^{i\theta} = \cos\theta + i\sin\theta. \tag{2–104}$$

If we allow complex numbers x as solutions of the differential equation, then the arbitrary constants C_1 and C_2 must also be complex in order for Eq. (2–103) to be the general solution. The solution of the physical problem must be real, hence we must choose C_1 and C_2 so that x turns out to be real. The sum of two complex numbers is real if one is the complex conjugate of the other. If

$$C = a + ib, \tag{2–105}$$

and

$$C^* = a - ib, \tag{2–106}$$

then

$$C + C^* = 2a, \quad C - C^* = 2ib. \tag{2–107}$$

Now $e^{i\omega_0 t}$ is the complex conjugate of $e^{-i\omega_0 t}$, so that if we set $C_1 = C, C_2 = C^*$, then x will be real:

$$x = C e^{i\omega_0 t} + C^* e^{-i\omega_0 t}. \tag{2–108}$$

We could evaluate x by using Eqs. (2–104), (2–105), and (2–106), but the algebra is simpler if we make use of the polar representation of a complex number:

$$C = a + ib = re^{i\theta}, \tag{2–109}$$

$$C^* = a - ib = re^{-i\theta}, \tag{2–110}$$

where

$$r = (a^2 + b^2)^{\frac{1}{2}}, \quad \tan\theta = \frac{b}{a}, \tag{2–111}$$

$$a = r\cos\theta, \quad b = r\sin\theta. \tag{2–112}$$

The reader should verify that these equations follow algebraically from Eq. (2–104). If we represent C as a point in the complex plane, then a and b are its rectangular coordinates, and r and θ are its polar coordinates. Using the polar representation of C, Eq. (2–108) becomes (we set $r = \frac{1}{2}A$)

$$x = \frac{1}{2}A e^{i(\omega_0 t + \theta)} + \frac{1}{2}A e^{-i(\omega_0 t + \theta)}$$
$$= A\cos(\omega_0 t + \theta). \tag{2–113}$$

This is the general real solution of Eq. (2–84). It differs from the solution (2–94) only by a shift of $\pi/2$ in the phase constant θ.

Setting $B_1 = A \cos \theta$, $B_2 = -A \sin \theta$, we can write our solution in another form:

$$x = B_1 \cos \omega_0 t + B_2 \sin \omega_0 t. \tag{2–114}$$

The constants A, θ, or B_1, B_2, are to be obtained in terms of the initial values x_0, v_0 at $t = 0$ by setting

$$x_0 = A \cos \theta = B_1, \tag{2–115}$$
$$v_0 = -\omega_0 A \sin \theta = \omega_0 B_2. \tag{2–116}$$

The solutions are easily obtained:

$$A = \left(x_0^2 + \frac{v_0^2}{\omega_0^2} \right)^{\frac{1}{2}}, \tag{2–117}$$

$$\tan \theta = -\frac{v_0}{x_0 \omega_0}, \tag{2–118}$$

or

$$B_1 = x_0, \tag{2–119}$$

$$B_2 = \frac{v_0}{\omega_0}. \tag{2–120}$$

Another way of handling Eq. (2–103) would be to notice that, since Eq. (2–84) contains only real coefficients, a complex function can satisfy it only if both real and imaginary parts satisfy it separately. (The proof of this statement is a matter of substituting $x = u + iw$ and carrying out a little algebra.) Hence if a solution is (we set $r = A$)

$$\begin{aligned} x = C e^{i\omega_0 t} &= A e^{i(\omega_0 t + \theta)} \\ &= A \cos(\omega_0 t + \theta) + iA \sin(\omega_0 t + \theta), \end{aligned} \tag{2–121}$$

then both the real and imaginary parts of this solution must separately be solutions, and we have either solution (2–113) or (2–94). We can carry through the solutions of linear equations like this, and perform any algebraic operations we please on them in their complex form (so long as we do not multiply two complex numbers together), with the understanding that at each step what we are really concerned with is only the real part or only the imaginary part. This procedure is often useful in the treatment of problems involving harmonic oscillations, and we shall use it in Section 2–10.

It is often very convenient to represent a sinusoidal function as a complex exponential:

$$\cos \theta = \text{Real part of } e^{i\theta} = \frac{e^{i\theta} + e^{-i\theta}}{2}, \tag{2–122}$$

$$\sin \theta = \text{Imaginary part of } e^{i\theta} = \frac{e^{i\theta} - e^{-i\theta}}{2i}. \tag{2–123}$$

Exponential functions are easier to handle algebraically than sines and cosines. The reader will find the relations (2–122), (2–123), and (2–104) useful in deriving trigonometric formulas. The power series for the sine and cosine functions are readily obtained by expanding $e^{i\theta}$ in a power series and separating the real and imaginary parts. The trigonometric rule for $\sin(A + B)$ and $\cos(A + B)$ can be easily obtained from the algebraic rule for adding exponents. Many other examples could be cited.

2–9 The damped harmonic oscillator. The equation of motion for a particle subject to a linear restoring force and a frictional force proportional to its velocity is [Eq. (2–85)]

$$m\ddot{x} + b\dot{x} + kx = 0, \tag{2-124}$$

where the dots stand for time derivatives. Applying the method of Section 2–8, we make the substitution (2–98) and obtain

$$mp^2 + bp + k = 0. \tag{2-125}$$

The solution is

$$p = -\frac{b}{2m} \pm \left[\left(\frac{b}{2m}\right)^2 - \frac{k}{m}\right]^{\frac{1}{2}}. \tag{2-126}$$

We distinguish three cases: (a) $k/m > (b/2m)^2$, (b) $k/m < (b/2m)^2$, and (c) $k/m = (b/2m)^2$.

In case (a), we make the substitutions

$$\omega_0 = \sqrt{\frac{k}{m}}, \tag{2-127}$$

$$\gamma = \frac{b}{2m}, \tag{2-128}$$

$$\omega_1 = (\omega_0^2 - \gamma^2)^{\frac{1}{2}}, \tag{2-129}$$

where γ is called the damping coefficient and $(\omega_0/2\pi)$ is the natural frequency of the undamped oscillator. There are now two solutions for p:

$$p = -\gamma \pm i\omega_1. \tag{2-130}$$

The general solution of the differential equation is therefore

$$x = C_1 e^{-\gamma t + i\omega_1 t} + C_2 e^{-\gamma t - i\omega_1 t}. \tag{2-131}$$

Setting

$$C_1 = \tfrac{1}{2}Ae^{i\theta}, \quad C_2 = \tfrac{1}{2}Ae^{-i\theta}, \tag{2-132}$$

we have

$$x = Ae^{-\gamma t}\cos(\omega_1 t + \theta). \tag{2-133}$$

This corresponds to an oscillation of frequency $(\omega_1/2\pi)$ with an amplitude $Ae^{-\gamma t}$ which decreases exponentially with time. The constants A and θ

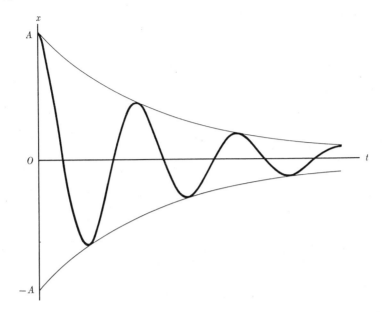

FIG. 2–4. Motion of damped harmonic oscillator. Heavy curve: $x = Ae^{-\gamma t} \cos \omega t$, $\gamma = \omega/8$. Light curve: $x = \pm Ae^{-\gamma t}$.

depend upon the initial conditions. The frequency of oscillation is less than without damping. The solution (2–133) can also be written

$$x = e^{-\gamma t}(B_1 \cos \omega_1 t + B_2 \sin \omega_1 t). \tag{2–134}$$

In terms of the constants ω_0 and γ, Eq. (2–124) can be written

$$\ddot{x} + 2\gamma\dot{x} + \omega_0^2 x = 0. \tag{2–135}$$

This form of the equation is often used in discussing mechanical oscillations.

The total energy of the oscillator is

$$E = \tfrac{1}{2}m\dot{x}^2 + \tfrac{1}{2}kx^2. \tag{2–136}$$

In the important case of small damping, $\gamma \ll \omega_0$, we can set $\omega_1 \doteq \omega_0$ and neglect γ compared with ω_0, and we have for the energy corresponding to the solution (2–133), approximately,

$$E \doteq \tfrac{1}{2}kA^2 e^{-2\gamma t} = E_0 e^{-2\gamma t}. \tag{2–137}$$

Thus the energy falls off exponentially at twice the rate at which the amplitude decays. The fractional rate of decline or *logarithmic derivative* of E is

$$\frac{1}{E}\frac{dE}{dt} = \frac{d \ln E}{dt} = -2\gamma. \tag{2–138}$$

We now consider case (b), $(\omega_0 < \gamma)$. In this case, the two solutions for p are

$$p = -\gamma_1 = -\gamma - (\gamma^2 - \omega_0^2)^{\frac{1}{2}},$$
$$p = -\gamma_2 = -\gamma + (\gamma^2 - \omega_0^2)^{\frac{1}{2}}. \qquad (2\text{–}139)$$

The general solution is

$$x = C_1 e^{-\gamma_1 t} + C_2 e^{-\gamma_2 t}. \qquad (2\text{–}140)$$

These two terms both decline exponentially with time, one at a faster rate than the other. The constants C_1 and C_2 may be chosen to fit the initial conditions. The reader should determine them for two important cases: $x_0 \neq 0, v_0 = 0$ and $x_0 = 0, v_0 \neq 0$, and draw curves $x(t)$ for the two cases.

In case (c), $(\omega_0 = \gamma)$, we have only one solution for p:

$$p = -\gamma. \qquad (2\text{–}141)$$

The corresponding solution for x is

$$x = e^{-\gamma t}. \qquad (2\text{–}142)$$

We now show that, in this case, another solution is

$$x = te^{-\gamma t}. \qquad (2\text{–}143)$$

To prove this, we compute

$$\dot{x} = e^{-\gamma t} - \gamma te^{-\gamma t},$$
$$\ddot{x} = -2\gamma e^{-\gamma t} + \gamma^2 te^{-\gamma t}. \qquad (2\text{–}144)$$

The left side of Eq. (2–135) is, for this x,

$$\ddot{x} + 2\gamma\dot{x} + \omega_0^2 x = (\omega_0^2 - \gamma^2)te^{-\gamma t}. \qquad (2\text{–}145)$$

This is zero if $\omega_0 = \gamma$. Hence the general solution in case $\omega_0 = \gamma$ is

$$x = (C_1 + C_2 t)e^{-\gamma t}. \qquad (2\text{–}146)$$

This function declines exponentially with time at a rate intermediate between that of the two exponential terms in Eq. (2–140):

$$\gamma_1 > \gamma > \gamma_2. \qquad (2\text{–}147)$$

Hence the solution (2–146) falls to zero faster after a sufficiently long time than the solution (2–140), except in the case $C_2 = 0$ in Eq. (2–140). Cases (a), (b), and (c) are important in problems involving mechanisms which approach an equilibrium position under the action of a frictional damping force, e.g., pointer reading meters, hydraulic and pneumatic spring returns for doors, etc. In most cases, it is desired that the mechanism move quickly and smoothly to its equilibrium position. For a given damping coefficient γ, or for a given ω_0, this is accomplished in the shortest time without overshoot if $\omega_0 = \gamma$ [case (c)]. This case is called *critical damping*. If $\omega_0 < \gamma$, the system is said to be *overdamped;* it behaves sluggishly and does not return as quickly to $x = 0$ as for critical damping. If $\omega_0 > \gamma$, the system is said to be *underdamped;* the coordinate x then overshoots the value $x = 0$ and oscillates. Note that at critical damping, $\omega_1 = 0$, so that the period of oscillation becomes infinite. The behavior is shown in Fig. 2–5 for the case of a system displaced from equilibrium and released ($x_0 \neq 0$, $v_0 = 0$). The reader should draw similar curves for the case where the system is given a sharp blow at $t = 0$ (i.e., $x_0 = 0$, $v_0 \neq 0$).

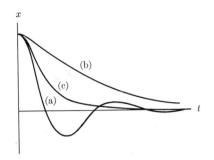

FIG. 2–5. Return of harmonic oscillator to equilibrium. (a) Underdamped. (b) Overdamped. (c) Critically damped.

2–10 The forced harmonic oscillator. The harmonic oscillator subject to an external applied force is governed by Eq. (2–86). In order to simplify the problem of solving this equation, we state the following theorem:

THEOREM III. *If $x_i(t)$ is a solution of an inhomogeneous linear equation [e.g., Eq. (2–86)], and $x_h(t)$ is a solution of the corresponding homogeneous equation [e.g., Eq. (2–85)], then $x(t) = x_i(t) + x_h(t)$ is also a solution of the inhomogeneous equation.*

This theorem applies whether the coefficients in the equation are constants or functions of t. The proof is a matter of straightforward substitution, and is left to the reader. In consequence of Theorem III, if we know the general solution x_h of the homogeneous equation (2–85) (we found this in Section 2–9), then we need find only one particular solution x_i of the inhomogeneous equation (2–86). For we can add x_i to x_h and obtain a solution of Eq. (2–86) which contains two arbitrary constants and is therefore the general solution.

The most important case is that of a sinusoidally oscillating applied force. If the applied force oscillates with angular frequency ω and amplitude F_0, the equation of motion is

$$m \frac{d^2x}{dt^2} + b \frac{dx}{dt} + kx = F_0 \cos(\omega t + \theta_0), \qquad (2\text{–}148)$$

where θ_0 is a constant specifying the phase of the applied force. There are, of course, many solutions of Eq. (2–148), of which we need find only one. From physical considerations, we expect that one solution will be a steady oscillation of the coordinate x at the same frequency as the applied force:

$$x = A_s \cos(\omega t + \theta_s). \qquad (2\text{–}149)$$

The amplitude A_s and phase θ_s of the oscillations in x will have to be determined by substituting Eq. (2–149) in Eq. (2–148). This procedure is straightforward and leads to the correct answer. The algebra is simpler, however, if we write the force as the real part of a complex function:*

$$F(t) = Re(F_0 e^{i\omega t}), \tag{2–150}$$
$$F_0 = F_0 e^{i\theta_0}. \tag{2–151}$$

Thus if we can find a solution $x(t)$ of

$$m\frac{d^2x}{dt^2} + b\frac{dx}{dt} + kx = F_0 e^{i\omega t}, \tag{2–152}$$

then, by splitting the equation into real and imaginary parts, we can show that the real part of $x(t)$ will satisfy Eq. (2–148). We assume a solution of the form

$$x = x_0 e^{i\omega t},$$

so that

$$\dot{x} = i\omega x_0 e^{i\omega t}, \quad \ddot{x} = -\omega^2 x_0 e^{i\omega t}. \tag{2–153}$$

Substituting in Eq. (2–152), we solve for x_0:

$$x_0 = \frac{F_0/m}{\omega_0^2 - \omega^2 + 2i\gamma\omega}. \tag{2–154}$$

The solution of Eq. (2–152) is therefore

$$x = x_0 e^{i\omega t} = \frac{(F_0/m)e^{i\omega t}}{\omega_0^2 - \omega^2 + 2i\gamma\omega}. \tag{2–155}$$

We are often more interested in the velocity

$$\dot{x} = \frac{i\omega F_0}{m} \frac{e^{i\omega t}}{\omega_0^2 - \omega^2 + 2i\gamma\omega}. \tag{2–156}$$

The simplest way to write Eq. (2–156) is to express all complex factors in polar form [Eq. (2–109)]:

$$i = e^{i\pi/2}, \tag{2–157}$$
$$\omega_0^2 - \omega^2 + 2i\gamma\omega = [(\omega_0^2 - \omega^2)^2 + 4\gamma^2\omega^2]^{\frac{1}{2}} \exp\left(i\tan^{-1}\frac{2\gamma\omega}{\omega_0^2 - \omega^2}\right). \tag{2–158}$$

If we use these expressions, Eq. (2–156) becomes

$$\dot{x} = \frac{\omega F_0}{m[(\omega_0^2 - \omega^2)^2 + 4\gamma^2\omega^2]^{\frac{1}{2}}} e^{i(\omega t + \theta_0 + \beta)}, \tag{2–159}$$

where

$$\beta = \frac{\pi}{2} - \tan^{-1}\frac{2\gamma\omega}{\omega_0^2 - \omega^2} = \tan^{-1}\frac{\omega_0^2 - \omega^2}{2\gamma\omega}, \tag{2–160}$$

---

* Note the use of Roman type (F, x) to distinguish complex quantities from the corresponding real quantities (F, x) which are their real parts.

$$\sin \beta = \frac{\omega_0^2 - \omega^2}{[(\omega_0^2 - \omega^2)^2 + 4\gamma^2\omega^2]^{\frac{1}{2}}}, \tag{2-161}$$

$$\cos \beta = \frac{2\gamma\omega}{[(\omega_0^2 - \omega^2)^2 + 4\gamma^2\omega^2]^{\frac{1}{2}}}. \tag{2-162}$$

By Eq. (2–159),

$$\dot{x} = Re(\dot{\mathrm{x}})$$
$$= \frac{F_0}{m} \frac{\omega}{[(\omega_0^2 - \omega^2)^2 + 4\gamma^2\omega^2]^{\frac{1}{2}}} \cos(\omega t + \theta_0 + \beta), \tag{2-163}$$

and

$$x = Re(\mathrm{x}) = Re\left(\frac{\dot{\mathrm{x}}}{i\omega}\right)$$
$$= \frac{F_0}{m} \frac{1}{[(\omega_0^2 - \omega^2)^2 + 4\gamma^2\omega^2]^{\frac{1}{2}}} \sin(\omega t + \theta_0 + \beta). \tag{2-164}$$

This is a particular solution of Eq. (2–148) containing no arbitrary constants. By Theorem III and Eq. (2–133), the general solution (for the underdamped oscillator) is

$$x = Ae^{-\gamma t}\cos(\omega_1 t + \theta) + \frac{F_0/m}{[(\omega_0^2 - \omega^2)^2 + 4\gamma^2\omega^2]^{\frac{1}{2}}}\sin(\omega t + \theta_0 + \beta). \tag{2-165}$$

This solution contains two arbitrary constants A, θ, whose values are determined by the initial values x_0, v_0 at $t = 0$. The first term dies out exponentially in time and is called the *transient*. The second term is called

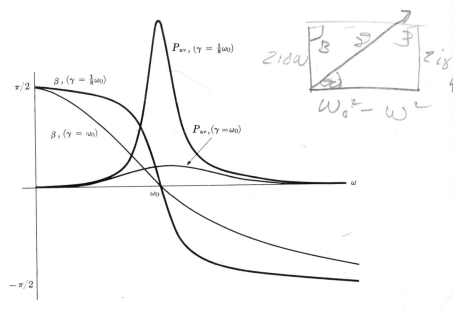

Fig. 2–6. Power and phase of forced harmonic oscillations.

the *steady state*, and oscillates with constant amplitude. The transient depends on the initial conditions. The steady state which remains after the transient dies away is independent of the initial conditions.

In the steady state, the rate at which work is done on the oscillator by the applied force is

$$\dot{x}F(t) = \frac{F_0^2}{m} \frac{\omega}{[(\omega^2 - \omega_0^2)^2 + 4\gamma^2\omega^2]^{\frac{1}{2}}} \cos(\omega t + \theta_0) \cos(\omega t + \theta_0 + \beta)$$

$$= \frac{F_0^2 \, \omega \cos\beta \cos^2(\omega t + \theta_0)}{m[(\omega^2 - \omega_0^2)^2 + 4\gamma^2\omega^2]^{\frac{1}{2}}} - \frac{F_0^2 \, \omega \sin\beta \sin 2(\omega t + \theta_0)}{2m[(\omega^2 - \omega_0^2)^2 + 4\gamma^2\omega^2]^{\frac{1}{2}}}. \quad (2\text{-}166)$$

The last term on the right is zero on the average, while the average value of $\cos^2(\omega t + \theta_0)$ over a complete cycle is $\frac{1}{2}$. Hence the average power delivered by the applied force is

$$P_{av} = \langle \dot{x}F(t)\rangle_{av} = \frac{F_0^2 \cos\beta}{2m} \frac{\omega}{[(\omega^2 - \omega_0^2)^2 + 4\gamma^2\omega^2]^{\frac{1}{2}}}, \quad (2\text{-}167)$$

or

$$P_{av} = \tfrac{1}{2}F_0\dot{x}_m \cos\beta, \quad (2\text{-}168)$$

where $\dot{x}_m$ is the maximum value of $\dot{x}$. A similar relation holds for power delivered to an electrical circuit. The factor $\cos\beta$ is called the *power factor*. In the electrical case, β is the phase angle between the current and the applied emf. Using formula (2-162) for $\cos\beta$, we can rewrite Eq. (2-167):

$$P_{av} = \frac{F_0^2}{m} \frac{\gamma\omega^2}{(\omega^2 - \omega_0^2)^2 + 4\gamma^2\omega^2}. \quad (2\text{-}169)$$

It is easy to show that in the steady state power is supplied to the oscillator at the same average rate that power is being dissipated by friction, as of course it must be. The power P_{av} has a maximum for $\omega = \omega_0$. In Fig. 2-6, the power P_{av} (in arbitrary units) and the phase β of steady state forced oscillations are plotted against ω for two values of γ. The heavy curves are for small damping; the light curves are for greater damping. Formula (2-169) can be simplified somewhat in case $\gamma \ll \omega_0$. In this case, P_{av} is large only near the resonant frequency ω_0, and we shall deduce a formula valid near $\omega = \omega_0$. Defining

$$\Delta\omega = \omega - \omega_0, \quad (2\text{-}170)$$

and assuming $\Delta\omega \ll \omega_0$, we have

$$(\omega^2 - \omega_0^2) = (\omega + \omega_0)\Delta\omega \doteq 2\omega_0\,\Delta\omega, \quad (2\text{-}171)$$

$$\omega^2 \doteq \omega_0^2. \quad (2\text{-}172)$$

Hence

$$P_{\text{av}} \doteq \frac{F_0^2}{4m} \frac{\gamma}{(\Delta\omega)^2 + \gamma^2}. \tag{2-173}$$

This simple formula gives a good approximation to P_{av} near resonance. The corresponding formula for β is

$$\cos\beta \doteq \frac{\gamma}{[(\Delta\omega)^2 + \gamma^2]^{\frac{1}{2}}}, \quad \sin\beta \doteq \frac{-\Delta\omega}{[(\Delta\omega)^2 + \gamma^2]^{\frac{1}{2}}}. \tag{2-174}$$

When $\omega \ll \omega_0$, $\beta \doteq \pi/2$, and Eq. (2-164) becomes

$$x \doteq \frac{F_0}{\omega_0^2 m} \cos(\omega t + \theta_0) = \frac{F(t)}{k}. \tag{2-175}$$

This result is easily interpreted physically; when the force varies slowly, the particle moves in such a way that the applied force is just balanced by the restoring force. When $\omega \gg \omega_0$, $\beta \doteq -\pi/2$, and Eq. (2-164) becomes

$$x \doteq -\frac{F_0}{\omega^2 m} \cos(\omega t + \theta_0) = -\frac{F(t)}{\omega^2 m}. \tag{2-176}$$

The motion now depends only on the mass of the particle and on the frequency of the applied force, and is independent of the friction and the restoring force. This result is, in fact, identical with that obtained in Section 2-3 [see Eqs. (2-15) and (2-19)] for a free particle subject to an oscillating force.

We can apply the result (2-165) to the case of an electron bound to an equilibrium position $x = 0$ by an elastic restoring force, and subject to an oscillating electric field:

$$E_x = E_0 \cos\omega t, \tag{2-177}$$

$$F = -eE_0 \cos\omega t. \tag{2-178}$$

The motion will be given by

$$x = Ae^{-\gamma t} \cos(\omega_1 t + \theta) - \frac{eE_0}{m} \frac{\sin(\omega t + \beta)}{[(\omega^2 - \omega_0^2)^2 + 4\gamma^2\omega^2]^{\frac{1}{2}}}. \tag{2-179}$$

The first term on the right in (2-179) is eventually damped out, and in any case would be zero on the average over a large number of electrons oscillating with different phases θ. Expanding the second term, we get

$$
\begin{aligned}
x &= -\frac{eE_0}{m} \frac{\sin\beta \cos\omega t}{[(\omega^2 - \omega_0^2)^2 + 4\gamma^2\omega^2]^{\frac{1}{2}}} - \frac{eE_0}{m} \frac{\cos\beta \sin\omega t}{[(\omega^2 - \omega_0^2)^2 + 4\gamma^2\omega^2]^{\frac{1}{2}}} \\
&= \frac{-eE_0 \cos\omega t}{m} \frac{\omega_0^2 - \omega^2}{[(\omega^2 - \omega_0^2)^2 + 4\gamma^2\omega^2]} - \frac{eE_0 \sin\omega t}{m} \frac{2\gamma\omega}{[(\omega^2 - \omega_0^2)^2 + 4\gamma^2\omega^2]}.
\end{aligned} \tag{2-180}
$$

The first term represents an oscillation of x in phase with the applied force at low frequencies, 180° out of phase at high frequencies. The second term represents an oscillation of x that is 90° out of phase with the applied force, the velocity $\dot{x}$ for this term being in phase with the applied force. Hence the second term corresponds to an absorption of energy from the applied force. The second term contains a factor γ and is therefore small, if $\gamma \ll \omega_0$, except near resonance. If we imagine a dielectric medium consisting of electrons bound by elastic forces to positions of equilibrium, then the first term in Eq. (2–180) will represent an electric polarization proportional to the applied oscillating electric field, while the second term will represent an absorption of energy from the electric field. Near the resonant frequency, the dielectric medium will absorb energy, and will be opaque to electromagnetic radiation. Above the resonant frequency, the displacement of the electrons is out of phase with the applied force, and the resulting electric polarization will be out of phase with the applied electric field. The dielectric constant and index of refraction will be less than one. For very high frequencies, the first term of Eq. (2–180) approaches the last term of Eq. (2–19), and the electrons behave as if they were free. Below the resonant frequency, the electric polarization will be in phase with the applied electric field, and the dielectric constant and index of refraction will be greater than one.

Computing the dielectric constant from the first term in Eq. (2–180), in the same manner as for a free electron [see Eqs. (2–20)–(2–26)], we find, for N electrons per unit volume:

$$\epsilon = 1 + \frac{4\pi N e^2}{m} \frac{\omega_0^2 - \omega^2}{(\omega_0^2 - \omega^2)^2 + 4\gamma^2\omega^2}. \qquad (2\text{–}181)$$

The index of refraction for electromagnetic waves ($\mu = 1$) is

$$n = \frac{c}{v} = (\mu\epsilon)^{\frac{1}{2}} = \epsilon^{\frac{1}{2}}. \qquad (2\text{–}182)$$

For very high or very low frequencies, Eq. (2–181) becomes

$$\epsilon \doteq 1 + \frac{4\pi N e^2}{m\omega_0^2}, \quad \omega \ll \omega_0, \qquad (2\text{–}183)$$

$$\epsilon \doteq 1 - \frac{4\pi N e^2}{m\omega^2}, \quad \omega \gg \omega_0. \qquad (2\text{–}184)$$

The mean rate of energy absorption per unit volume is given by Eq. (2–169):

$$\frac{dE}{dt} = \frac{N e^2 E_0^2}{m} \frac{\gamma\omega^2}{(\omega^2 - \omega_0^2)^2 + 4\gamma^2\omega^2}. \qquad (2\text{–}185)$$

The resulting dielectric constant and energy absorption versus frequency are plotted in Fig. 2–7. Thus the dielectric constant is constant and greater than one at low frequencies, increases as we approach the resonant frequency, falls to less than one in the region of "anomalous dispersion" where there is strong absorption of electromagnetic radiation, and then rises, approaching one at high fre-quencies. The index of refraction will follow a similar curve. This is precisely the sort of behavior which

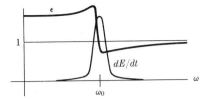

Fig. 2–7. Dielectric constant and energy absorption for medium containing harmonic oscillators.

is exhibited by matter in all forms. Glass, for example, has a constant dielec-tric constant at low frequencies; in the region of visible light its index of refraction increases with frequency; and it becomes opaque in a certain band in the ultraviolet. X-rays are transmitted with an index of refrac-tion very slightly less than one. A more realistic model of a transmitting medium would result from assuming several different resonant frequencies corresponding to electrons bound with various values of the spring con-stant k. This picture is then capable of explaining most of the features in the experimental curves for ϵ or n vs. frequency. Not only is there qualita-tive agreement, but the formulas (2–181)–(2–185) agree quantitatively with experimental results, provided the constants N, ω_0, and γ are properly chosen for each material. The success of this theory was one of the reasons for the adoption, until the year 1913, of the "jelly model" of the atom, in which electrons were imagined embedded in a positively charged jelly in which they oscillated as harmonic oscillators. The experiments of Ruther-ford in 1913 forced physicists to adopt the "planetary" model of the atom, but this model was unable to explain even qualitatively the optical and electromagnetic properties of matter until the advent of quantum mechan-ics. The result of the quantum mechanical treatment is that, for the inter-action of matter and radiation, the simple oscillator picture gives essentially correct results when the constants are properly chosen.*

We now consider an applied force $F(t)$ which is large only during a short time interval δt and is zero or negligible at all other times. Such a force is called an impulse, and corresponds to a sudden blow. We assume the oscillator initially at rest at $x = 0$, and we assume the time δt so short that the mass moves only a negligibly small distance while the force is acting. According to Eq. (2–4), the momentum just after the force is applied will equal the impulse delivered by the force:

$$mv_0 = p_0 = \int_{t_0}^{t_0+\delta t} F \, dt, \qquad (2\text{–}186)$$

* See John C. Slater, *Quantum Theory of Matter*. New York: McGraw-Hill Book Co., 1951. (Page 378.)

where v_0 is the velocity at $t_0 + \delta t$, just after the impulse. After $t_0 + \delta t$, the applied force is zero, and the oscillator must move according to Eq. (2–133), if the damping is less than critical. We are assuming δt so small that the oscillator does not move appreciably during this time, hence we choose $\theta = -(\pi/2) - \omega_1 t_0$, in order that $x = 0$ at $t = t_0$:

$$x = Ae^{-\gamma t} \sin [\omega_1(t - t_0)]. \tag{2–187}$$

The velocity at $t = t_0$ is

$$v_0 = \omega_1 A e^{-\gamma t_0}. \tag{2–188}$$

Thus

$$A = \frac{v_0}{\omega_1} e^{\gamma t_0}. \tag{2–189}$$

The solution when an impulse p_0 is delivered at $t = t_0$ to an oscillator at rest is therefore

$$x = \begin{cases} 0, & t \leq t_0, \\ \dfrac{p_0}{m\omega_1} e^{-\gamma(t-t_0)} \sin [\omega_1(t - t_0)], & t > t_0. \end{cases} \tag{2–190}$$

Here we have neglected the short time δt during which the force acts.

We see that the result of an impulse type force depends only on the total impulse p_0 delivered, and is independent of the particular form of the function $F(t)$, provided only that $F(t)$ is negligible except during a very short time interval δt. Several possible forms of $F(t)$ which have this property are listed below:

$$F(t) = \begin{cases} 0, & t < t_0, \\ p_0/\delta t, & t_0 \leq t \leq t_0 + \delta t, \\ 0, & t > t_0 + \delta t, \end{cases} \tag{2–191}$$

$$F(t) = \frac{p_0 \delta t}{\pi} \frac{1}{(t - t_0)^2 + (\delta t)^2}, \quad -\infty < t < \infty, \tag{2–192}$$

$$F(t) = \frac{p_0}{\delta t \sqrt{\pi}} \exp \left[-\frac{(t - t_0)^2}{(\delta t)^2} \right], \quad -\infty < t < \infty. \tag{2–193}$$

The reader may verify that each of these functions is negligible except within an interval of the order of δt around t_0, and that the total impulse delivered by each is p_0.

2–11 The principle of superposition. Harmonic oscillator with arbitrary applied force. An important property of the harmonic oscillator is that its motion $x(t)$, when subject to an applied force $F(t)$ which can be regarded as the sum of two or more other forces $F_1(t)$, $F_2(t)$, ..., is the sum of the motions $x_1(t)$, $x_2(t)$, ..., which it would have if each of the forces $F_n(t)$ were acting separately. This principle applies to small mechanical vibrations, electrical vibrations, sound waves, electromagnetic waves, and all physical phenomena governed by linear differential equations. The principle is expressed in the following theorem:

THEOREM IV.   *Let the (finite or infinite*) set of functions $x_n(t)$, n = 1,2,3, ..., be solutions of the equations*

$$m\ddot{x}_n + b\dot{x}_n + kx_n = F_n(t), \qquad (2\text{-}194)$$

and let

$$F(t) = \sum_n F_n(t). \qquad (2\text{-}195)$$

Then the function

$$x(t) = \sum_n x_n(t) \qquad (2\text{-}196)$$

satisfies the equation

$$m\ddot{x} + b\dot{x} + kx = F(t). \qquad (2\text{-}197)$$

To prove this theorem, we substitute Eq. (2-196) in the left side of Eq. (2-197):

$$m\ddot{x} + b\dot{x} + kx = m \sum_n \ddot{x}_n + b \sum_n \dot{x}_n + k \sum_n x_n$$

$$= \sum_n (m\ddot{x}_n + b\dot{x}_n + kx_n)$$

$$= \sum_n F_n(t)$$

$$= F(t).$$

This theorem enables us to find a solution of Eq. (2-197) whenever the force $F(t)$ can be expressed as a sum of forces $F_n(t)$ for which the solutions of the corresponding equations (2-194) can be found. In particular, whenever $F(t)$ can be written as a sum of sinusoidally oscillating terms:

$$F(t) = \sum_n C_n \cos(\omega_n t + \theta_n), \qquad (2\text{-}198)$$

a particular solution of Eq. (2-197) will be, by Theorem IV and Eq. (2-164),

$$x = \sum_n \frac{C_n}{m} \frac{1}{[(\omega_n^2 - \omega_0^2)^2 + 4\gamma^2\omega_n^2]^{\frac{1}{2}}} \sin(\omega_n t + \theta_n + \beta_n), \qquad (2\text{-}199)$$

$$\beta_n = \tan^{-1} \frac{\omega_0^2 - \omega_n^2}{2\gamma\omega_n}.$$

The general solution is then

$$x = Ae^{-\gamma t}\cos(\omega_1 t + \theta) + \sum_n \frac{C_n}{m} \frac{\sin(\omega_n t + \theta_n + \beta_n)}{[(\omega_n^2 - \omega_0^2)^2 + 4\gamma^2\omega_n^2]^{\frac{1}{2}}}, \qquad (2\text{-}200)$$

where A and θ are, as usual, to be chosen to make the solution (2-200) fit the initial conditions.

We can write Eqs. (2-198) and (2-199) in a different form by setting

$$A_n = C_n \cos\theta_n, \quad B_n = -C_n \sin\theta_n. \qquad (2\text{-}201)$$

---

* When the set of functions is infinite, there are certain mathematical restrictions which need not concern us here.

Then

$$F(t) = \sum_n (A_n \cos \omega_n t + B_n \sin \omega_n t),$$ (2-202)

and

$$x = \sum_n \frac{A_n \sin (\omega_n t + \beta_n) - B_n \cos (\omega_n t + \beta_n)}{m[(\omega_n^2 - \omega_0^2)^2 + 4\gamma^2\omega_n^2]^{\frac{1}{2}}}.$$ (2-203)

An important case of this kind is that of a periodic force $F(t)$, that is, a force such that

$$F(t + T) = F(t),$$ (2-204)

where T is the period of the force. For any continuous function $F(t)$ satisfying Eq. (2-204) (and, in fact, even for only piecewise continuous functions), it can be shown that $F(t)$ can always be written as a sum of sinusoidal functions:

$$F(t) = \tfrac{1}{2}A_0 + \sum_{n=1}^{\infty}\left(A_n \cos \frac{2\pi nt}{T} + B_n \sin \frac{2\pi nt}{T}\right),$$ (2-205)

where

$$A_n = \frac{2}{T} \int_0^T F(t) \cos \frac{2\pi nt}{T} \, dt, \quad n = 0,1,2,\ldots,$$

$$B_n = \frac{2}{T} \int_0^T F(t) \sin \frac{2\pi nt}{T} \, dt, \quad n = 1,2,3,\ldots.$$ (2-206)

This result enables us, at least in principle, to solve the problem of the forced oscillator for any periodically varying force. The sum in Eq. (2-205) is called a *Fourier series*.* The actual computation of the solution by this method is in most cases rather laborious, particularly the fitting of the constants A,θ in Eq. (2-200) to the initial conditions. However the knowledge that such a solution exists is often useful in itself. If any of the frequencies $2\pi n/T$ coincides with the natural frequency ω_0 of the oscillator, then the corresponding terms in the series in Eqs. (2-199) or (2-203) will be relatively much larger than the rest. Thus a force which oscillates nonsinusoidally at half the frequency ω_0 may cause the oscillator to perform a nearly sinusoidal oscillation at its natural frequency ω_0.

A generalization of the Fourier series theorem [Eqs. (2-205) and (2-206)] applicable to nonperiodic forces is the Fourier integral theorem, which allows us to represent any continuous (or piecewise continuous) function $F(t)$, subject to certain limitations, as a superposition of harmonically oscillating forces. By means of Fourier series and integrals, we may solve Eq. (2-197) for almost any physically reasonable force $F(t)$. We shall not pursue the subject further here. Suffice it to say that while the methods

---

* For a proof of the above statements and a more complete discussion of Fourier series, see Dunham Jackson, *Fourier Series and Orthogonal Polynomials*. Menasha, Wisconsin: George Banta Pub. Co., 1941. (Chapter 1.)

of Fourier series and Fourier integrals are of considerable practical
value in solving vibration problems,
their greatest importance in physics
probably lies in the fact that in principle such a solution exists.   Many
important results can be deduced
without ever actually evaluating the
series or integrals at all.

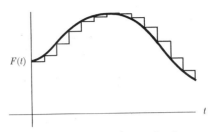

FIG. 2–8.   Representation of a force as
a sum of impulses. Heavy curve: $F(t)$.
Light curve: $\Sigma_n F_n(t)$.

   A method of solution known as
Green's method is based on the solu-
tion (2–190) for an impulse type force.   We can think of any force $F(t)$ as the
sum of a series of impulses, each acting during a short time δt and delivering
an impulse $F(t)\,\delta t$:

$$F(t) \doteq \sum_{n=-\infty}^{\infty} F_n(t), \qquad (2\text{–}207)$$

$$F_n(t) = \begin{cases} 0, & \text{if } t < t_n, \text{ where } t_n = n\,\delta t, \\ F(t_n), & \text{if } t_n \le t \le t_{n+1}, \\ 0, & \text{if } t > t_{n+1}. \end{cases} \qquad (2\text{–}208)$$

As $\delta t \to 0$, the sum of all the impulse forces $F_n(t)$ will approach $F(t)$.   (See
Fig. 2–8.)   According to Theorem IV and Eq. (2–190), a solution of
Eq. (2–197) for a force given by Eq. (2–207) is

$$x(t) \doteq \sum_{n=-\infty}^{n_0} \frac{F(t_n)\,\delta t}{m\omega_1} e^{-\gamma(t-t_n)} \sin\,[\omega_1(t - t_n)], \qquad (2\text{–}209)$$

where $t_{n_0} \le t < t_{n_0+1}$.   If we let $\delta t \to 0$ and write $t_n = t'$, Eq. (2–209) becomes

$$x(t) = \int_{-\infty}^{t} \frac{F(t')}{m\omega_1} e^{-\gamma(t-t')} \sin\,[\omega_1(t - t')]\,dt'. \qquad (2\text{–}210)$$

The function

$$G(t,t') = \begin{cases} 0, & \text{if } t' > t, \\ \dfrac{e^{-\gamma(t-t')}}{m\omega_1} \sin\,[\omega_1(t - t')], & \text{if } t' \le t \end{cases} \qquad (2\text{–}211)$$

is called the *Green's function* for Eq. (2–197).   In terms of Green's function,

$$x(t) = \int_{-\infty}^{\infty} G(t,t')F(t')\,dt'. \qquad (2\text{–}212)$$

If the force $F(t)$ is zero for $t < t_0$, then the solution (2–210) will give
$x(t) = 0$ for $t < t_0$.   This solution is therefore already adjusted to fit the
initial condition that the oscillator be at rest before the application of the
force.   For any other initial condition, a transient given by Eq. (2–133),

with appropriate values of A and θ, will have to be added. The solution (2–210) is useful in studying the transient behavior of a mechanical system or electrical circuit when subject to forces of various kinds.

PROBLEMS

1. A particle with an initial velocity v_0 is subject to a force given by Eq. (2–192). (a) Find $v(t)$ and $x(t)$. (b) Show that as $\delta t \to 0$, the motion approaches motion at constant velocity with an abrupt change in velocity at $t = t_0$ of amount p_0/m.

2. A particle initially at rest is subject, beginning at $t = 0$, to a force

$$F = F_0 e^{-\gamma t} \cos (\omega t + \theta).$$

(a) Find its motion. (b) How does the final velocity depend on θ, and on ω? [*Hint:* the algebra is simplified by writing $\cos (\omega t + \theta)$ in terms of complex exponential functions.]

3. A boat with initial velocity v_0 is slowed by a frictional force

$$F = -be^{\alpha v}.$$

(a) Find its motion. (b) Find the time and the distance required to stop.

4. A jet engine which develops a constant maximum thrust F_0 is used to power a plane with a frictional drag proportional to the square of the velocity. If the plane starts at $t = 0$ with a negligible velocity and accelerates with maximum thrust, find its velocity $v(t)$.

5. A particle is subject to a force

$$F = -kx + \frac{a}{x^3}.$$

(a) Find the potential $V(x)$, describe the nature of the solutions, and find the solution $x(t)$. (b) Can you give a simple interpretation of the motion when $E^2 \gg ka$?

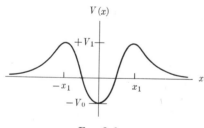

$V(x)$

$+V_1$

$-x_1$ x_1 x

$-V_0$

FIG. 2–9.

6. An alpha-particle in a nucleus is held by a potential having the shape shown in Fig. 2–9. (a) Describe the kinds of motion that are possible. (b) Devise a function $V(x)$ having this general form and having the values $-V_0$ and V_1 at $x = 0$ and $x = \pm x_1$, and find the corresponding force.

7. Derive the solutions (2–69) and (2–70) for a falling body subject to a frictional force proportional to the square of the velocity.

8. A body of mass m falls from rest through a medium which exerts a frictional drag $be^{\alpha|v|}$. (a) Find its velocity $v(t)$. (b) What is the terminal velocity? (c) Expand your solution in a power series in t, keeping terms up to t^2. (d) Why does the solution fail to agree with Eq. (1–28) even for short times t?

9. A projectile is fired vertically upward with an initial velocity v_0. Find its motion, assuming a frictional drag proportional to the square of the velocity. (Constant g.)

10. Derive equations analogous to Eqs. (2–80) and (2–81) for the motion of a body whose velocity is greater than the escape velocity. [*Hint:* Set $\sinh \beta = (Ex/mMG)^{\frac{1}{2}}$.]

11. Find the motion of a body projected upward from the earth with a velocity equal to the escape velocity. Neglect air resistance.

12. Find the general solution for the motion of a body subject to a linear repelling force $F = kx$. Show that this is the type of motion to be expected in the neighborhood of a point of unstable equilibrium.

13. The potential energy for the force between two atoms in a diatomic molecule has the approximate form:

$$V(x) = -\frac{a}{x^6} + \frac{b}{x^{12}},$$

where x is the distance between the atoms, and a,b are positive constants. (a) Find the force. (b) Assuming one of the atoms is very heavy and remains at rest while the other moves along a straight line, describe the possible motions. (c) Find the equilibrium distance, and the period of small oscillations about the equilibrium position if the mass of the lighter atom is m.

14. Starting with $e^{2i\theta} = (e^{i\theta})^2$, obtain formulas for $\sin 2\theta$, $\cos 2\theta$ in terms of $\sin \theta$, $\cos \theta$.

15. Find the general solution of the equations:

(a) $m\ddot{x} + b\dot{x} - kx = 0,$
(b) $m\ddot{x} - b\dot{x} + kx = 0.$

Discuss the physical interpretation of these equations and their solutions, assuming that they are the equations of motion of a particle.

16. Show that when $\omega_0^2 - \gamma^2$ is very small, the underdamped solution (2–133) is approximately equal to the critically damped solution (2–146), for a short time interval. What is the relation between the constants C_1, C_2 and A, θ? This result suggests how one may obtain the additional solution (2–143) in the critical case.

17. A mass m subject to a linear restoring force $-kx$ and damping $-b\dot{x}$ is displaced a distance x_0 from equilibrium and released with zero initial velocity. Find the motion in the underdamped, critically damped, and overdamped cases.

18. A force $F_0 \cos (\omega t + \theta_0)$ acts on a damped harmonic oscillator beginning at $t = 0$. (a) What must be the initial values of x and v in order that there be no transient? (b) If $x_0 = v_0 = 0$, find the amplitude A and phase θ of the transient in terms of F_0, θ_0.

19. An undamped harmonic oscillator of mass m, natural frequency ω_0, is initially at rest and is subject at $t = 0$ to a blow so that it starts from $x_0 = 0$ with initial velocity v_0 and oscillates freely until $t = 3\pi/2\omega_0$. From this time on, a force $F = B \cos (\omega t + \theta)$ is applied. Find the values which B, θ must have in order that the motion after $t = 3\pi/2\omega_0$ shall be purely sinusoidal, without transients ($\omega < \omega_0$).

20. An underdamped harmonic oscillator is subject to an applied force

$$F = F_0 e^{-at} \cos (\omega t + \theta).$$

Find a particular solution by expressing F as the real part of a complex exponential function and looking for a solution for x having the same exponential time dependence.

21. (a) Find the motion of a damped harmonic oscillator subject to a constant applied force F_0, by guessing a "steady state" solution of the inhomogeneous equation (2–86) and adding a solution of the homogeneous equation. (b) Solve the

same problem by making the substitution $x' = x - a$, and choosing the constant a so as to reduce the equation in x' to the homogeneous equation (2–85). Hence show that the effect of the application of a constant force is merely to shift the equilibrium position without affecting the nature of the oscillations.

22. Find the motion of a mass m subject to a restoring force $-kx$, and to a damping force $(\pm)\mu mg$ due to dry sliding friction. Show that the oscillations are isochronous (period independent of amplitude) with the amplitude of oscillation decreasing by $2\mu g/\omega_0^2$ during each half cycle until the mass comes to a stop. (*Hint:* Use the result of problem 21. When the force has a different algebraic form at different times during the motion, as here, where the sign of the damping force must be chosen so that the force is always opposed to the velocity, it is necessary to solve the equation of motion separately for each interval of time during which a particular expression for the force is to be used, and to choose as initial conditions for each time interval the final position and velocity of the preceding time interval.)

23. An undamped harmonic oscillator ($\gamma = 0$), initially at rest, is subject to a force given by Eq. (2–191). (a) Find $x(t)$. (b) For a fixed p_0, for what value of δt is the final amplitude of oscillation greatest? (c) Show that as $\delta t \to 0$, your solution approaches that given by Eq. (2–190).

24. Find the solution analogous to Eq. (2–190) for a critically damped harmonic oscillator subject to an impulse p_0 delivered at $t = t_0$.

25. (a) Find, using the principle of superposition, the motion of an underdamped oscillator [$\gamma = (1/3)\omega_0$] initially at rest and subject, after $t = 0$, to a force

$$F = A \sin \omega_0 t + B \sin 3\omega_0 t,$$

where ω_0 is the natural frequency of the oscillator. (b) What ratio of B to A is required in order for the forced oscillation at frequency $3\omega_0$ to have the same amplitude as that at frequency ω_0?

26. Find, by the Fourier series method, the steady state solution for the damped harmonic oscillator subject to a force

$$F(t) = \begin{cases} 0, & \text{if } nT < t \le (n + \tfrac{1}{2})T, \\ F_0, & \text{if } (n + \tfrac{1}{2})T < t \le (n + 1)T, \end{cases}$$

where n is any integer, and $T = 6\pi/\omega_0$, where ω_0 is the resonance frequency of the oscillator. Show that if $\gamma \ll \omega_0$, the motion is nearly sinusoidal with period $T/3$.

27. An underdamped oscillator initially at rest is acted upon, beginning at $t = 0$, by a force

$$F = F_0 e^{-at}.$$

Find its motion by using Green's solution (2–210).

28. Using the result of problem 24, find by Green's method the motion of a critically damped oscillator initially at rest and subject to a force $F(t)$.

CHAPTER 3

MOTION OF A PARTICLE IN TWO OR THREE DIMENSIONS

3–1 Vector algebra. The discussion of motion in two or three dimensions is vastly simplified by the introduction of the concept of a vector. A *vector* is defined geometrically as a physical quantity characterized by a magnitude and a direction in space. Examples are velocity, force, and position with respect to a fixed origin. Schematically, we represent a vector by an arrow whose length and direction represent the magnitude and direction of the vector. We shall represent a vector by a letter in boldface type. The same letter in ordinary italics will represent the magnitude of the vector (see Fig. 3–1). The magnitude of a vector may also be represented by vertical bars enclosing the vector symbol:

$$A = |\mathbf{A}|. \tag{3–1}$$

Two vectors are equal if they have the same magnitude and direction; the concept of vector itself makes no reference to any particular location.*

A quantity represented by an ordinary (positive or negative) number is often called a *scalar*, to distinguish it from a vector. We define a product of a vector $\mathbf{A}$ and a positive scalar c as a vector $c\mathbf{A}$ in the same direction as $\mathbf{A}$ of magnitude cA. If c is negative, we define $c\mathbf{A}$ as having the magnitude $|c|A$ and a direction opposite to $\mathbf{A}$. (See Fig. 3–2.) It follows from this definition that

$$|c\mathbf{A}| = |c|\,|\mathbf{A}|. \tag{3–2}$$

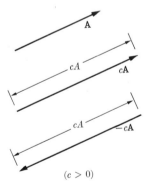

$(c > 0)$

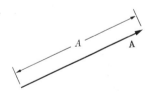

Fig. 3–1. A vector $\mathbf{A}$ and its magnitude A.

Fig. 3–2. Definition of multiplication of a vector by a scalar.

---

* A distinction is sometimes made between "free" vectors, which have no particular location in space; "sliding," vectors which may be located anywhere along a line; and "fixed" vectors, which must be located at a definite point in space. We prefer here to regard the vector as distinguished by its magnitude and direction alone, so that two vectors may be regarded as equal if they have the same magnitude and direction, regardless of their position in space.

It is also readily shown, on the basis of this definition, that multiplication by a scalar is associative in the following sense:

$$(cd)\ \mathbf{A} = c(d\mathbf{A}).\qquad(3\text{--}3)$$

It is sometimes convenient to be able to write the scalar to the right of the vector, and we define $\mathbf{A}c$ as meaning the same vector as $c\mathbf{A}$:

$$\mathbf{A}c = c\mathbf{A}.\qquad(3\text{--}4)$$

We define the sum $(\mathbf{A} + \mathbf{B})$ of two vectors $\mathbf{A},\mathbf{B}$ as the vector which extends from the tail of $\mathbf{A}$ to the tip of $\mathbf{B}$ when $\mathbf{A}$ is drawn with its tip at the tail of $\mathbf{B}$, as in Fig. 3–3. This definition is equivalent to the usual parallelogram rule, and is more convenient to use. It is readily extended to the sum of any number of vectors, as in Fig. 3–4.

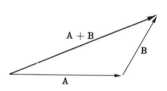

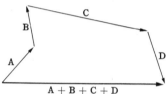

Fig. 3–3. Definition of addition of two vectors.

Fig. 3–4. Addition of several vectors.

On the basis of the definition given in Fig. 3–3, we can readily prove that vector addition is commutative and associative:

$$\mathbf{A} + \mathbf{B} = \mathbf{B} + \mathbf{A},\qquad(3\text{--}5)$$
$$(\mathbf{A} + \mathbf{B}) + \mathbf{C} = \mathbf{A} + (\mathbf{B} + \mathbf{C}).\qquad(3\text{--}6)$$

According to Eq. (3–6), we may omit parentheses in writing a vector sum, since the order of adding does not matter. From the definitions given by Figs. 3–2 and 3–3, we can also prove the following distributive laws:

$$c(\mathbf{A} + \mathbf{B}) = c\mathbf{A} + c\mathbf{B},\qquad(3\text{--}7)$$
$$(c + d)\mathbf{A} = c\mathbf{A} + d\mathbf{A}.\qquad(3\text{--}8)$$

These statements can be proved by drawing diagrams representing the right and left members of each equation according to the definitions given.

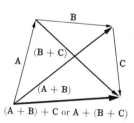

$(\mathbf{A} + \mathbf{B}) + \mathbf{C}$ or $\mathbf{A} + (\mathbf{B} + \mathbf{C})$

Fig. 3–5. Proof of Eq. (3–6).

For example, the diagram in Fig. 3–5 makes it evident that the result of adding $\mathbf{C}$ to $(\mathbf{A} + \mathbf{B})$ is the same as the result of adding $(\mathbf{B} + \mathbf{C})$ to $\mathbf{A}$.

According to Eqs. (3–3) through (3–8), the sum and product we have defined have most of the algebraic properties of sums and products of ordinary numbers. This is the justification for calling them sums and

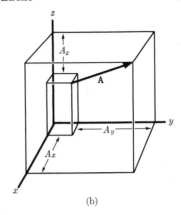

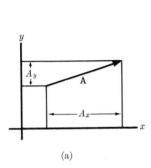

FIG. 3–6a. Components of a vector in a plane.

FIG. 3–6b. Components of a vector in space.

products. Thus it is unnecessary to commit these results to memory. We need only remember that we can manipulate these sums and products just as we manipulate numbers in ordinary algebra with the one exception that the product defined by Fig. 3–2 can be formed only between a scalar and a vector, and the result is a vector.

A vector may be represented algebraically in terms of its *components* or *projections* along a set of coordinate axes. Drop perpendiculars from the tail and tip of the vector onto the coordinate axes as in Fig. 3–6. Then the component of the vector along any axis is defined as the length of the segment cut off on the axis by these perpendiculars. The component is taken as positive or negative according to whether the projection of the tip of the vector lies in the positive or negative direction along the axis from the projection of the tail. The components of a vector $\mathbf{A}$ along x-, y-, and z-axes will be written A_x, A_y, and A_z. The notation (A_x, A_y, A_z) will sometimes be used to represent the vector $\mathbf{A}$:

$$\mathbf{A} = (A_x, A_y, A_z). \tag{3–9}$$

If we define vectors $\mathbf{i, j, k}$ of unit length along the x-, y-, z-axes respectively, then we can write any vector as a sum of products of its components with $\mathbf{i, j, k}$:

$$\mathbf{A} = A_x\mathbf{i} + A_y\mathbf{j} + A_z\mathbf{k}. \tag{3–10}$$

The correctness of this formula can be made evident by drawing a diagram in which the three vectors on the right, which are parallel to the three axes, are added to give $\mathbf{A}$. Figure 3–7 shows this construction for the two-dimensional case.

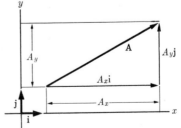

FIG. 3–7. Diagrammatic proof of the formula $\mathbf{A} = A_x\mathbf{i} + A_y\mathbf{j}$.

We now have two equivalent ways of defining a vector: geometrically as quantity with a magnitude and direction in space, or algebraically as a set of three numbers (A_x, A_y, A_z), which we call its components.* The operations of addition and multiplication by a scalar, which are defined geometrically in Figs. 3–2 and 3–3 in terms of the lengths and directions of the vectors involved, can also be defined algebraically as operations on the components of the vectors. Thus $c\mathbf{A}$ is the vector whose components are the components of $\mathbf{A}$, each multiplied by c:

$$c\mathbf{A} = (cA_x, cA_y, cA_z), \tag{3–11}$$

and $\mathbf{A} + \mathbf{B}$ is the vector whose components are obtained by adding the components of $\mathbf{A}$ and $\mathbf{B}$:

$$\mathbf{A} + \mathbf{B} = (A_x + B_x,\ A_y + B_y,\ A_z + B_z). \tag{3–12}$$

The equivalence of the definitions (3–11) and (3–12) to the corresponding geometrical definitions can be demonstrated by drawing suitable diagrams. Figure 3–8 constitutes a proof of Eq. (3–12) for the two-dimensional case. All vectors are drawn in Fig. 3–8 so that their components are positive; for a complete proof, similar diagrams should be drawn for the cases where one or both components of either vector are negative. The length of a vector can be defined algebraically as follows:

$$|\mathbf{A}| = (A_x^2 + A_y^2 + A_z^2)^{\frac{1}{2}}, \tag{3–13}$$

where the positive square root is to be taken.

We can now give algebraic proofs of Eqs. (3–2), (3–3), (3–5), (3–6), (3–7), and (3–8), based on the definitions (3–11), (3–12), and (3–13). For example, to prove Eq. (3–7), we show that each component of the left side agrees with each component on the right. For the x-component, the proof runs:

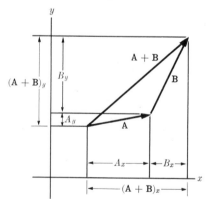

FIG. 3–8. Proof of equivalence of algebraic and geometric definitions of vector addition.

---

* These two ways of defining a vector are not quite equivalent as given here, for the algebraic definition requires that a coordinate system be set up, whereas the geometric definition does not refer to any particular set of axes. This flaw can be remedied by making the algebraic definition also independent of any particular set of axes. This is done by studying how the components change when the axes are changed, and defining a vector algebraically as a set of three quantities which transform in a certain way when the axes are changed. This refinement will not concern us in this text.

$$[c(\mathbf{A} + \mathbf{B})]_x = c(\mathbf{A} + \mathbf{B})_x \qquad \text{[by Eq. (3–11)]}$$
$$= c(A_x + B_x) \qquad \text{[by Eq. (3–12)]}$$
$$= cA_x + cB_x$$
$$= (c\mathbf{A})_x + (c\mathbf{B})_x \qquad \text{[by Eq. (3–11)]}$$
$$= (c\mathbf{A} + c\mathbf{B})_x. \qquad \text{[by Eq. (3–12)]}$$

Since all components are treated alike in the definitions (3–11), (3–12), (3–13), the same proof holds for the y- and z-components, and hence the vectors on the left and right sides of Eq. (3–7) are equal.

In view of the equivalence of the geometrical and algebraic definitions of the vector operations, it is unnecessary, for geometrical applications, to give both an algebraic and a geometric proof of each formula of vector algebra. Either a geometric or an algebraic proof, whichever is easiest, will suffice. However, there are important cases in physics where we have to consider sets of quantities which behave algebraically like the components of vectors although they cannot be interpreted geometrically as quantities with a magnitude and direction in ordinary space. In order that we may apply the rules of vector algebra in such applications, it is important to know that all of these rules can be proved purely algebraically from the algebraic definitions of the vector operations. We shall have only one example of such a nongeometrical vector in this text. The geometric approach has the advantage of enabling us to visualize the meanings of the various vector notations and formulas. The algebraic approach simplifies certain proofs, and has the further advantage that it makes possible wide applications of the mathematical concept of vector, including many cases where the ordinary geometric meaning is no longer retained.

We may define subtraction of vectors in terms of addition and multiplication by -1:

$$\mathbf{A} - \mathbf{B} = \mathbf{A} + (-\mathbf{B}) = (A_x - B_x, \, A_y - B_y, \, A_z - B_z). \qquad (3–14)$$

The difference $\mathbf{A} - \mathbf{B}$ may be found geometrically according to either of the two schemes shown in Fig. 3–9. Subtraction of vectors may be shown to have all the algebraic properties to be expected by analogy with subtraction of numbers.

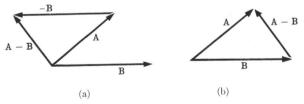

(a)   (b)

FIG. 3–9. Two methods of subtraction of vectors.

It is useful to define a *scalar product* $(\mathbf{A} \cdot \mathbf{B})$ of two vectors $\mathbf{A}$ and $\mathbf{B}$ as the product of their magnitudes times the cosine of the angle between them:

$$\mathbf{A} \cdot \mathbf{B} = AB \cos \theta. \tag{3-15}$$

The scalar product is a scalar or number. It is also called the *dot product* or *inner product*, and can also be defined as the product of the magnitude of either vector times the projection of the other along it. An example of its use is the expression for the work done when a force $\mathbf{F}$ acts through a distance $\mathbf{s}$ not necessarily parallel to it:

$$W = Fs \cos \theta = \mathbf{F} \cdot \mathbf{s}.$$

We are entitled to call $\mathbf{A} \cdot \mathbf{B}$ a product because it has the following algebraic properties which are easily proved from the geometrical definition (3–15):

$$(c\mathbf{A}) \cdot \mathbf{B} = \mathbf{A} \cdot (c\mathbf{B}) = c(\mathbf{A} \cdot \mathbf{B}), \tag{3-16}$$
$$\mathbf{A} \cdot (\mathbf{B} + \mathbf{C}) = \mathbf{A} \cdot \mathbf{B} + \mathbf{A} \cdot \mathbf{C}, \tag{3-17}$$
$$\mathbf{A} \cdot \mathbf{B} = \mathbf{B} \cdot \mathbf{A}, \tag{3-18}$$
$$\mathbf{A} \cdot \mathbf{A} = A^2. \tag{3-19}$$

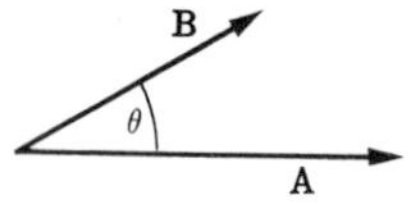

Fig. 3–10. Angle between two vectors.

These equations mean that we can treat the dot product algebraically like a product in the algebra of ordinary numbers, provided we keep in mind that the two factors must be vectors and the resulting product is a scalar. The following statements are also consequences of the definition (3–15), where $\mathbf{i}$, $\mathbf{j}$, and $\mathbf{k}$ are the unit vectors along the three coordinate axes:

$$\mathbf{i} \cdot \mathbf{i} = \mathbf{j} \cdot \mathbf{j} = \mathbf{k} \cdot \mathbf{k} = 1,$$
$$\mathbf{i} \cdot \mathbf{j} = \mathbf{j} \cdot \mathbf{k} = \mathbf{k} \cdot \mathbf{i} = 0. \tag{3-20}$$
$$\mathbf{A} \cdot \mathbf{B} = AB, \quad \text{when } \mathbf{A} \text{ is parallel to } \mathbf{B}, \tag{3-21}$$
$$\mathbf{A} \cdot \mathbf{B} = 0, \quad \text{when } \mathbf{A} \text{ is perpendicular to } \mathbf{B}. \tag{3-22}$$

Notice that, according to Eq. (3–22), the dot product of two vectors is zero if they are perpendicular, even though neither vector is of zero length. The dot product can also be defined algebraically in terms of components:

$$\mathbf{A} \cdot \mathbf{B} = A_x B_x + A_y B_y + A_z B_z. \tag{3-23}$$

To prove that Eq. (3–23) is equivalent to the geometric definition (3–15), we write $\mathbf{A}$ and $\mathbf{B}$ in the form given by Eq. (3–10), and make use of Eqs. (3–16), (3–17), (3–18), and (3–20), which follow from Eq. (3–15):

$$\begin{aligned}
\mathbf{A} \cdot \mathbf{B} &= (\mathbf{i}A_x + \mathbf{j}A_y + \mathbf{k}A_z) \cdot (\mathbf{i}B_x + \mathbf{j}B_y + \mathbf{k}B_z) \\
&= (\mathbf{i} \cdot \mathbf{i})A_x B_x + (\mathbf{i} \cdot \mathbf{j})A_x B_y + (\mathbf{i} \cdot \mathbf{k})A_x B_z + (\mathbf{j} \cdot \mathbf{i})A_y B_x + \mathbf{j} \cdot \mathbf{j}A_y B_y \\
&\quad + \mathbf{j} \cdot \mathbf{k}A_y B_z + \mathbf{k} \cdot \mathbf{i}A_z B_x + \mathbf{k} \cdot \mathbf{j}A_z B_y + \mathbf{k} \cdot \mathbf{k}A_z B_z \\
&= A_x B_x + A_y B_y + A_z B_z.
\end{aligned}$$

This proves Eq. (3–23). The properties (3–16) to (3–20) can all be proved readily from the algebraic definition (3–23) as well as from the geometric definition (3–15). We can regard Eqs. (3–21) and (3–22) as algebraic definitions of *parallel* and *perpendicular*.

Another product convenient to define is the *vector product*, also called the *cross product* or *outer product*. The cross product $(\mathbf{A} \times \mathbf{B})$ of two vectors $\mathbf{A}$ and $\mathbf{B}$ is defined as a vector perpendicular to the plane of $\mathbf{A}$ and $\mathbf{B}$ whose magnitude is the area of the parallelogram having $\mathbf{A}$ and $\mathbf{B}$ as sides. The sense or direction of $(\mathbf{A} \times \mathbf{B})$ is defined as the direction of advance of a right-hand screw rotated from $\mathbf{A}$ toward $\mathbf{B}$. (See Fig. 3–11.) The length of $(\mathbf{A} \times \mathbf{B})$, in terms of the angle θ between the two vectors, is given by

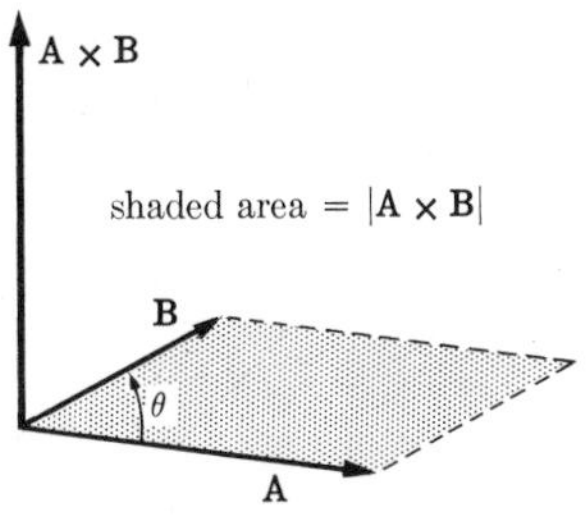

FIG. 3–11. Definition of vector product.

$$|\mathbf{A} \times \mathbf{B}| = AB \sin \theta. \quad (3\text{–}24)$$

Note that the scalar product of two vectors is a scalar or number, while the vector product is a new vector. The vector product has the following algebraic properties which can be proved from the definition given in Fig. 3–11:*

$$\mathbf{A} \times \mathbf{B} = -\mathbf{B} \times \mathbf{A}, \quad (3\text{–}25)$$
$$(c\mathbf{A}) \times \mathbf{B} = \mathbf{A} \times (c\mathbf{B}) = c(\mathbf{A} \times \mathbf{B}), \quad (3\text{–}26)$$
$$\mathbf{A} \times (\mathbf{B} + \mathbf{C}) = (\mathbf{A} \times \mathbf{B}) + (\mathbf{A} \times \mathbf{C}), \quad (3\text{–}27)$$
$$\mathbf{A} \times \mathbf{A} = 0, \quad (3\text{–}28)$$
$$\mathbf{A} \times \mathbf{B} = 0, \quad \text{when } \mathbf{A} \text{ is parallel to } \mathbf{B}, \quad (3\text{–}29)$$
$$|\mathbf{A} \times \mathbf{B}| = AB, \quad \text{when } \mathbf{A} \text{ is perpendicular to } \mathbf{B}, \quad (3\text{–}30)$$
$$\mathbf{i} \times \mathbf{i} = \mathbf{j} \times \mathbf{j} = \mathbf{k} \times \mathbf{k} = 0,$$
$$\mathbf{i} \times \mathbf{j} = \mathbf{k}, \quad \mathbf{j} \times \mathbf{k} = \mathbf{i}, \quad \mathbf{k} \times \mathbf{i} = \mathbf{j}. \quad (3\text{–}31)$$

Hence the cross product can be treated algebraically like an ordinary product with the exception that the order of multiplication must not be changed, and provided we keep in mind that the two factors must be vectors and the result is a vector. Switching the order of factors in a cross product changes the sign. This is the first unexpected deviation of the rules of vector algebra from those of ordinary algebra. The reader should therefore memorize Eq. (3–25). Equations (3–29) and (3–30), as well as the analogous Eqs. (3–21) and (3–22), are also worth remembering. (It goes without saying that all geometrical and algebraic definitions should be memorized.) In a repeated vector product like $(\mathbf{A} \times \mathbf{B}) \times (\mathbf{C} \times \mathbf{D})$, the parentheses cannot be omitted or rearranged, for the result of carrying out the multiplications in a different order is not, in general, the same. [See,

---

* Here $\mathbf{0}$ stands for the vector of zero length, sometimes called the *null vector*. It has no particular direction in space. It has the properties:

$$\mathbf{A} + \mathbf{0} = \mathbf{A}, \; \mathbf{A} \cdot \mathbf{0} = 0, \; \mathbf{A} \times \mathbf{0} = 0, \; \mathbf{A} - \mathbf{A} = 0, \; \mathbf{0} = (0,0,0).$$

for example, Eqs. (3–35) and (3–36).] Notice that according to Eq. (3–29) the cross product of two vectors may be null without either vector being the null vector.

From Eqs. (3–25) to (3–31), using Eq. (3–10) to represent **A** and **B**, we can prove that the geometric definition (Fig. 3–11) is equivalent to the following algebraic definition of the cross product:

$$\mathbf{A} \times \mathbf{B} = (A_y B_z - A_z B_y, \; A_z B_x - A_x B_z, \; A_x B_y - A_y B_x). \qquad (3\text{–}32)$$

We can also write **A** × **B** as a determinant:

$$\mathbf{A} \times \mathbf{B} = \begin{vmatrix} \mathbf{i} & \mathbf{j} & \mathbf{k} \\ A_x & A_y & A_z \\ B_x & B_y & B_z \end{vmatrix}. \qquad (3\text{–}33)$$

Expansion of the right side of Eq. (3–33) according to the ordinary rules for determinants yields Eq. (3–32). Again the properties (3–25) to (3–31) follow also from the algebraic definition (3–32).

The following useful identities can be proved:

$$\mathbf{A} \cdot (\mathbf{B} \times \mathbf{C}) = (\mathbf{A} \times \mathbf{B}) \cdot \mathbf{C}, \qquad (3\text{–}34)$$
$$\mathbf{A} \times (\mathbf{B} \times \mathbf{C}) = \mathbf{B}(\mathbf{A} \cdot \mathbf{C}) - \mathbf{C}(\mathbf{A} \cdot \mathbf{B}), \qquad (3\text{–}35)$$
$$(\mathbf{A} \times \mathbf{B}) \times \mathbf{C} = \mathbf{B}(\mathbf{A} \cdot \mathbf{C}) - \mathbf{A}(\mathbf{B} \cdot \mathbf{C}), \qquad (3\text{–}36)$$
$$\mathbf{i} \cdot (\mathbf{j} \times \mathbf{k}) = 1. \qquad (3\text{–}37)$$

The first three of these should be committed to memory. Equation (3–34) allows us to interchange dot and cross in the scalar triple product. The quantity **A** · (**B** × **C**) can be shown to be the volume of the parallelepiped whose edges are **A**,**B**,**C**, with positive or negative sign depending on whether **A**,**B**,**C** are in the same relative orientation as **i**,**j**,**k**, that is, depending on whether a right-hand screw rotated from **A** toward **B** would advance along **C** in the positive or negative direction. The triple vector product formulas (3–35) and (3–36) are easy to remember if we note that the positive term on the right in each case is the middle vector (**B**) times the scalar product (**A** · **C**) of the other two, while the negative term is the other vector within the parentheses times the scalar product of the other two.

As an example of the use of the vector product, the rule for the force exerted by a magnetic field of induction **B** on a moving electric charge q (esu) can be expressed as

$$\mathbf{F} = \frac{q}{c} \mathbf{v} \times \mathbf{B},$$

where c is the speed of light, and **v** is the velocity of the charge. This equation gives correctly both the magnitude and direction of the force. The reader will remember that the subject of electricity and magnetism is full of right- and left-hand rules. Vector quantities whose directions are determined by right- or left-hand rules generally turn out to be expressible as cross products.

3-2 Applications to a set of forces acting on a particle. According to the principles set down in Section 1–3, if a set of forces $F_1, F_2, \ldots, F_n$ act on a particle, the total force F, which determines its acceleration, is to be obtained by taking the vector sum of the forces $F_1, F_2, \ldots, F_n$:

$$F = F_1 + F_2 + \cdots + F_n. \tag{3–38}$$

The forces $F_1, F_2, \ldots, F_n$ are often referred to as *component* forces, and F is called their *resultant*. The term *component* is here used in a more general sense than in the preceding section, where the components of a vector were defined as the projections of the vector on a set of coordinate axes. When *component* is meant in this sense as one of a set of vectors whose sum is F, we shall use the term *(vector) component*. In general, unless otherwise indicated, the term *component* of a vector F in a certain direction will mean the perpendicular projection of the vector F on a line in that direction. In symbols, the component of F in the direction of the unit vector n is

$$F_n = n \cdot F. \tag{3–39}$$

In this sense, the component of F is not a vector, but a number. The components of F along the x-, y-, and z-axes are the components in the sense of Eq. (3–39) in the directions i, j, and k.

If the forces $F_1, F_2, \ldots, F_n$ are given, the sum may be determined graphically by drawing a careful scale diagram according to the definition of Fig. 3–3 or 3–4. The sum may also be determined analytically by drawing a rough sketch of the sum diagram and using trigonometry to calculate the magnitude and direction of the vector F. If, for example, two vectors are to be added, the sum can be found by using the cosine and sine laws. In Fig. 3–12, F_1, F_2, and θ are given, and the magnitude and direction of the sum F are calculated from

$$F^2 = F_1^2 + F_2^2 - 2F_1F_2 \cos \theta, \tag{3–40}$$

$$\frac{F_1}{\sin \beta} = \frac{F_2}{\sin \alpha} = \frac{F}{\sin \theta}. \tag{3–41}$$

Note that the first of these equations can be obtained by squaring, in the sense of the dot product, the equation

$$F = F_1 + F_2. \tag{3–42}$$

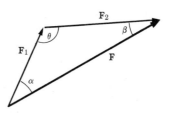

FIG. 3–12. Sum of two forces.

Taking the dot product of each member of this equation with itself, we obtain

$$F \cdot F = F^2 = F_1 \cdot F_1 + 2F_1 \cdot F_2 + F_2 \cdot F_2$$
$$= F_1^2 + F_2^2 - 2F_1F_2 \cos \theta.$$

(Note that θ in Fig. 3–12 is the supplement of the angle between F_1 and F_2 as defined by Fig. 3–10.) This technique can be applied to obtain directly the magnitude of the sum of any number of vectors in terms of their lengths and the angles between them. Simply square Eq. (3–38), and split up the right side according to the laws of vector algebra into a sum of squares and dot products of the component forces. The angle between $\mathbf{F}$ and any of the component forces can be found by crossing or dotting the component vector into Eq. (3–38). For example, in the case of a sum of two forces, we cross $\mathbf{F}_1$ into Eq. (3–42):

$$\mathbf{F}_1 \times \mathbf{F} = \mathbf{F}_1 \times \mathbf{F}_1 + \mathbf{F}_1 \times \mathbf{F}_2.$$

We take the magnitude of each side, using Eqs. (3–28) and (3–24):

$$F_1 F \sin \alpha = F_1 F_2 \sin \theta,$$

or

$$\frac{F}{\sin \theta} = \frac{F_2}{\sin \alpha}.$$

When a sum of more than two vectors is involved, it is usually simpler to take the dot product of the component vector with each side of Eq. (3–38).

The vector sum in Eq. (3–38) can also be obtained by adding separately the components of $\mathbf{F}_1, \ldots, \mathbf{F}_n$ along any convenient set of axes:

$$\begin{aligned}
F_x &= F_{1x} + F_{2x} + \cdots + F_{nx}, \\
F_y &= F_{1y} + F_{2y} + \cdots + F_{ny}, \\
F_z &= F_{1z} + F_{2z} + \cdots + F_{nz}.
\end{aligned} \tag{3–43}$$

When a sum of a large number of vectors is to be found, this is likely to be the quickest method. The reader should use his ingenuity in combining and modifying these methods to suit the problem at hand. Obviously, if a set of vectors is to be added which contains a group of parallel vectors, it will be simpler to add these parallel vectors first before trying to apply the methods of the preceding paragraph.

Just as the various forces acting on a particle are to be added vectorially to give the total force, so, conversely, the total force, or any individual force, acting on a particle may be resolved in any convenient manner into a sum of (vector) component forces which may be considered as acting individually on the particle. Thus in the problem discussed in Section 1–7 (Fig. 1–4), the reaction force F exerted by the plane on the brick is resolved into a normal component N and a frictional component f. The effect of the force F on the motion of the brick is the same as that of the forces N and f acting together. If it is desired to resolve a force $\mathbf{F}$ into a sum of (vector) component forces in two or three perpendicular directions, this can be done by taking the perpendicular projections of $\mathbf{F}$ in these directions, as in Fig. 3–6. The magnitudes of the vector components of $\mathbf{F}$, along a set of perpendicular directions, are just the ordinary components of $\mathbf{F}$ in these directions in the sense of Eq. (3–39).

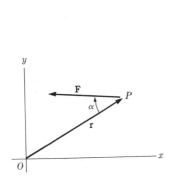

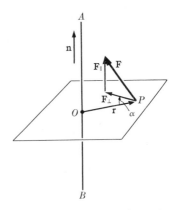

FIG. 3–13. Force **F** acting at point **r** relative to O.

FIG. 3–14.   Moment of a force about an axis in space.

If a force **F** in the xy-plane acts on a particle at the point P, we define the *torque*, or *moment* of the force **F** about the origin O (Fig. 3–13) as the product of the distance $\overline{OP}$ and the component of **F** perpendicular to **r**:

$$N_O = rF \sin \alpha. \qquad (3\text{–}44)$$

The moment N_O of the force **F** about the point O is defined as positive when **F** acts in a counterclockwise direction about O as in Fig. 3–13, and negative when **F** acts in a clockwise direction.   We can define in a similar way the moment about O of any vector quantity located at the point P.   The concept of moment will be found useful in our study of the mechanics of particles and rigid bodies.   The geometrical and algebraic properties of torques will be studied in detail in Chapter 5.   Notice that torque can be defined in terms of the vector product:

$$N_O = \pm |\mathbf{r} \times \mathbf{F}|, \qquad (3\text{–}45)$$

where the $+$ or $-$ sign is used according to whether the vector $\mathbf{r} \times \mathbf{F}$ points in the positive or negative direction along the z-axis.

We can generalize the above definition of torque to the three-dimensional case by defining the torque or moment of a force **F**, acting at a point P, about an axis $\overline{AB}$ (Fig. 3–14).   Let **n** be a unit vector in the direction of $\overline{AB}$, and let **F** be resolved into vector components parallel and perpendicular to $\overline{AB}$:

$$\mathbf{F} = \mathbf{F}_{\parallel} + \mathbf{F}_{\perp}, \qquad (3\text{–}46)$$

where

$$\mathbf{F}_{\parallel} = \mathbf{n}(\mathbf{n} \cdot \mathbf{F}), \qquad (3\text{–}47)$$
$$\mathbf{F}_{\perp} = \mathbf{F} - \mathbf{F}_{\parallel}.$$

We now define the moment of $\mathbf{F}$ about the axis $\overline{AB}$ as the moment, defined by Eq. (3–44) or (3–45), of the force $\mathbf{F}_\perp$, in a plane through the point P perpendicular to $\overline{AB}$, about the point O at which the axis $\overline{AB}$ passes through this plane:

$$N_{AB} = \pm rF_\perp \sin \alpha = \pm |\mathbf{r} \times \mathbf{F}_\perp|, \tag{3–48}$$

where the $+$ or $-$ sign is used, depending on whether $\mathbf{r} \times \mathbf{F}_\perp$ is in the same or opposite direction to $\mathbf{n}$. According to this definition, a force like $\mathbf{F}_\parallel$ parallel to $\overline{AB}$ has no torque or moment about $\overline{AB}$. Since $\mathbf{r} \times \mathbf{F}_\parallel$ is perpendicular to $\mathbf{n}$,

$$\begin{aligned}
\mathbf{n} \cdot (\mathbf{r} \times \mathbf{F}) &= \mathbf{n} \cdot [\mathbf{r} \times (\mathbf{F}_\parallel + \mathbf{F}_\perp)] \\
&= \mathbf{n} \cdot (\mathbf{r} \times \mathbf{F}_\parallel) + \mathbf{n} \cdot (\mathbf{r} \times \mathbf{F}_\perp) \\
&= \mathbf{n} \cdot (\mathbf{r} \times \mathbf{F}_\perp) \\
&= \pm |\mathbf{r} \times \mathbf{F}_\perp|.
\end{aligned}$$

Hence we can define N_{AB} in a neater way as follows:

$$N_{AB} = \mathbf{n} \cdot (\mathbf{r} \times \mathbf{F}). \tag{3–49}$$

This definition automatically includes the proper sign, and does not require a resolution of $\mathbf{F}$ into $\mathbf{F}_\parallel$ and $\mathbf{F}_\perp$. Furthermore, $\mathbf{r}$ can now be drawn to P from any point on the axis $\overline{AB}$, since a component of $\mathbf{r}$ parallel to $\overline{AB}$, like a component of $\mathbf{F}$ parallel to $\overline{AB}$, gives a component in the cross product perpendicular to $\mathbf{n}$ which disappears from the dot product.

Equation (3–49) suggests the definition of a *vector torque* or *vector moment*, about a point O, of a force $\mathbf{F}$ acting at a point P, as follows:

$$\mathbf{N}_O = \mathbf{r} \times \mathbf{F}, \tag{3–50}$$

where $\mathbf{r}$ is the vector from O to P. The vector torque $\mathbf{N}_O$ has, according to Eq. (3–49), the property that its component in any direction is the torque, in the previous sense, of the force $\mathbf{F}$ about an axis through O in that direction. Hereafter the term torque will usually mean the vector torque defined by Eq. (3–50). Torque about an axis $\overline{AB}$ in the previous sense will be called the component of torque along $\overline{AB}$. We can define the vector moment of any vector located at a point P, about a point O, by an equation analogous to Eq. (3–50).

3–3 Differentiation and integration of vectors. A vector $\mathbf{A}$ may be a function of a scalar quantity, say t, in the sense that with each value of t a certain vector $\mathbf{A}(t)$ is associated, or algebraically in the sense that its components may be functions of t:

$$\mathbf{A} = \mathbf{A}(t) = [A_x(t), A_y(t), A_z(t)]. \tag{3–51}$$

The most common example is that of a vector function of the time; for example the velocity of a moving particle is a function of the time: $\mathbf{v}(t)$. Other cases also occur, however; for example, in Eq. (3–76), the vector $\mathbf{n}$ is a function of the angle θ.   We may define the derivative of the vector $\mathbf{A}$ with respect to t in analogy with the usual definition of the derivative of a scalar function (see Fig. 3–15):

$$\frac{d\mathbf{A}}{dt} = \lim_{\Delta t \to 0} \frac{\mathbf{A}(t + \Delta t) - \mathbf{A}(t)}{\Delta t}. \tag{3–52}$$

(Division by Δt here means multiplication by $1/\Delta t$.)   We may also define the vector derivative algebraically in terms of its components:

$$\frac{d\mathbf{A}}{dt} = \left(\frac{dA_x}{dt}, \frac{dA_y}{dt}, \frac{dA_z}{dt}\right) = \mathbf{i}\frac{dA_x}{dt} + \mathbf{j}\frac{dA_y}{dt} + \mathbf{k}\frac{dA_z}{dt}. \tag{3–53}$$

As an example, if $\mathbf{v}(t)$ is the vector velocity of a particle, its vector acceleration $\mathbf{a}$ is

$$\mathbf{a} = \frac{d\mathbf{v}}{dt}.$$

Examples of the calculation of vector derivatives based on either definition (3–52) or (3–53) will be given in Sections 3–4 and 3–5.

The following properties of vector differentiation can be proved by straightforward calculation from the algebraic definition (3–53), or they may be proved from the definition (3–52) in the same way the analogous properties are proved for differentiation of a scalar function:

$$\frac{d}{dt}(\mathbf{A} + \mathbf{B}) = \frac{d\mathbf{A}}{dt} + \frac{d\mathbf{B}}{dt}, \tag{3–54}$$

$$\frac{d}{dt}(f\mathbf{A}) = \frac{df}{dt}\mathbf{A} + f\frac{d\mathbf{A}}{dt}, \tag{3–55}$$

$$\frac{d}{dt}(\mathbf{A} \cdot \mathbf{B}) = \frac{d\mathbf{A}}{dt} \cdot \mathbf{B} + \mathbf{A} \cdot \frac{d\mathbf{B}}{dt}, \tag{3–56}$$

$$\frac{d}{dt}(\mathbf{A} \times \mathbf{B}) = \frac{d\mathbf{A}}{dt} \times \mathbf{B} + \mathbf{A} \times \frac{d\mathbf{B}}{dt}. \tag{3–57}$$

These results imply that differentiation of vector sums and products obeys the same algebraic rules as differentiation of sums and products in ordinary calculus, except, however, that the order of factors in the cross product must not be changed [Eq. (3–57)].   To prove Eq. (3–55), for example, from the definition (3–53), we simply show by direct calculation that the corresponding components on both sides of the equation are equal, making use of the definitions and properties of the vector operations introduced in the preceding section.   For the x-component, the proof runs:

$$\left[\frac{d}{dt}\,(f\mathbf{A})\right]_x = \frac{d}{dt}\,(f\mathbf{A})_x \qquad \text{[by Eq. (3–53)]}$$

$$= \frac{d}{dt}\,(fA_x) \qquad \text{[by Eq. (3–11)]}$$

$$= \frac{df}{dt}\,A_x + f\frac{dA_x}{dt} \qquad \begin{array}{l}\text{[standard rule of ordi-}\\ \text{nary calculus]}\end{array}$$

$$= \frac{df}{dt}\,A_x + f\left(\frac{d\mathbf{A}}{dt}\right)_x \qquad \text{[by Eq. (3–53)]}$$

$$= \left(\frac{df}{dt}\,\mathbf{A}\right)_x + \left(f\frac{d\mathbf{A}}{dt}\right)_x \qquad \text{[by Eq. (3–11)]}$$

$$= \left(\frac{df}{dt}\,\mathbf{A} + f\frac{d\mathbf{A}}{dt}\right)_x. \qquad \text{[by Eq. (3–12)]}$$

As another example, to prove Eq. (3–56) from the definition (3–52), we proceed as in the proof of the corresponding theorem for products of ordinary scalar functions. We shall use the symbol Δ to stand for the increment in the values of any function between t and $t + \Delta t$; the increment $\Delta\mathbf{A}$ of a vector $\mathbf{A}$ is defined in Fig. 3–15. Using this definition of Δ, and the rules of vector algebra given in the preceding section, we have

$$\frac{\Delta(\mathbf{A}\cdot\mathbf{B})}{\Delta t} = \frac{(\mathbf{A}+\Delta\mathbf{A})\cdot(\mathbf{B}+\Delta\mathbf{B}) - \mathbf{A}\cdot\mathbf{B}}{\Delta t}$$

$$= \frac{(\Delta\mathbf{A})\cdot\mathbf{B} + \mathbf{A}\cdot(\Delta\mathbf{B}) + (\Delta\mathbf{A})\cdot(\Delta\mathbf{B})}{\Delta t}$$

$$= \frac{(\Delta\mathbf{A})\cdot\mathbf{B}}{\Delta t} + \frac{\mathbf{A}\cdot(\Delta\mathbf{B})}{\Delta t} + \frac{(\Delta\mathbf{A})\cdot(\Delta\mathbf{B})}{\Delta t}$$

$$= \frac{\Delta\mathbf{A}}{\Delta t}\cdot\mathbf{B} + \mathbf{A}\cdot\frac{\Delta\mathbf{B}}{\Delta t} + \frac{(\Delta\mathbf{A})\cdot(\Delta\mathbf{B})}{\Delta t}. \qquad (3\text{–}58)$$

When $\Delta t \to 0$, the left side of Eq. (3–58) approaches the left side of Eq. (3–56), and the first two terms on the right side of Eq. (3–58) approach the two terms on the right of Eq. (3–56), while the last term on the right of Eq. (3–58) vanishes. The rigorous justification of this limit process is exactly similar to the justification required for the corresponding process in ordinary calculus.

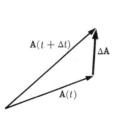

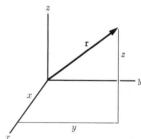

Fig. 3–15. Vector increment $\Delta\mathbf{A} =$ $\mathbf{A}(t + \Delta t) - \mathbf{A}(t)$.

Fig. 3–16. The position vector $\mathbf{r}$ of the point (x, y, z).

In treating motions in three-dimensional space, we often meet scalar and vector quantities which have a definite value at every point in space. Such quantities are functions of the space coordinates, commonly x, y, and z. They may also be thought of as functions of the position vector $\mathbf{r}$ from the origin to the point x,y,z (Fig. 3–16). We thus distinguish scalar point functions

$$u(\mathbf{r}) = u(x,y,z),$$

and vector point functions

$$\mathbf{A}(\mathbf{r}) = \mathbf{A}(x,y,z) = [A_x(x,y,z),\ A_y(x,y,z),\ A_z(x,y,z)].$$

An example of a scalar point function is the potential energy $V(x,y,z)$ of a particle moving in three dimensions. An example of a vector point function is the electric field intensity $\mathbf{E}(x,y,z)$. Scalar and vector point functions are often functions of the time t as well as of the point x,y,z in space.

If we are given a curve C in space, and a vector function $\mathbf{A}$ defined at points along this curve, we may consider the *line integral* of $\mathbf{A}$ along C:

$$\int_C \mathbf{A} \cdot d\mathbf{r}.$$

To define the line integral, imagine the curve C divided into small segments, and let any segment be represented by a vector $d\mathbf{r}$ in the direction of the segment and of length equal to the length of the segment. Then the curve consists of the successive vectors $d\mathbf{r}$ laid end to end. Now for each segment, form the product $\mathbf{A} \cdot d\mathbf{r}$, where $\mathbf{A}$ is the value of the vector function at the position of that segment. The line integral above is defined as the limit of the sums of the products $\mathbf{A} \cdot d\mathbf{r}$ as the number of segments increases without limit, while the length $|d\mathbf{r}|$ of every segment approaches zero. As an example, the work done by a force $\mathbf{F}$, which may vary from point to point, on a particle which moves along a curve C is

$$W = \int_C \mathbf{F} \cdot d\mathbf{r},$$

which is a generalization, to the case of a varying force and an arbitrary curve C, of the formula

$$W = \mathbf{F} \cdot \mathbf{s},$$

for a constant force acting on a body moving along a straight line segment $\mathbf{s}$. The reason for using the symbol $d\mathbf{r}$ to represent a segment of the curve is that if $\mathbf{r}$ is the position vector from the origin to a point on the curve, then $d\mathbf{r}$ is the increment in $\mathbf{r}$ (see Fig. 3–15) from one end to the other of the corresponding segment. If we write $\mathbf{r}$ in the form

$$\mathbf{r} = \mathbf{i}x + \mathbf{j}y + \mathbf{k}z, \qquad (3\text{–}59)$$

then

$$d\mathbf{r} = \mathbf{i}\,dx + \mathbf{j}\,dy + \mathbf{k}\,dz, \qquad (3\text{–}60)$$

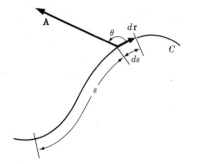

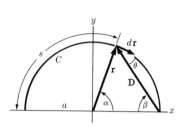

FIG. 3–17. Elements involved in the line integral.

FIG. 3–18.

where dx,dy,dz are the differences in the coordinates of the two ends of the segment. If s is the distance measured along the curve from some fixed point, we may express the line integral as an ordinary integral over the coordinate s:

$$\int_C \mathbf{A} \cdot d\mathbf{r} = \int A \cos \theta \, ds, \qquad (3\text{–}61)$$

where θ is the angle between $\mathbf{A}$ and the tangent to the curve at each point. (See Fig. 3–17.) This formula may be used to evaluate the integral if we know A and $\cos \theta$ as functions of s. We may also write the integral, using Eq. (3–60), as

$$\int_C \mathbf{A} \cdot d\mathbf{r} = \int_C (A_x \, dx + A_y \, dy + A_z \, dz). \qquad (3\text{–}62)$$

One of the most convenient ways to represent a curve in space is to give the three coordinates (x,y,z) or, equivalently, the position vector $\mathbf{r}$ as functions of a parameter s which has a definite value assigned to each point of the curve. The parameter s is often, though not necessarily, the distance measured along the curve from some reference point, as in Fig. 3–17, and in Eq. (3–61). The parameter s may also be the time at which a moving particle arrives at any given point on the curve. If we know $\mathbf{A}(\mathbf{r})$ and $\mathbf{r}(s)$, then the line integral can be evaluated from the formula

$$\int_C \mathbf{A} \cdot d\mathbf{r} = \int \left(\mathbf{A} \cdot \frac{d\mathbf{r}}{ds} \right) ds$$
$$= \int \left(A_x \frac{dx}{ds} + A_y \frac{dy}{ds} + A_z \frac{dz}{ds} \right) ds. \qquad (3\text{–}63)$$

The right member of this equation is an ordinary integral over the variable s.

As an example of the calculation of a line integral, let us compute the work done on a particle moving in a semicircle of radius a about the origin in the xy-plane, by a force attracting the particle toward the point $(x = a, y = 0)$ and proportional to the distance of the particle from the point $(a,0)$. Using the notation indicated in Fig. 3–18, we can write down the following relations:

$$\beta = \tfrac{1}{2}(\pi - \alpha),$$

$$\theta = \frac{\pi}{2} - \beta = \tfrac{1}{2}\alpha,$$

$$D^2 = 2a^2(1 - \cos \alpha),$$

$$D = 2a \sin \frac{\alpha}{2},$$

$$\mathbf{F} = -k\mathbf{D},$$

$$F = kD = 2ka \sin \frac{\alpha}{2},$$

$$s = a(\pi - \alpha).$$

Using these relations, we can evaluate the work done, using Eq. (3–61):

$$W = \int_C \mathbf{F} \cdot d\mathbf{r}$$

$$= \int_{s=0}^{\pi a} F \cos \theta \, ds$$

$$= -\int_{\alpha = \pi}^{0} 2ka^2 \sin \frac{\alpha}{2} \cos \frac{\alpha}{2} \, d\alpha$$

$$= -4ka^2 \int_{\theta = \frac{\pi}{2}}^{0} \sin \theta \cos \theta \, d\theta$$

$$= 2ka^2.$$

In order to calculate the same integral from Eq. (3–63), we express $\mathbf{r}$ and $\mathbf{F}$ along the curve as functions of the parameter α:

$$x = a \cos \alpha, \quad y = a \sin \alpha,$$

$$F_x = kD \cos \beta = 2ka \sin^2 \frac{\alpha}{2} = ka(1 - \cos \alpha),$$

$$F_y = -kD \sin \beta = -2ka \sin \frac{\alpha}{2} \cos \frac{\alpha}{2} = -ka \sin \alpha.$$

The work is now, according to Eq. (3–63),

$$W = \int_C \mathbf{F} \cdot d\mathbf{r}$$

$$= \int_{\alpha = \pi}^{0} \left(F_x \frac{dx}{d\alpha} + F_y \frac{dy}{d\alpha} \right) d\alpha$$

$$= \int_{\pi}^{0} [-ka^2(1 - \cos \alpha) \sin \alpha - ka^2 \sin \alpha \cos \alpha] \, d\alpha$$

$$= ka^2 \int_0^{\pi} \sin \alpha \, d\alpha$$

$$= 2ka^2.$$

3–4 Kinematics in a plane. Kinematics is the science which describes the possible motions of mechanical systems without regard to the dynamical laws which determine which motions actually occur. In studying the kinematics of a particle in a plane, we shall be concerned with methods for describing the position of a particle, and the path followed by the particle, and with methods for finding the various components of its velocity and acceleration.

The simplest method of locating a particle in a plane is to set up two perpendicular axes and to specify any position by its rectangular coordinates x,y with respect to these axes (Fig. 3–19). Equivalently, we may specify the position vector $\mathbf{r} = (x,y)$ from the origin to the position of the particle. If we locate a position by specifying the vector $\mathbf{r}$, then we need to specify in addition only the origin O from which the vector is drawn. If we specify the coordinates x,y, then we must also specify the coordinate axes from which x,y are measured.

Having set up a coordinate system, we next wish to describe the path of a particle in the plane. A curve in the xy-plane may be specified by giving y as a function of x along the curve, or vice versa:

$$y = y(x), \tag{3–64}$$

or

$$x = x(y). \tag{3–65}$$

Forms (3–64) and (3–65), however, are not convenient in many cases, for example when the curve doubles back on itself. We may also specify the curve by giving a relation between x and y,

$$f(x,y) = 0, \tag{3–66}$$

such that the curve consists of those points whose coordinates satisfy this relation. An example is the equation of a circle:

$$x^2 + y^2 - a^2 = 0.$$

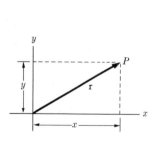

FIG. 3–19. Position vector and rectangular coordinates of a point P in a plane.

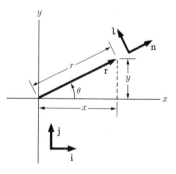

FIG. 3–20. Plane polar coordinates.

One of the most convenient ways to represent a curve is in terms of a parameter s:

$$x = x(s), \quad y = y(s), \tag{3-67}$$

or

$$\mathbf{r} = \mathbf{r}(s).$$

The parameter s has a unique value at each point of the curve. As s varies, the point $[x(s),y(s)]$ traces out the curve. The parameter s may, for example, be the distance measured along the curve from some fixed point. The equations of a circle can be expressed in terms of a parameter θ in the form

$$x = a \cos \theta, \quad y = a \sin \theta,$$

where θ is the angle between the x-axis and the radius a to the point (x,y) on the circle. In terms of the distance s measured around the circle,

$$x = a \cos \frac{s}{a}, \quad y = a \sin \frac{s}{a}.$$

In mechanical problems, the parameter is usually the time, in which case Eqs. (3–67) specify not only the path of the particle, but also the rate at which the particle traverses the path. If a particle travels with constant speed v around a circle, its position at any time t may be given by

$$x = a \cos \frac{vt}{a}, \quad y = a \sin \frac{vt}{a}.$$

If a particle moves along the path given by Eq. (3–67), we may specify its motion by giving $s(t)$, or by specifying directly

$$x = x(t), \quad y = y(t), \tag{3-68}$$

or

$$\mathbf{r} = \mathbf{r}(t). \tag{3-69}$$

The velocity and acceleration, and their components, are given by

$$\mathbf{v} = \frac{d\mathbf{r}}{dt} = \mathbf{i}\frac{dx}{dt} + \mathbf{j}\frac{dy}{dt},$$
$$v_x = \frac{dx}{dt}, \quad v_y = \frac{dy}{dt}, \tag{3-70}$$

$$\mathbf{a} = \frac{d\mathbf{v}}{dt} = \frac{d^2\mathbf{r}}{dt^2} = \mathbf{i}\frac{d^2x}{dt^2} + \mathbf{j}\frac{d^2y}{dt^2},$$
$$a_x = \frac{d^2x}{dt^2}, \quad a_y = \frac{d^2y}{dt^2}. \tag{3-71}$$

Polar coordinates, shown in Fig. 3–20, are convenient in many problems. The coordinates r,θ are related to x,y by the following equations:

$$x = r \cos \theta, \quad y = r \sin \theta, \tag{3-72}$$

and

$$r = (x^2 + y^2)^{\frac{1}{2}},$$ (3–73)

$$\theta = \tan^{-1}\frac{y}{x} = \sin^{-1}\frac{y}{(x^2 + y^2)^{\frac{1}{2}}} = \cos^{-1}\frac{x}{(x^2 + y^2)^{\frac{1}{2}}}.$$

We define unit vectors **n**,**l** in the directions of increasing r and θ, respectively, as shown. The vectors **n**,**l** are functions of the angle θ, and are related to **i**,**j** by the equations

$$\mathbf{n} = \mathbf{i}\cos\theta + \mathbf{j}\sin\theta,$$
$$\mathbf{l} = -\mathbf{i}\sin\theta + \mathbf{j}\cos\theta.$$ (3–74)

Equations (3–74) follow by inspection of Fig. 3–20. Differentiating, we obtain the important formulas

$$\frac{d\mathbf{n}}{d\theta} = \mathbf{l}, \quad \frac{d\mathbf{l}}{d\theta} = -\mathbf{n}.$$ (3–75)

Formulas (3–75) can also be obtained by studying Fig. 3–21 (remembering that $|\mathbf{n}| = |\mathbf{l}| = 1$). The position vector **r** is given very simply in terms of polar coordinates:

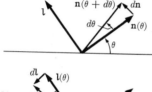

FIG. 3–21. Increments in the vectors **n** and **l**.

$$\mathbf{r} = r\mathbf{n}(\theta).$$ (3–76)

We may describe the motion of a particle in polar coordinates by specifying $r(t),\theta(t)$, thus determining the position vector $\mathbf{r}(t)$. The velocity vector is

$$\mathbf{v} = \frac{d\mathbf{r}}{dt} = \frac{dr}{dt}\mathbf{n} + r\frac{d\mathbf{n}}{d\theta}\frac{d\theta}{dt}$$
$$= \dot{r}\mathbf{n} + r\dot{\theta}\mathbf{l}.$$ (3–77)

Thus we obtain the components of velocity in the **n**,**l** directions:

$$v_r = \dot{r}, \quad v_\theta = r\dot{\theta}.$$ (3–78)

The acceleration vector is

$$\mathbf{a} = \frac{d\mathbf{v}}{dt} = \ddot{r}\mathbf{n} + \dot{r}\frac{d\mathbf{n}}{d\theta}\frac{d\theta}{dt} + \dot{r}\dot{\theta}\mathbf{l} + r\ddot{\theta}\mathbf{l} + r\dot{\theta}\frac{d\mathbf{l}}{d\theta}\frac{d\theta}{dt}$$
$$= (\ddot{r} - r\dot{\theta}^2)\mathbf{n} + (r\ddot{\theta} + 2\dot{r}\dot{\theta})\mathbf{l}.$$ (3–79)

The components of acceleration are

$$a_r = \ddot{r} - r\dot{\theta}^2, \quad a_\theta = r\ddot{\theta} + 2\dot{r}\dot{\theta}.$$ (3–80)

The term $r\dot{\theta}^2 = v_\theta^2/r$ is called the *centripetal acceleration* arising from motion in the θ direction. If $\ddot{r} = \dot{r} = 0$, the path is a circle, and $a_r = -v_\theta^2/r$. This result is familiar from elementary physics. The term $2\dot{r}\dot{\theta}$ is sometimes called the coriolis acceleration.

3–5 Kinematics in three dimensions.   The development in the preceding section for kinematics in two dimensions utilizing rectangular coordinates can be extended immediately to the three-dimensional case.   A point is specified by its coordinates x,y,z, with respect to chosen rectangular axes in space, or by its position vector $\mathbf{r} = (x,y,z)$ with respect to a chosen origin.   A path in space may be represented in the form of two equations in x, y, and z:

$$f(x,y,z) = 0, \quad g(x,y,z) = 0. \tag{3–81}$$

Each equation represents a surface.   The path is the intersection of the two surfaces.   A path may also be represented parametrically:

$$x = x(s), \quad y = y(s), \quad z = z(s). \tag{3–82}$$

Velocity and acceleration are again given by

$$\mathbf{v} = \frac{d\mathbf{r}}{dt} = \mathbf{i}v_x + \mathbf{j}v_y + \mathbf{k}v_z, \tag{3–83}$$

$$v_x = \frac{dx}{dt}, \quad v_y = \frac{dy}{dt}, \quad v_z = \frac{dz}{dt}, \tag{3–84}$$

and

$$\mathbf{a} = \frac{d\mathbf{v}}{dt} = \mathbf{i}a_x + \mathbf{j}a_y + \mathbf{k}a_z, \tag{3–85}$$

$$a_x = \frac{d^2x}{dt^2}, \quad a_y = \frac{d^2y}{dt^2}, \quad a_z = \frac{d^2z}{dt^2}. \tag{3–86}$$

Many coordinate systems other than cartesian are useful for special problems.   Perhaps the most widely used are spherical polar coordinates and cylindrical polar coordinates.   Cylindrical polar coordinates (ρ,φ,z) are defined as in Fig. 3–22, or by the equations

$$x = \rho \cos \varphi, \quad y = \rho \sin \varphi, \quad z = z, \tag{3–87}$$

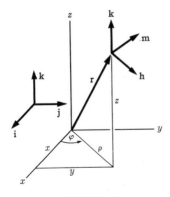

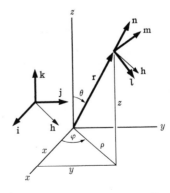

Fig. 3–22.   Cylindrical polar coordinates.

Fig. 3–23.   Spherical polar coordinates.

and, conversely,

$$\rho = (x^2 + y^2)^{\frac{1}{2}},$$

$$\varphi = \tan^{-1}\frac{y}{x} = \sin^{-1}\frac{y}{(x^2 + y^2)^{\frac{1}{2}}} = \cos^{-1}\frac{x}{(x^2 + y^2)^{\frac{1}{2}}}, \qquad (3\text{–}88)$$

$$z = z.$$

A system of unit vectors **h,m,k**, in the directions of increasing ρ,φ,z, respectively, is shown in Fig. 3–22. **k** is constant, but **m** and **h** are functions of φ, just as in plane polar coordinates:

$$\mathbf{h} = \mathbf{i}\cos\varphi + \mathbf{j}\sin\varphi, \quad \mathbf{m} = -\mathbf{i}\sin\varphi + \mathbf{j}\cos\varphi, \qquad (3\text{–}89)$$

and, likewise,

$$\frac{d\mathbf{h}}{d\varphi} = \mathbf{m}, \quad \frac{d\mathbf{m}}{d\varphi} = -\mathbf{h}. \qquad (3\text{–}90)$$

The position vector **r** can be expressed in cylindrical coordinates in the form

$$\mathbf{r} = \rho\mathbf{h} + z\mathbf{k}. \qquad (3\text{–}91)$$

Differentiating, we obtain for velocity and acceleration, using Eq. (3–90):

$$\mathbf{v} = \frac{d\mathbf{r}}{dt} = \dot{\rho}\mathbf{h} + \rho\dot{\varphi}\mathbf{m} + \dot{z}\mathbf{k}, \qquad (3\text{–}92)$$

$$\mathbf{a} = \frac{d\mathbf{v}}{dt} = (\ddot{\rho} - \rho\dot{\varphi}^2)\mathbf{h} + (\rho\ddot{\varphi} + 2\dot{\rho}\dot{\varphi})\mathbf{m} + \ddot{z}\mathbf{k}. \qquad (3\text{–}93)$$

Since **k,m,h** form a set of mutually perpendicular unit vectors, any vector **A** can be expressed in terms of its components along **k,m,h**:

$$\mathbf{A} = A_\rho\mathbf{h} + A_\varphi\mathbf{m} + A_z\mathbf{k}. \qquad (3\text{–}94)$$

It must be noted that since **h** and **m** are functions of φ, the set of components (A_ρ, A_φ, A_z) refers in general to a specific point in space at which the vector **A** is to be located, or at least to a specific value of the coordinate φ. Thus the components of a vector in cylindrical coordinates, and in fact in all systems of curvilinear coordinates, depend not only on the vector itself, but also on its location in space. If **A** is a function of a parameter, say t, then we may compute its derivative by differentiating Eq. (3–94), but we must be careful to take account of the variation of **h** and **m** if the location of the vector is also changing with t (e.g., if **A** is the force acting on a moving particle):

$$\frac{d\mathbf{A}}{dt} = \left(\frac{dA_\rho}{dt} - A_\varphi\frac{d\varphi}{dt}\right)\mathbf{h} + \left(\frac{dA_\varphi}{dt} + A_\rho\frac{d\varphi}{dt}\right)\mathbf{m} + \frac{dA_z}{dt}\mathbf{k}. \qquad (3\text{–}95)$$

Formulas (3–92) and (3–93) are special cases of Eq. (3–95). A formula for $d\mathbf{A}/dt$ could have been worked out also for the case of polar coordinates in two dimensions considered in the preceding section, and would, in fact, have been exactly analogous to Eq. (3–95) except that the last term would be missing.

Spherical polar coordinates (r,θ,φ) are defined as in Fig. 3–23 or by the equations

$$x = r \sin \theta \cos \varphi, \quad y = r \sin \theta \sin \varphi, \quad z = r \cos \theta. \qquad (3\text{–}96)$$

The expressions for x and y follow if we note that $\rho = r \sin \theta$, and use Eq. (3–87); the formula for z is evident from the diagram. Conversely,

$$r = (x^2 + y^2 + z^2)^{\frac{1}{2}}, \ \theta = \tan^{-1} \frac{(x^2 + y^2)^{\frac{1}{2}}}{z}, \ \varphi = \tan^{-1} \frac{y}{x}. \qquad (3\text{–}97)$$

Unit vectors $\mathbf{n},\mathbf{l},\mathbf{m}$ appropriate to spherical coordinates are indicated in Fig. 3–23, where $\mathbf{m}$ is the same vector as in cylindrical coordinates. The unit vector $\mathbf{h}$ is also useful in obtaining relations involving $\mathbf{n}$ and $\mathbf{l}$. We note that $\mathbf{k},\mathbf{h},\mathbf{n},\mathbf{l}$, all lie in one vertical plane. From the figure, and Eq. (3–89), we have

$$\mathbf{n} = \mathbf{k} \cos \theta + \mathbf{h} \sin \theta = \mathbf{k} \cos \theta + \mathbf{i} \sin \theta \cos \varphi + \mathbf{j} \sin \theta \sin \varphi,$$
$$\mathbf{l} = -\mathbf{k} \sin \theta + \mathbf{h} \cos \theta = -\mathbf{k} \sin \theta + \mathbf{i} \cos \theta \cos \varphi + \mathbf{j} \cos \theta \sin \varphi, \quad (3\text{–}98)$$
$$\mathbf{m} = -\mathbf{i} \sin \varphi + \mathbf{j} \cos \varphi.$$

By differentiating these formulas, or more easily by inspection of the diagram (as in Fig. 3–21), noting that variation of θ, with φ and r fixed, corresponds to rotation in the $\mathbf{k},\mathbf{n},\mathbf{h},\mathbf{l}$ plane, while variation of φ, with θ and r fixed, corresponds to rotation around the z-axis, we find

$$\frac{\partial \mathbf{n}}{\partial \theta} = \mathbf{l}, \qquad \frac{\partial \mathbf{n}}{\partial \varphi} = \mathbf{m} \sin \theta,$$
$$\frac{\partial \mathbf{l}}{\partial \theta} = -\mathbf{n}, \qquad \frac{\partial \mathbf{l}}{\partial \varphi} = \mathbf{m} \cos \theta, \qquad\qquad (3\text{–}99)$$
$$\frac{\partial \mathbf{m}}{\partial \theta} = 0, \qquad \frac{\partial \mathbf{m}}{\partial \varphi} = -\mathbf{h} = -\mathbf{n} \sin \theta - \mathbf{l} \cos \theta.$$

In spherical coordinates the position vector is simply

$$\mathbf{r} = r\mathbf{n}(\theta,\varphi). \qquad (3\text{–}100)$$

Differentiating and using Eqs. (3–99), we obtain the velocity and acceleration:

$$\mathbf{v} = \frac{d\mathbf{r}}{dt} = \dot{r}\mathbf{n} + r\dot{\theta}\mathbf{l} + r\dot{\varphi} \, (\sin \theta)\mathbf{m}, \qquad\qquad (3\text{–}101)$$

$$\mathbf{a} = \frac{d\mathbf{v}}{dt} = (\ddot{r} - r\dot{\theta}^2 - r\dot{\varphi}^2 \sin^2 \theta)\mathbf{n} + (r\ddot{\theta} + 2\dot{r}\dot{\theta} - r\dot{\varphi}^2 \sin \theta \cos \theta)\mathbf{l}$$
$$+ (r\ddot{\varphi} \sin \theta + 2\dot{r}\dot{\varphi} \sin \theta + 2r\dot{\theta}\dot{\varphi} \cos \theta)\mathbf{m}. \quad (3\text{–}102)$$

Again, **n,m,l** form a set of mutually perpendicular unit vectors, and any vector **A** may be represented in terms of its spherical components:

$$\mathbf{A} = A_r\mathbf{n} + A_\theta\mathbf{l} + A_\varphi\mathbf{m}. \tag{3–103}$$

Here again the components depend not only on **A** but also on its location. If **A** is a function of t, then

$$\frac{d\mathbf{A}}{dt} = \left(\frac{dA_r}{dt} - A_\theta\frac{d\theta}{dt} - A_\varphi\sin\theta\frac{d\varphi}{dt}\right)\mathbf{n}$$
$$+ \left(\frac{dA_\theta}{dt} + A_r\frac{d\theta}{dt} - A_\varphi\cos\theta\frac{d\varphi}{dt}\right)\mathbf{l}$$
$$+ \left(\frac{dA_\varphi}{dt} + A_r\sin\theta\frac{d\varphi}{dt} + A_\theta\cos\theta\frac{d\varphi}{dt}\right)\mathbf{m}. \tag{3–104}$$

3–6 Elements of vector analysis. A scalar function $u(x,y,z)$ has three derivatives, which may be thought of as the components of a vector point function called the *gradient* of u:

$$\text{grad } u = \left(\frac{\partial u}{\partial x}, \frac{\partial u}{\partial y}, \frac{\partial u}{\partial z}\right) = \mathbf{i}\frac{\partial u}{\partial x} + \mathbf{j}\frac{\partial u}{\partial y} + \mathbf{k}\frac{\partial u}{\partial z}. \tag{3–105}$$

We may also define grad u geometrically as a vector whose direction is the direction in which u increases most rapidly and whose magnitude is the *directional derivative* of u, i.e., the rate of increase of u per unit distance, in that direction. That this geometrical definition is equivalent to the algebraic definition (3–105) can be seen by taking the differential of u:

$$du = \frac{\partial u}{\partial x}\,dx + \frac{\partial u}{\partial y}\,dy + \frac{\partial u}{\partial z}\,dz. \tag{3–106}$$

Equation (3–106) has the form of a scalar product of grad u with the vector $d\mathbf{r}$ whose components are dx,dy,dz:

$$du = d\mathbf{r} \cdot \text{grad } u. \tag{3–107}$$

Geometrically, du is the change in u when we move from the point $\mathbf{r} = (x,y,z)$ to a nearby point $\mathbf{r} + d\mathbf{r} = (x + dx, y + dy, z + dz)$. By Eq. (3–15): $A \cdot B = A B \cos \theta$

$$du = |d\mathbf{r}|\,|\text{grad } u|\cos\theta, \tag{3–108}$$

where θ is the angle between $d\mathbf{r}$ and grad u. Thus at a fixed small distance $|d\mathbf{r}|$ from the point $\mathbf{r}$, the change in u is a maximum when $d\mathbf{r}$ is in the same direction as grad u, and then:

$$|\text{grad } u| = \frac{du}{|d\mathbf{r}|}.$$

This confirms the geometrical description of grad u given above. An alternative geometrical definition of grad u is that it is a vector such that the change in u, for an arbitrary small change of position $d\mathbf{r}$, is given by Eq. (3–107).

In a purely symbolic way, the right member of Eq. (3–105) can be thought of as the "product" of a "vector":

$$\boldsymbol{\nabla} = \left(\frac{\partial}{\partial x}, \frac{\partial}{\partial y}, \frac{\partial}{\partial z}\right) = \mathbf{i}\frac{\partial}{\partial x} + \mathbf{j}\frac{\partial}{\partial y} + \mathbf{k}\frac{\partial}{\partial z}, \qquad (3\text{–}109)$$

with the scalar function u:

$$\text{grad } u = \boldsymbol{\nabla} u. \qquad (3\text{–}110)$$

The symbol $\boldsymbol{\nabla}$ is pronounced "del." $\boldsymbol{\nabla}$ itself is not a vector in the geometrical sense, but an operation on a function u which gives a vector $\boldsymbol{\nabla} u$. However, algebraically, $\boldsymbol{\nabla}$ has properties nearly identical with those of a vector. The reason is that the differentiation symbols $(\partial/\partial x, \partial/\partial y, \partial/\partial z)$ have algebraic properties like those of ordinary numbers except when they act on a product of functions:

$$\frac{\partial}{\partial x}(u + v) = \frac{\partial u}{\partial x} + \frac{\partial v}{\partial x}, \quad \frac{\partial}{\partial x}\frac{\partial}{\partial y}u = \frac{\partial}{\partial y}\frac{\partial}{\partial x}u, \qquad (3\text{–}111)$$

and

$$\frac{\partial}{\partial x}(au) = a\frac{\partial u}{\partial x}, \qquad (3\text{–}112)$$

provided a is constant. However,

$$\frac{\partial}{\partial x}(uv) = \frac{\partial u}{\partial x}v + u\frac{\partial v}{\partial x}. \qquad (3\text{–}113)$$

In this one respect differentiation operators differ algebraically from ordinary numbers. If $\partial/\partial x$ were a number, $\partial/\partial x(uv)$ would equal either $u(\partial/\partial x)v$ or $v(\partial/\partial x)u$. Thus we may say that $\partial/\partial x$ behaves algebraically as a number except that when it operates on a product, the result is a sum of terms in which each factor is differentiated separately, as in Eq. (3–113). A similar remark applies to the symbol $\boldsymbol{\nabla}$. It behaves algebraically as a vector, except that when it operates on a product it must be treated also as a differentiation operation. This rule enables us to write down a large number of identities involving the $\boldsymbol{\nabla}$ symbol, based on vector identities. We shall require very few of these in this text, and shall not list them here.*

We can form the scalar product of $\boldsymbol{\nabla}$ with a vector point function $\mathbf{A}(x,y,z)$, and this is called the *divergence* of $\mathbf{A}$:

$$\text{div } \mathbf{A} = \boldsymbol{\nabla} \cdot \mathbf{A} = \frac{\partial A_x}{\partial x} + \frac{\partial A_y}{\partial y} + \frac{\partial A_z}{\partial z}. \qquad (3\text{–}114)$$

---

* For a more complete treatment of vector analysis, see H. B. Phillips, *Vector Analysis*. New York: John Wiley & Sons, 1933.

The geometrical meaning of div **A** is given by the following theorem, called the divergence theorem, or Gauss' theorem:

$$\iiint_V \nabla \cdot \mathbf{A}\, dV = \iint_S \mathbf{n} \cdot \mathbf{A}\, dS, \qquad (3\text{–}115)$$

where V is a given volume, S is the surface bounding the volume V, and **n** is a unit vector perpendicular to the surface S pointing out from the volume at each point of S (Fig. 3–24). Thus $\mathbf{n} \cdot \mathbf{A}$ is the component of **A** normal to S, and Eq. (3–115) says that the "total amount of $\nabla \cdot \mathbf{A}$ inside V" is equal to the "total flux of **A** outward through the surface S." If **v** represents the velocity of a moving fluid at any point in space, then

$$\iint_S \mathbf{n} \cdot \mathbf{v}\, dS$$

represents the volume of fluid flowing across S per second. If the fluid is incompressible, then according to Eq. (3–115),

$$\iiint_V \nabla \cdot \mathbf{v}\, dV$$

would represent the total volume of fluid being produced within the volume V per second. Hence $\nabla \cdot \mathbf{v}$ would be positive at sources from which the fluid is flowing, and negative at "sinks" into which it is flowing. We omit the proof of Gauss' theorem [Eq. (3–115)]; it may be found in any book on vector analysis.*

We can also form a cross product of ∇ with a vector point function $\mathbf{A}(x,y,z)$, and this is called the *curl* of **A**:

$$\operatorname{curl} \mathbf{A} = \nabla \times \mathbf{A} = \mathbf{i}\left(\frac{\partial A_z}{\partial y} - \frac{\partial A_y}{\partial z}\right) + \mathbf{j}\left(\frac{\partial A_x}{\partial z} - \frac{\partial A_z}{\partial x}\right) + \mathbf{k}\left(\frac{\partial A_y}{\partial x} - \frac{\partial A_x}{\partial y}\right).$$
$$(3\text{–}116)$$

The geometrical meaning of the curl is given by Stokes' theorem:

$$\iint_S \mathbf{n} \cdot (\nabla \times \mathbf{A})\, dS = \int_C \mathbf{A} \cdot d\mathbf{r}, \qquad (3\text{–}117)$$

where S is any surface in space, **n** is the unit vector normal to S, and C is the curve bounding S, $d\mathbf{r}$ being taken in that direction in which a man would walk around C if his left hand were on the inside and his head in the direction of **n**. (See Fig. 3–25.) According to Eq. (3–117), curl **A** at any point is a measure of the extent to which the vector function **A** circles around that point. A good example is the magnetic field around a wire carrying an electric current, where the curl of the magnetic field intensity is propor-

---

* See, e.g., Phillips, *op. cit.* Chapter 3, Section 32.

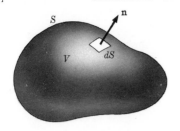

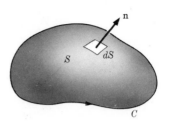

FIG. 3-24. A volume V bounded by a surface S.

FIG. 3-25. A surface S bounded by a curve C.

tional to the current density. We omit the proof of Stokes' theorem [Eq. (3–117)], which will be required only once in the present text.*

The reader should not be bothered by the difficulty of fixing these ideas in his mind. Understanding of new mathematical concepts like these comes to most people only slowly, as they are put to use. The definitions are recorded here for future use. One cannot be expected to be familiar with them until he has seen how they are used in physical problems.

The symbolic vector $\boldsymbol{\nabla}$ can also be expressed in cylindrical coordinates in terms of its components along $\mathbf{h,m,k}$. (See Fig. 3–22.) We note that if $u = u(\rho,\varphi,z)$,

$$du = \frac{\partial u}{\partial \rho}\, d\rho + \frac{\partial u}{\partial \varphi}\, d\varphi + \frac{\partial u}{\partial z}\, dz, \tag{3–118}$$

and, from Eqs. (3–91) and (3–90),

$$d\mathbf{r} = \mathbf{h}\, d\rho + \mathbf{m}\rho\, d\varphi + \mathbf{k}\, dz, \tag{3–119}$$

a result whose geometric significance will be evident from Fig. 3–22. Hence, if we write

$$\boldsymbol{\nabla} = \mathbf{h}\frac{\partial}{\partial \rho} + \frac{\mathbf{m}}{\rho}\frac{\partial}{\partial \varphi} + \mathbf{k}\frac{\partial}{\partial z}, \tag{3–120}$$

we will have, since $\mathbf{h,m,k}$ are a set of mutually perpendicular unit vectors,

$$du = d\mathbf{r} \cdot \boldsymbol{\nabla} u, \tag{3–121}$$

as required by the geometrical definition of $\boldsymbol{\nabla} u = \mathrm{grad}\ u$. [See the remarks following Eq. (3–107).] A formula for $\boldsymbol{\nabla}$ could have been worked out also for the case of polar coordinates in two dimensions and would have been exactly analogous to Eq. (3–120) except that the term in z would be missing. In applying the symbol $\boldsymbol{\nabla}$ to expressions involving vectors expressed in cylindrical coordinates [Eq. (3–94)], it must be remembered that the unit vectors $\mathbf{h}$ and $\mathbf{m}$ are functions of φ and subject to differentiation when they occur after $\partial/\partial\varphi$.

We may also find the vector $\boldsymbol{\nabla}$ in spherical coordinates (Fig. 3–23) by noting that

$$du = \frac{\partial u}{\partial r}\, dr + \frac{\partial u}{\partial \theta}\, d\theta + \frac{\partial u}{\partial \varphi}\, d\varphi, \tag{3–122}$$

and

$$d\mathbf{r} = \mathbf{n}\, dr + \mathbf{l}r\, d\theta + \mathbf{m}r\sin\theta\, d\varphi. \tag{3–123}$$

---

* For the proof see Phillips, *op. cit.* Chapter 3, Section 29.

Hence

$$\boldsymbol{\nabla} = \mathbf{n}\frac{\partial}{\partial r} + \frac{1}{r}\frac{\partial}{\partial \theta} + \frac{\mathbf{m}}{r\sin\theta}\frac{\partial}{\partial \varphi}, \tag{3-124}$$

in order that Eq. (3-121) may hold.   Again we caution that in working with Eq. (3-124), the dependence of $\mathbf{n},\mathbf{l},\mathbf{m}$, on θ,φ must be kept in mind.   For example, the divergence of a vector function $\mathbf{A}$ expressed in spherical coordinates [Eq. (3-103)] is

$$\begin{aligned}
\boldsymbol{\nabla}\cdot\mathbf{A} &= \mathbf{n}\cdot\frac{\partial\mathbf{A}}{\partial r} + \frac{1}{r}\cdot\frac{\partial\mathbf{A}}{\partial\theta} + \frac{\mathbf{m}}{r\sin\theta}\cdot\frac{\partial\mathbf{A}}{\partial\varphi} \\
&= \frac{\partial A_r}{\partial r} + \frac{1}{r}\left(\frac{\partial A_\theta}{\partial\theta} + A_r\right) + \frac{1}{r\sin\theta}\left(\frac{\partial A_\varphi}{\partial\varphi} + A_r\sin\theta + A_\theta\cos\theta\right) \\
&= \frac{\partial A_r}{\partial r} + \frac{2A_r}{r} + \frac{1}{r}\frac{\partial A_\theta}{\partial\theta} + \frac{A_\theta}{r\tan\theta} + \frac{1}{r\sin\theta}\frac{\partial A_\varphi}{\partial\varphi} \\
&= \frac{1}{r^2}\frac{\partial}{\partial r}(r^2 A_r) + \frac{1}{r\sin\theta}\frac{\partial}{\partial\theta}(\sin\theta A_\theta) + \frac{1}{r\sin\theta}\frac{\partial A_\varphi}{\partial\varphi}.
\end{aligned}$$

(In the above calculation, we use the fact that $\mathbf{l},\mathbf{m},\mathbf{n}$ are a set of mutually perpendicular unit vectors.)

3-7 Momentum and energy theorems.   Newton's second law, as formulated in Chapter 1, leads, in two or three dimensions, to the vector equation

$$m\frac{d^2\mathbf{r}}{dt^2} = \mathbf{F}. \tag{3-125}$$

In two dimensions, this is equivalent to two component equations, in three dimensions, to three, which are, in cartesian coordinates,

$$m\frac{d^2x}{dt^2} = F_x, \quad m\frac{d^2y}{dt^2} = F_y, \quad m\frac{d^2z}{dt^2} = F_z. \tag{3-126}$$

In this section, we prove, using Eq. (3-125), some theorems for motion in two or three dimensions which are the vector analogs to those proved in Section 2-1 for one-dimensional motion.

The linear momentum vector $\mathbf{p}$ of a particle is to be defined, according to Eq. (1-10), as follows:

$$\mathbf{p} = m\mathbf{v}. \tag{3-127}$$

Equations (3-125) and (3-126) can then be written

$$\frac{d}{dt}(m\mathbf{v}) = \frac{d\mathbf{p}}{dt} = \mathbf{F}, \tag{3-128}$$

or, in component form,

$$\frac{dp_x}{dt} = F_x, \quad \frac{dp_y}{dt} = F_y, \quad \frac{dp_z}{dt} = F_z. \tag{3-129}$$

If we multiply by dt, and integrate from t_1 to t_2, we obtain the change in momentum between t_1 and t_2:

$$\mathbf{p}_2 - \mathbf{p}_1 = m\mathbf{v}_2 - m\mathbf{v}_1 = \int_{t_1}^{t_2} \mathbf{F}\, dt. \tag{3-130}$$

The integral on the right is the impulse delivered by the force, and is a vector whose components are the corresponding integrals of the components of **F**. In component form:

$$p_{x_2} - p_{x_1} = \int_{t_1}^{t_2} F_x \, dt, \quad p_{y_2} - p_{y_1} = \int_{t_1}^{t_2} F_y \, dt, \quad p_{z_2} - p_{z_1} = \int_{t_1}^{t_2} F_z \, dt. \quad (3\text{–}131)$$

In order to obtain an equation for the rate of change of kinetic energy, we proceed as in Section 2–1, multiplying Eqs. (3–126) by v_x, v_y, v_z, respectively, to obtain

$$\frac{d}{dt}\left(\tfrac{1}{2}mv_x^2\right) = F_x v_x, \quad \frac{d}{dt}\left(\tfrac{1}{2}mv_y^2\right) = F_y v_y, \quad \frac{d}{dt}\left(\tfrac{1}{2}mv_z^2\right) = F_z v_z. \quad (3\text{–}132)$$

Adding these equations, we have

$$\frac{d}{dt}\left[\tfrac{1}{2}m(v_x^2 + v_y^2 + v_z^2)\right] = F_x v_x + F_y v_y + F_z v_z,$$

or

$$\frac{d}{dt}\left(\tfrac{1}{2}mv^2\right) = \frac{dT}{dt} = \mathbf{F} \cdot \mathbf{v}. \quad (3\text{–}133)$$

This equation can also be deduced from the vector equation (3–125) by taking the dot product with **v** on each side, and noting that

$$\frac{d}{dt}(v^2) = \frac{d}{dt}(\mathbf{v} \cdot \mathbf{v}) = \frac{d\mathbf{v}}{dt} \cdot \mathbf{v} + \mathbf{v} \cdot \frac{d\mathbf{v}}{dt} = 2\mathbf{v} \cdot \frac{d\mathbf{v}}{dt}.$$

Thus, by Eq. (3–132),

$$\mathbf{F} \cdot \mathbf{v} = m\mathbf{v} \cdot \frac{d\mathbf{v}}{dt} = \tfrac{1}{2}m\frac{d(v^2)}{dt} = \frac{d}{dt}\left(\tfrac{1}{2}mv^2\right).$$

Multiplying Eq. (3–133) by dt, and integrating, we obtain the integrated form of the energy theorem:

$$T_2 - T_1 = \tfrac{1}{2}mv_2^2 - \tfrac{1}{2}mv_1^2 = \int_{t_1}^{t_2} \mathbf{F} \cdot \mathbf{v} \, dt. \quad (3\text{–}134)$$

Since $\mathbf{v}\,dt = d\mathbf{r}$, if **F** is given as a function of **r**, we can write the right member of Eq. (3–134) as a line integral:

$$T_2 - T_1 = \int_{r_1}^{r_2} \mathbf{F} \cdot d\mathbf{r}, \quad (3\text{–}135)$$

where the integral is to be taken along the path followed by the particle between the points r_1 and r_2. The integral on the right in Eqs. (3–134) and (3–135) is the work done on the particle by the force between the times t_1 and t_2. Note how the vector notation brings out the analogy between the one- and the two- or three-dimensional cases of the momentum and energy theorems.

3–8 Plane and vector angular momentum theorems. If a particle moves in a plane, we define its angular momentum L_O about a point O as the moment of its momentum vector about the point O, that is, as the product of its distance from O times the component of momentum perpendicular to the line joining the particle to O. The subscript o will usually be omitted, except when moments about more than one origin enter into the discussion, but it must be remembered that angular momentum, like torque, refers to a particular origin about which moments are taken. The angular momentum L is taken as positive when the particle is moving in a counter-clockwise sense with respect to O; L is expressed most simply in terms of polar coordinates with O as origin. Let the particle have mass m. Then its momentum is $m\mathbf{v}$, and the component of momentum perpendicular to the radius vector from O is mv_θ (Fig. 3–26), so that, if we use Eq. (3–78),

$$L = rmv_\theta = mr^2\dot\theta. \qquad (3\text{–}136)$$

If we write the force in terms of its polar components:

$$\mathbf{F} = \mathbf{n}F_r + \mathbf{1}F_\theta, \qquad (3\text{–}137)$$

then in plane polar coordinates the equation of motion, Eq. (3–125), be-

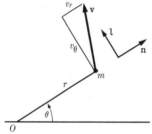

comes, by Eq. (3–80),

$$ma_r = m\ddot r - mr\dot\theta^2 = F_r, \qquad (3\text{–}138)$$
$$ma_\theta = mr\ddot\theta + 2m\dot r\dot\theta = F_\theta. \qquad (3\text{–}139)$$

We now note that

$$\frac{dL}{dt} = 2mr\dot r\dot\theta + mr^2\ddot\theta.$$

Thus, multiplying Eq. (3–139) by r, we have

FIG. 3–26.   Components of velocity in a plane.

$$\frac{dL}{dt} = \frac{d}{dt}(mr^2\dot\theta) = rF_\theta = N. \qquad (3\text{–}140)$$

The quantity rF_θ is the torque exerted by the force $\mathbf{F}$ about the point O. Integrating Eq. (3–140), we obtain the integrated form of the angular momentum theorem for motion in a plane:

$$L_2 - L_1 = mr_2^2\dot\theta_2 - mr_1^2\dot\theta_1 = \int_{t_1}^{t_2} rF_\theta\, dt. \qquad (3\text{–}141)$$

We can generalize the definition of angular momentum to apply to three-dimensional motion by defining the angular momentum of a particle about an axis in space as the moment of its momentum vector about this axis, just as in Section 3–2 we defined the moment of a force about an axis. The development is most easily carried out in cylindrical coordinates with the z-axis as the axis about which moments are to be taken. The generalization of theorems (3–140) and (3–141) to this case is then easily proved in analogy with the proof given above. This development is left as an exercise.

As a final generalization of the concept of angular momentum, we define the vector angular momentum L_O about a point O as the vector moment of the momentum vector about O:

$$L_O = \mathbf{r} \times \mathbf{p} = m(\mathbf{r} \times \mathbf{v}), \qquad (3\text{-}142)$$

where the vector $\mathbf{r}$ is taken from the point O as origin to the position of the particle of mass m. Again we shall omit the subscript o when no confusion can arise. The component of the vector $\mathbf{L}$ in any direction is the moment of the momentum vector $\mathbf{p}$ about an axis in that direction through O.

By taking the cross product of $\mathbf{r}$ with both members of the vector equation of motion [Eq. (3–125)], we obtain

$$\mathbf{r} \times \left(m \frac{d\mathbf{v}}{dt} \right) = \mathbf{r} \times \mathbf{F}. \qquad (3\text{-}143)$$

By the rules of vector algebra and vector calculus,

$$\begin{aligned}
\frac{d\mathbf{L}}{dt} &= \frac{d}{dt} \left[\mathbf{r} \times (m\mathbf{v}) \right] \\
&= \mathbf{r} \times \frac{d}{dt} (m\mathbf{v}) + \frac{d\mathbf{r}}{dt} \times (m\mathbf{v}) \\
&= \mathbf{r} \times \frac{d}{dt} (m\mathbf{v}) + \mathbf{v} \times (m\mathbf{v}) \\
&= \mathbf{r} \times \left(m \frac{d\mathbf{v}}{dt} \right).
\end{aligned}$$

We substitute this result in Eq. (3–143):

$$\frac{d\mathbf{L}}{dt} = \mathbf{r} \times \mathbf{F} = \mathbf{N}. \qquad (3\text{-}144)$$

The time rate of change of the vector angular momentum of a particle is equal to the vector torque acting on it. The integrated form of the angular momentum theorem is

$$\mathbf{L}_2 - \mathbf{L}_1 = \int_{t_1}^{t_2} \mathbf{N} \, dt. \qquad (3\text{-}145)$$

The theorems for plane angular momentum and for angular momentum about an axis follow from the vector angular momentum theorems by taking components in the appropriate direction.

3–9 Discussion of the general problem of two- and three-dimensional motion. If the force $\mathbf{F}$ is given, in general as a function $\mathbf{F}(\mathbf{v},\mathbf{r},t)$ of position, velocity, and time, the equations of motion (3–126) become a set of three (or, in two dimensions, two) simultaneous second order differential equations:

$$m \frac{d^2x}{dt^2} = F_x(\dot{x},\dot{y},\dot{z},x,y,z,t),$$

$$m \frac{d^2y}{dt^2} = F_y(\dot{x},\dot{y},\dot{z},x,y,z,t), \tag{3-146}$$

$$m \frac{d^2z}{dt^2} = F_z(\dot{x},\dot{y},\dot{z},x,y,z,t).$$

If we are given the position $\mathbf{r}_0 = (x_0,y_0,z_0)$, and the velocity $\mathbf{v}_0 = (v_{x_0},v_{y_0},v_{z_0})$ at any instant t_0, Eqs. (3–146) give us $d^2\mathbf{r}/dt^2$, and from $\mathbf{r},\dot{\mathbf{r}},\ddot{\mathbf{r}}$, at time t, we can determine $\mathbf{r},\dot{\mathbf{r}}$ a short time later or earlier at $t + dt$, thus extending the functions $\mathbf{r},\dot{\mathbf{r}},\ddot{\mathbf{r}}$, into the past and future with the help of Eqs. (3–146). This argument can be made mathematically rigorous, and leads to an existence theorem guaranteeing the existence of a unique solution of these equations for any given position and velocity at an initial instant t_0. We note that the general solution of Eqs. (3–146) involves the six "arbitrary" constants $x_0,y_0,z_0,v_{x_0},v_{y_0},v_{z_0}$. Instead of these six constants, we might specify any other six quantities from which they can be determined. (In two dimensions, we will have two second order differential equations and four initial constants.)

In general, the solution of the three simultaneous equations (3–146) will be much more difficult than the solution of the single equation (2–9) for one-dimensional motion. The reason for the greater difficulty is that, in general, all the variables x,y,z and their derivatives are involved in all three equations, which makes the problem of the same order of difficulty as a single sixth order differential equation. [In fact, the set of Eqs. (3–146) can be shown to be equivalent to a single sixth order equation.] If each force component involved only the corresponding coordinate and its derivatives,

$$F_x = F_x(\dot{x},x,t), \quad F_y = F_y(\dot{y},y,t), \quad F_z = F_z(\dot{z},z,t), \tag{3-147}$$

then the three equations (3–146) would be independent of one another. We could solve for $x(t),y(t),z(t)$ separately as three independent problems in one-dimensional motion. The most important example of this case is probably when the force is given as a function of time only:

$$\mathbf{F} = \mathbf{F}(t) = [F_x(t),F_y(t),F_z(t)]. \tag{3-148}$$

The x, y, and z equations of motion can then each be solved separately by the method given in Section 2–3. The case of a frictional force proportional to the velocity will also be an example of the type (3–147). Other cases will sometimes occur, for example, the three-dimensional harmonic oscillator (e.g., a baseball in a tubful of gelatine, or an atom in a crystal lattice), for which the force is

$$F_x = -k_x x, \quad F_y = -k_y y, \quad F_z = -k_z z, \tag{3-149}$$

when the axes are suitably chosen. The problem now splits into three separate linear harmonic oscillator problems in x, y, and z. In most cases, however, we are not so fortunate, and Eq. (3–147) does not hold. Special methods are available for solving certain classes of two- and three-dimensional problems. Some of these will be developed in this chapter. Problems not solvable by such methods are always, in principle, solvable by various numerical methods of integrating sets of equations like Eqs. (3–146) to get approximate solutions to any required degree of accuracy. Such methods are even more tedious in the three-dimensional case than in the one-dimensional case, and are usually impractical unless one has the services of one of the large automatic computing machines.

When we try to extend the idea of potential energy to two or three dimensions, we will find that having the force given as $\mathbf{F}(\mathbf{r})$, a function of $\mathbf{r}$ alone, is not sufficient to guarantee the existence of a potential energy function $V(\mathbf{r})$. In the one-dimensional case, we found that if the force is given as a function of position alone, a potential energy function can always be defined by Eq. (2–41). Essentially, the reason is that in one dimension, a particle which travels from x_1 to x_2 and returns to x_1 must return by the same route, so that if the force is a function of position alone, the work done by the force on the particle during its return trip must necessarily be the same as that expended against the force in going from x_1 to x_2. In three dimensions, a particle can travel from $\mathbf{r}_1$ to $\mathbf{r}_2$ and return by a different route, so that even if $\mathbf{F}$ is a function of $\mathbf{r}$, the particle may be acted on by a different force on the return trip and the work done may not be the same. In Section 3–12 we shall formulate a criterion to determine when a potential energy $V(\mathbf{r})$ exists.

When $V(\mathbf{r})$ exists, a conservation of energy theorem still holds, and the total energy $(T + V)$ is a constant of the motion. However, whereas in one dimension the energy integral is always sufficient to enable us to solve the problem at least in principle (Section 2–5), in two and three dimensions this is no longer the case. If x is the only coordinate, then if we know a relation $(T + V = E)$ between x and $\dot{x}$, we can solve for $\dot{x} = f(x)$ and reduce the problem to one of carrying out a single integration. But with coordinates x,y,z, one relation between $x,y,z,\dot{x},\dot{y},\dot{z}$ is not enough. We would need to know five such relations, in general, in order to eliminate, for example, x, y, $\dot{x}$, and $\dot{y}$, and find $\dot{z} = f(z)$. In the two-dimensional case, we would need three relations between $x,y,\dot{x},\dot{y}$ to solve the problem by this method. To find four more relations like the energy integral from Eqs. (3–146) (or two more in two dimensions) is hopeless in most cases. In fact, such relations do not usually exist. Often, however, we can find other quantities (e.g., the angular momentum) which are constants of the motion, and thus obtain one or two more relations between $x,y,z,\dot{x},\dot{y},\dot{z}$, which in many cases will be enough to allow a solution of the problem. Examples will be given later.

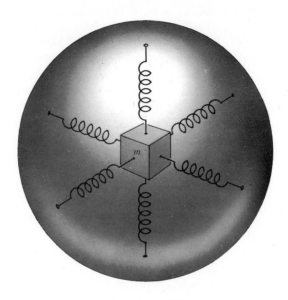

FIG. 3–27.   Model of a three-dimensional harmonic oscillator.

3–10 The harmonic oscillator in two and three dimensions.   In this section and the next, we consider a few simple problems in which the force has the form of Eqs. (3–147), so that the equations of motion separate into independent equations in x, y, and z.   Mathematically, we then simply have three separate problems, each of the type considered in Chapter 2. The only new feature will be the interpretation of the three solutions $x(t),y(t),z(t)$ as representing a motion in three-dimensional space.

We first consider briefly the solution of the problem of the three-dimensional harmonic oscillator without damping, whose equations of motion are

$$m\ddot{x} = -k_x x, \quad m\ddot{y} = -k_y y, \quad m\ddot{z} = -k_z z. \qquad (3\text{–}150)$$

A model could be constructed by suspending a mass between three perpendicular sets of springs (Fig. 3–27).   The solutions of these equations, we know from Section 2–8:

$$
\begin{aligned}
x &= A_x \cos{(\omega_x t + \theta_x)}, & \omega_x^2 &= k_x/m, \\
y &= A_y \cos{(\omega_y t + \theta_y)}, & \omega_y^2 &= k_y/m, \\
z &= A_z \cos{(\omega_z t + \theta_z)}, & \omega_z^2 &= k_z/m.
\end{aligned}
\qquad (3\text{–}151)
$$

The six constants $(A_x, A_y, A_z, \theta_x, \theta_y, \theta_z)$ depend on the initial values $x_0, y_0, z_0, \dot{x}_0, \dot{y}_0, \dot{z}_0$.   Each coordinate oscillates independently with simple harmonic motion at a frequency depending on the corresponding restoring force

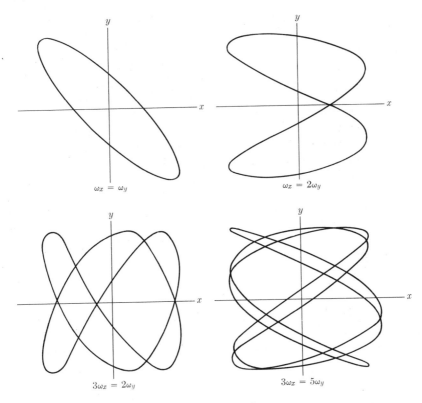

$$\omega_x = \omega_y$$

$$\omega_x = 2\omega_y$$

$$3\omega_x = 2\omega_y$$

$$3\omega_x = 5\omega_y$$

Fig. 3–28.   Lissajous figures.

coefficient, and on the mass.   The resulting motion of the particle takes place within a rectangular box of dimensions $2A_x \times 2A_y \times 2A_z$ about the origin.   If the angular frequencies $\omega_x, \omega_y, \omega_z$ are commensurable, that is, if for some set of integers (n_x, n_y, n_z),

$$\frac{\omega_x}{n_x} = \frac{\omega_y}{n_y} = \frac{\omega_z}{n_z}, \tag{3-152}$$

then the path of the mass m in space is closed, and the motion is periodic. If (n_x, n_y, n_z) are chosen so that they have no common integral factor, then the period of the motion is

$$\tau = \frac{2\pi n_x}{\omega_x} = \frac{2\pi n_y}{\omega_y} = \frac{2\pi n_z}{\omega_z}. \tag{3-153}$$

During one period, the coordinate x makes n_x oscillations, the coordinate y makes n_y oscillations, and the coordinate z makes n_z oscillations, so that the particle returns at the end of the period to its initial position and velocity.   In the two-dimensional case, if the path of the oscillating particle is plotted for various combinations of frequencies ω_x and ω_y, and various phases θ_x and θ_y, many interesting and beautiful patterns are obtained. Such patterns are called *Lissajous figures* (Fig. 3–28), and may be produced mechanically by a mechanism designed to move a pencil or other writing device according to Eqs. (3–151). Similar patterns may be obtained electrically on a cathode-ray oscilloscope by sweeping horizontally and vertically with suitable oscillating voltages. If the frequencies $\omega_x, \omega_y, \omega_z$ are incommensurable, so that Eq. (3–152) does not hold for any set of integers, the motion is not periodic, and the path fills the entire box $2A_x \times 2A_y \times 2A_z$, in the sense that the particle eventually comes arbitrarily close to every point in the box. The discussion can readily be extended to the cases of damped and forced oscillations in two and three dimensions.

If the three constants k_x, k_y, k_z are all equal, the oscillator is said to be *isotropic*, that is, the same in all directions. In this case, the three frequencies $\omega_x, \omega_y, \omega_z$ are all equal and the motion is periodic, with each coordinate executing one cycle of oscillation in a period. The path can be shown to be an ellipse, a straight line, or a circle, depending on the amplitudes and phases $(A_x, A_y, A_z, \theta_x, \theta_y, \theta_z)$.

3–11 Projectiles. An important problem in the history of the science of mechanics is that of determining the motion of a projectile. A projectile moving under the action of gravity near the surface of the earth moves, if air resistance is neglected, according to the equation

$$m \frac{d^2\mathbf{r}}{dt^2} = -mg\mathbf{k}, \tag{3–154}$$

where the z-axis is taken in the vertical direction. In component form:

$$m \frac{d^2x}{dt^2} = 0, \tag{3–155}$$

$$m \frac{d^2y}{dt^2} = 0, \tag{3–156}$$

$$m \frac{d^2z}{dt^2} = -mg. \tag{3–157}$$

The solutions of these equations are

$$x = x_0 + v_{x_0}t, \tag{3–158}$$
$$y = y_0 + v_{y_0}t, \tag{3–159}$$
$$z = z_0 + v_{z_0}t - \tfrac{1}{2}gt^2, \tag{3–160}$$

or, in vector form,

$$\mathbf{r} = \mathbf{r}_0 + \mathbf{v}_0 t - \tfrac{1}{2}gt^2\mathbf{k}. \tag{3–161}$$

We assume the projectile starts from the origin $(0,0,0)$, with its initial velocity in the xz-plane, so that $v_{y_0} = 0$. This is no limitation on the motion of the projectile, but merely corresponds to a convenient choice of coordinate system. Equations (3–158), (3–159), (3–160) then become

$$x = v_{x_0}t, \tag{3-162}$$
$$y = 0, \tag{3-163}$$
$$z = v_{z_0}t - \tfrac{1}{2}gt^2. \tag{3-164}$$

These equations give a complete description of the motion of the projectile. Solving the first equation for t and substituting in the third, we have an equation for the path in the xz-plane:

$$z = \frac{v_{z_0}}{v_{x_0}}x - \frac{1}{2}\frac{g}{v_{x_0}^2}x^2. \tag{3-165}$$

This can be rewritten in the form

$$\left(x - \frac{v_{z_0}v_{x_0}}{g}\right)^2 = -2\frac{v_{x_0}^2}{g}\left(z - \frac{v_{z_0}^2}{2g}\right). \tag{3-166}$$

This is a parabola, concave downward, whose maximum altitude occurs at

$$z_m = \frac{v_{z_0}^2}{2g}, \tag{3-167}$$

and which crosses the horizontal plane $z = 0$ at the origin and at the point

$$x_m = 2\frac{v_{z_0}v_{x_0}}{g}. \tag{3-168}$$

If the surface of the earth is horizontal, x_m is the range of the projectile.

Let us now take account of air resistance by assuming a frictional force proportional to the velocity:

$$m\frac{d^2\mathbf{r}}{dt^2} = -mg\mathbf{k} - b\frac{d\mathbf{r}}{dt}. \tag{3-169}$$

In component notation, if we assume that the motion takes place in the xz-plane,

$$m\frac{d^2x}{dt^2} = -b\frac{dx}{dt}, \tag{3-170}$$

$$m\frac{d^2z}{dt^2} = -mg - b\frac{dz}{dt}. \tag{3-171}$$

It should be pointed out that the actual resistance of the air against a moving projectile is a complicated function of velocity, so that the solutions we obtain will be only approximate, although they indicate the general nature of the motion. If the projectile starts from the origin at $t = 0$, the solutions of Eqs. (3–170) and (3–171) are (see Sections 2–4 and 2–6)

$$v_x = v_{x_0}e^{-bt/m}, \tag{3-172}$$

$$x = \frac{mv_{x_0}}{b}(1 - e^{-bt/m}), \tag{3-173}$$

$$v_z = \left(\frac{mg}{b} + v_{z_0}\right) e^{-bt/m} - \frac{mg}{b}, \tag{3-174}$$

$$z = \left(\frac{m^2 g}{b^2} + \frac{m v_{z_0}}{b}\right)(1 - e^{-bt/m}) - \frac{mg}{b} t. \tag{3-175}$$

Solving Eq. (3-173) for t and substituting in Eq. (3-175), we obtain an equation for the trajectory:

$$z = \left(\frac{mg}{b v_{x_0}} + \frac{v_{z_0}}{v_{x_0}}\right) x - \frac{m^2 g}{b^2} \ln\left(\frac{m v_{x_0}}{m v_{x_0} - bx}\right). \tag{3-176}$$

For low air resistance, or short distances, when $(bx)/(mv_{x_0}) \ll 1$, we may expand in powers of $(bx)/(mv_{x_0})$ to obtain

$$z \doteq \frac{v_{z_0}}{v_{x_0}} x - \frac{1}{2}\frac{g}{v_{x_0}^2} x^2 - \frac{1}{3}\frac{bg}{m v_{x_0}^3} x^3 - \cdots . \tag{3-177}$$

Thus the trajectory starts out as a parabola, but for larger values of x (taking v_{x_0} as positive), z falls more rapidly than for a parabola. According to Eq. (3-176), as x approaches the value $(mv_{x_0})/b$, z approaches minus infinity, i.e., the trajectory ends as a vertical drop at $x = (mv_{x_0})/b$. From Eq. (3-174), we see that the vertical fall at the end of the trajectory takes place at the terminal velocity $-mg/b$. (The projectile may, of course, return to earth before reaching this part of its trajectory.) If we take the first three terms in Eq. (3-177) and solve for x when $z = 0$, we have approximately, if $x_m \ll mv_{x_0}/b$,

$$x_m \doteq \frac{2 v_{x_0} v_{z_0}}{g} - \frac{8}{3}\frac{b v_{z_0}^2 v_{x_0}}{mg^2} + \cdots . \tag{3-178}$$

The second term gives the first order correction to the range due to air resistance, and the first two terms will give a good approximation when the effect of air resistance is small. The extreme opposite case, when air resistance is predominant in determining range (Fig. 3-29), occurs when the vertical drop at $x = (mv_{x_0})/b$ begins above the horizontal plane $z = 0$. The range is then, approximately,

$$x_m \doteq \frac{m v_{x_0}}{b}, \quad \left(\frac{b v_{z_0}}{mg} \gg 1\right). \tag{3-179}$$

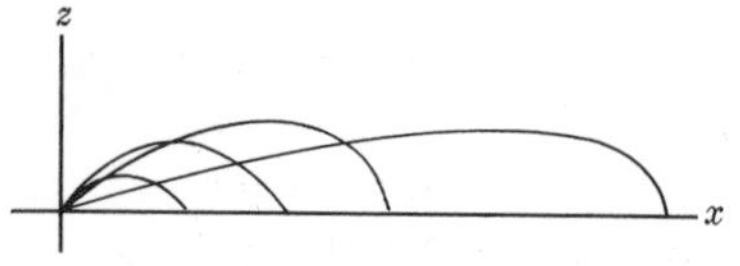

FIG. 3-29. Trajectories for maximum range for projectiles with various muzzle velocities.

We can treat (approximately) the problem of the effect of wind on the projectile by assuming the force of air resistance to be proportional to the relative velocity of the projectile with respect to the air:

$$m\frac{d^2\mathbf{r}}{dt^2} = -mg\mathbf{k} - b\left(\frac{d\mathbf{r}}{dt} - \mathbf{v}_w\right), \tag{3-180}$$

where $\mathbf{v}_w$ is the wind velocity.   If $\mathbf{v}_w$ is constant, the term $b\mathbf{v}_w$ in Eq. (3–180) behaves as a constant force added to $-mg\mathbf{k}$, and the problem is easily solved by the method above, the only difference being that there may be constant forces in addition to frictional forces in all three directions x,y,z.

The air resistance to a projectile decreases with altitude, so that a better form for the equation of motion of a projectile which rises to appreciable altitudes would be

$$m \frac{d^2\mathbf{r}}{dt^2} = -mg\mathbf{k} - be^{-z/h} \frac{d\mathbf{r}}{dt}, \qquad (3\text{–}181)$$

where h is the height (say about five miles) at which the air resistance falls to $1/e$ of its value at the surface of the earth.   In component form,

$$m\ddot{x} = -b\dot{x}e^{-z/h}, \quad m\ddot{y} = -b\dot{y}e^{-z/h}, \quad m\ddot{z} = -mg - b\dot{z}e^{-z/h}. \quad (3\text{–}182)$$

These equations are much harder to solve.   Since z appears in the x and y equations, we must first solve the z equation for $z(t)$ and substitute in the other two equations.   The z equation is not of any of the simple types discussed in Chapter 2.   The importance of this problem was brought out during the First World War, when it was discovered accidentally that aiming a cannon at a much higher elevation than that which had previously been believed to give maximum range resulted in a great increase in the range of the shell.   The reason is that the reduction in air resistance at altitudes of several miles more than makes up for the loss in horizontal component of muzzle velocity resulting from aiming the gun higher.

3–12 Potential energy.   If the force $\mathbf{F}$ acting on a particle is a function of its position $\mathbf{r} = (x,y,z)$, then the work done by the force when the particle moves from $\mathbf{r}_1$ to $\mathbf{r}_2$ is given by the line integral

$$\int_{\mathbf{r}_1}^{\mathbf{r}_2} \mathbf{F} \cdot d\mathbf{r}.$$

It is suggested that we try to define a potential energy $V(\mathbf{r}) = V(x,y,z)$ in analogy with Eq. (2–41) for one-dimensional motion, as the work done by the force on the particle when it moves from $\mathbf{r}$ to some chosen standard point $\mathbf{r}_s$:

$$V(\mathbf{r}) = -\int_{\mathbf{r}_s}^{\mathbf{r}} \mathbf{F}(\mathbf{r}) \cdot d\mathbf{r}. \qquad (3\text{–}183)$$

Such a definition implies, however, that the function $V(\mathbf{r})$ shall be a function only of the coordinates (x,y,z) of the point $\mathbf{r}$ (and of the standard point $\mathbf{r}_s$, which we regard as fixed), whereas in general the integral on the right depends upon the path of integration from $\mathbf{r}_s$ to $\mathbf{r}$.   Only if the integral on the right is independent of the path of integration will the definition be legitimate.

Let us assume that we have a force function $\mathbf{F}(x,y,z)$ such that the line integral in Eq. (3–183) is independent of the path of integration from $\mathbf{r}_s$ to any point $\mathbf{r}$. The value of the integral then depends only on $\mathbf{r}$ (and on $\mathbf{r}_s$), and Eq. (3–183) defines a potential energy function $V(\mathbf{r})$. The change in V when the particle moves from $\mathbf{r}$ to $\mathbf{r} + d\mathbf{r}$ is the negative of the work done by the force $\mathbf{F}$:

$$dV = -\mathbf{F} \cdot d\mathbf{r}. \qquad (3\text{–}184)$$

Comparing Eq. (3–184) with the geometrical definition [Eq. (3–107)] of the gradient, we see that

$$-\mathbf{F} = \text{grad } V,$$
$$\mathbf{F} = -\nabla V. \qquad (3\text{–}185)$$

Equation (3–185) may be regarded as the solution of Eq. (3–183) for $\mathbf{F}$ in terms of V. In component form,

$$F_x = -\frac{\partial V}{\partial x}, \quad F_y = -\frac{\partial V}{\partial y}, \quad F_z = -\frac{\partial V}{\partial z}. \qquad (3\text{–}186)$$

In seeking a condition to be satisfied by the function $\mathbf{F}(\mathbf{r})$ in order that the integral in Eq. (3–183) be independent of the path, we note that, since Eq. (3–28) can be proved from the algebraic definition of the cross product, it must hold also for the vector symbol ∇:

$$\nabla \times \nabla = 0. \qquad (3\text{–}187)$$

Applying $(\nabla \times \nabla)$ to the function V, we have

$$\nabla \times \nabla V = \text{curl (grad } V) = 0. \qquad (3\text{–}188)$$

Equation (3–188) can readily be verified by direct computation. From Eqs. (3–188) and (3–185), we have

$$\nabla \times \mathbf{F} = \text{curl } \mathbf{F} = 0. \qquad (3\text{–}189)$$

Since Eq. (3–189) has been deduced on the assumption that a potential function exists, it represents a necessary condition which must be satisfied by the force function $\mathbf{F}(x,y,z)$ before a potential function can be defined. We can show that Eq. (3–189) is also a sufficient condition for the existence of a potential by making use of Stokes' theorem [Eq. (3–117)]. By Stokes' theorem, if we consider any closed path C in space, the work done by the force $\mathbf{F}(\mathbf{r})$ when the particle travels around this path is

$$\int_C \mathbf{F} \cdot d\mathbf{r} = \iint_S \mathbf{n} \cdot (\nabla \times \mathbf{F}) \, dS, \qquad (3\text{–}190)$$

where S is a surface in space bounded by the closed curve C. If now Eq. (3–189) is assumed to hold, the integral on the right is zero, and we have, for any closed path C,

$$\int_C \mathbf{F} \cdot d\mathbf{r} = 0. \qquad (3\text{–}191)$$

But if the work done by the force **F** around any closed path is zero, then the work done in going from $\mathbf{r}_1$ to $\mathbf{r}_2$ will be independent of the path followed. For consider any two paths between $\mathbf{r}_1$ and $\mathbf{r}_2$, and let a closed path C be formed going from $\mathbf{r}_1$ to $\mathbf{r}_2$ by one path and returning to $\mathbf{r}_1$

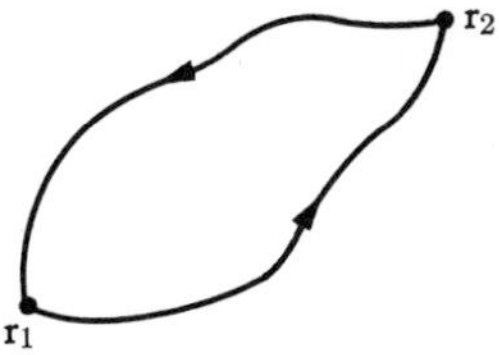

FIG. 3-30. Two paths between $\mathbf{r}_1$ and $\mathbf{r}_2$, forming a closed path.

by the other (Fig. 3-30). Since the work done around C is zero, the work going from $\mathbf{r}_1$ to $\mathbf{r}_2$ must be equal and opposite to that on the return trip, hence the work in going from $\mathbf{r}_1$ to $\mathbf{r}_2$ by either path is the same. Applying this argument to the integral on the right in Eq. (3-183), we see that the result is independent of the path of integration from $\mathbf{r}_s$ to $\mathbf{r}$, and therefore the integral is a function $V(\mathbf{r})$ of the upper limit alone, when the lower limit $\mathbf{r}_s$ is fixed. Thus Eq. (3-189) is both necessary and sufficient for the existence of a potential function $V(\mathbf{r})$ when the force is given as a function of position $\mathbf{F}(\mathbf{r})$.

When curl **F** is zero, we can express the work done by the force when the particle moves from $\mathbf{r}_1$ to $\mathbf{r}_2$ as the difference between the values of the potential energy at these points:

$$\int_{\mathbf{r}_1}^{\mathbf{r}_2} \mathbf{F} \cdot d\mathbf{r} = \int_{\mathbf{r}_1}^{\mathbf{r}_s} \mathbf{F} \cdot d\mathbf{r} + \int_{\mathbf{r}_s}^{\mathbf{r}_2} \mathbf{F} \cdot d\mathbf{r}$$
$$= V(\mathbf{r}_1) - V(\mathbf{r}_2). \qquad (3\text{-}192)$$

Combining Eq. (3-192) with the energy theorem (3-135), we have for any two times t_1 and t_2:

$$T_1 + V(\mathbf{r}_1) = T_2 + V(\mathbf{r}_2). \qquad (3\text{-}193)$$

Hence the total energy $(T + V)$ is again constant, and we have an energy integral for motion in three dimensions:

$$T + V = \tfrac{1}{2}m(\dot{x}^2 + \dot{y}^2 + \dot{z}^2) + V(x,y,z) = E. \qquad (3\text{-}194)$$

A force which is a function of position alone, and whose curl vanishes, is said to be *conservative*, because it leads to the theorem of conservation of kinetic plus potential energy [Eq. (3-194)].

In some cases, a force may be a function of both position and time $\mathbf{F}(\mathbf{r},t)$. If at any time t the curl of $\mathbf{F}(\mathbf{r},t)$ vanishes, then a potential energy function $V(\mathbf{r},t)$ can be defined as

$$V(\mathbf{r},t) = -\int_{\mathbf{r}_s}^{\mathbf{r}} \mathbf{F}(\mathbf{r},t) \cdot d\mathbf{r}, \qquad (3\text{-}195)$$

and we will have, for any time t such that $\nabla \times \mathbf{F}(\mathbf{r},t) = 0$,

$$\mathbf{F}(\mathbf{r},t) = -\nabla V(\mathbf{r},t). \qquad (3\text{-}196)$$

However, the conservation law of energy can no longer be proved, for Eq. (3–192) no longer holds. It is no longer true that the change in potential energy equals the negative of the work done on the particle, for the integral which defines the potential energy at time t is computed from the force function at that time, whereas the integral that defines the work is computed using at each point the force function at the time the particle passed through that point. Consequently, the energy $T + V$ is not a constant when **F** and V are functions of time, and such a force is not to be called a conservative force.

When the forces acting on a particle are conservative, Eq. (3–194) enables us to compute its speed as a function of its position. The energy E is fixed by the initial conditions of the motion. Equation (3–194), like Eq. (2–44), gives no information as to the direction of motion. This lack of knowledge of direction is much more serious in two and three dimensions, where there are an infinity of possible directions, than in one dimension, where there are only two opposite directions in which the particle may move. In one dimension, there is only one path along which the particle may move. In two or three dimensions, there are many paths, and unless we know the path of the particle, Eq. (3–194) alone allows us to say very little about the motion except that it can occur only in the region where $V(x,y,z) \leq E$. As an example, the potential energy of an electron in the attractive electric field of two protons (ionized hydrogen molecule $H_2{}^+$) is

$$V = -\frac{e^2}{r_1} - \frac{e^2}{r_2}, \tag{3–197}$$

where r_1, r_2 are the distances of the electron from the two protons. The function $V(x,y)$ (for motion in the xy-plane only) is plotted in Fig. 3–31 as a contour map, where the two protons are 2 A apart at the points $y = 0$, $x = \pm 1$ A, and the figures on the contours of constant potential energy are the corresponding potential energies in units of 10^{-12} erg. As long as $E < -46 \times 10^{-12}$ erg, the electron is confined to a region around one proton or the other, and we expect its motion will be either an oscillation through the attracting center or an orbit around it, depending on initial conditions. (These comments on the expected motion require some physical insight or experience in addition to what we can say from the energy integral alone.) For $0 > E > -46 \times 10^{-12}$ erg, the electron is confined to a region which includes both protons, and a variety of motions are possible. For $E > 0$, the electron is not confined to any finite region in the plane. For $E \ll -46 \times 10^{-12}$ erg, the electron is confined to a region where the equipotentials are nearly circles about one proton, and its motion will be practically the same as if the other proton were not there. For $E < 0$, but $|E| \ll 46 \times 10^{-12}$ erg, the electron *may* circle in an orbit far from the attracting centers, and its motion then will be approximately that of an electron bound to a single attracting center of charge $2e$, as the equipotential lines far from the attracting centers are again very nearly circles.

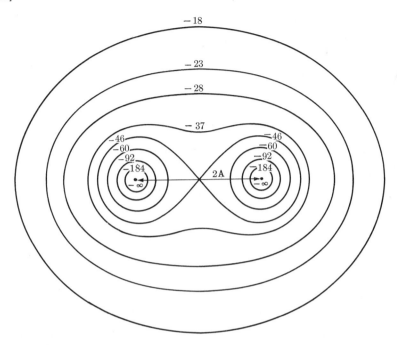

Fig. 3–31. Potential energy of electron in electric field of two protons 2 A apart. (Potential energies in units of 10^{-12} erg.)

Given a potential energy function $V(x,y,z)$, Eq. (3–186) enables us to compute the components of the corresponding force at any point. Conversely, given a force $F(x,y,z)$, we may compute its curl to determine whether a potential energy function exists for it. If all components of curl F are zero within any region of space, then within that region, F may be represented in terms of a potential energy function as $-\nabla V$. The potential energy is to be computed from Eq. (3–183). Furthermore, since curl $F = 0$, the result is independent of the path of integration, and we may compute the integral along any convenient path. As an example, consider the following two force functions:

(a) $F_x = axy$, $F_y = -az^2$, $F_z = -ax^2$,
(b) $F_x = ay(y^2 - 3z^2)$, $F_y = 3ax(y^2 - z^2)$, $F_z = -6axyz$,

where a is a constant. We compute the curl in each case:

(a) $\nabla \times F = i\left(\dfrac{\partial F_z}{\partial y} - \dfrac{\partial F_y}{\partial z}\right) + j\left(\dfrac{\partial F_x}{\partial z} - \dfrac{\partial F_z}{\partial x}\right) + k\left(\dfrac{\partial F_y}{\partial x} - \dfrac{\partial F_x}{\partial y}\right)$

$\qquad = (2az)i + (2ax)j - (ax)k$,

(b) $\nabla \times F = 0$.

In case (a), no potential energy exists. In case (b) there is a potential energy function, and we proceed to find it. Let us take $r_s = 0$, i.e., take the potential as zero at the origin. Since the components of force are given as functions of x, y, z, the simplest path of integration from $(0,0,0)$ to (x_0, y_0, z_0) along which to compute the integral in Eq. (3–183) is one which follows lines parallel to the coordinate axes, for example as shown in Fig. 3–32:

$$V(x_0, y_0, z_0) = -\int_{(0,0,0)}^{(x_0, y_0, z_0)} \mathbf{F} \cdot d\mathbf{r}$$

$$= -\int_{C_1} \mathbf{F} \cdot d\mathbf{r} - \int_{C_2} \mathbf{F} \cdot d\mathbf{r} - \int_{C_3} \mathbf{F} \cdot d\mathbf{r}.$$

Now along C_1, we have

$$y = z = 0, \quad F_x = F_y = F_z = 0, \quad d\mathbf{r} = \mathbf{i}\, dx.$$

Thus

$$\int_{C_1} \mathbf{F} \cdot d\mathbf{r} = \int_0^{x_0} F_x\, dx = 0.$$

Along C_2,

$$x = x_0, \quad z = 0,$$

$$F_x = ay^3, \quad F_y = 3ax_0y^2, \quad F_z = 0,$$

$$d\mathbf{r} = \mathbf{j}\, dy.$$

Thus

$$\int_{C_2} \mathbf{F} \cdot d\mathbf{r} = \int_0^{y_0} F_y\, dy = ax_0y_0^3.$$

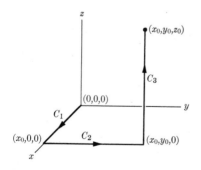

FIG. 3–32. A path of integration from $(0,0,0)$ to (x_0, y_0, z_0).

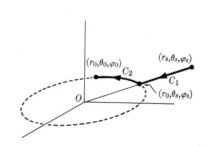

FIG. 3–33. Path of integration for a central force.

Along C_3,
$$x = x_0, \quad y = y_0,$$
$$F_x = ay_0(y_0^2 - 3z^2), \quad F_y = 3ax_0(y_0^2 - z^2), \quad F_z = -6ax_0y_0z,$$
$$d\mathbf{r} = \mathbf{k}\, dz.$$

Thus
$$\int_{C_3} \mathbf{F} \cdot d\mathbf{r} = \int_0^{z_0} F_z\, dz = -3ax_0y_0z_0^2.$$

Thus the potential energy, if the subscript zero is dropped, is
$$V(x,y,z) = -\, axy^3 + 3axyz^2.$$

It is readily verified that the gradient of this function is the force given by (b) above. In fact, one way to find the potential energy, which is often faster than the above procedure, is simply to try to guess a function whose gradient will give the required force.

An important case of a conservative force is the central force, a force directed always toward or away from a fixed center O, and whose magnitude is a function only of the distance from O. In spherical coordinates, with O as origin,
$$\mathbf{F} = \mathbf{n}F(r). \tag{3-198}$$

The cartesian components of a central force are (since $\mathbf{n} = \mathbf{r}/r$)
$$F_x = \frac{x}{r} F(r),$$
$$F_y = \frac{y}{r} F(r), \quad [r = (x^2 + y^2 + z^2)^{\frac{1}{2}}], \tag{3-199}$$
$$F_z = \frac{z}{r} F(r).$$

The curl of this force can be shown by direct computation to be zero, no matter what the function $F(r)$ may be. For example, we find
$$\frac{\partial F_x}{\partial y} = x \frac{d}{dr}\left(\frac{F(r)}{r}\right)\frac{\partial r}{\partial y} = \frac{xy}{r}\frac{d}{dr}\left(\frac{F(r)}{r}\right),$$
$$\frac{\partial F_y}{\partial x} = y \frac{d}{dr}\left(\frac{F(r)}{r}\right)\frac{\partial r}{\partial x} = \frac{xy}{r}\frac{d}{dr}\left(\frac{F(r)}{r}\right).$$

Therefore the z-component of curl $\mathbf{F}$ vanishes, and so, likewise, do the other two components. To compute the potential energy, we choose any standard point $\mathbf{r}_s$, and integrate from $\mathbf{r}_s$ to $\mathbf{r}_0$ along a path (Fig. 3–33) following a radius (C_1) from $\mathbf{r}_s$, whose coordinates are $(r_s, \theta_s, \varphi_s)$, to the point $(r_0, \theta_s, \varphi_s)$, then along a circle ($C_2$) of radius r_0 about the origin to the point $(r_0, \theta_0, \varphi_0)$. Along C_1,
$$d\mathbf{r} = \mathbf{n}\, dr,$$
$$\int_{C_1} \mathbf{F} \cdot d\mathbf{r} = \int_{r_s}^{r_0} F(r)\, dr.$$

Along C_2,

$$d\mathbf{r} = \mathbf{l}r\,d\theta + \mathbf{m}r \sin\theta\,d\varphi,$$

$$\int_{C_2} \mathbf{F} \cdot d\mathbf{r} = 0.$$

Thus

$$V(\mathbf{r}_0) = -\int_{r_s}^{r_0} \mathbf{F} \cdot d\mathbf{r} = -\int_{C_1} \mathbf{F} \cdot d\mathbf{r} - \int_{C_2} \mathbf{F} \cdot d\mathbf{r}$$

$$= -\int_{r_s}^{r_0} F(r)\,dr.$$

The potential energy is a function of r alone:

$$V(\mathbf{r}) = V(r) = -\int_{r_s}^{r} F(r)\,dr. \tag{3-200}$$

3–13 Motion under a central force.   A central force is a force of the form given by Eq. (3–198).   Physically, such a force represents an attraction [if $F(r) < 0$] or repulsion [if $F(r) > 0$] from a fixed point located at the origin $r = 0$.   In most cases where two particles interact with each other, the force between them is (at least primarily) a central force; that is, if either particle be located at the origin, the force on the other is given by Eq. (3–198).   Examples of attractive central forces are the gravitational force acting on a planet due to the sun, or the electrical attraction acting on an electron due to the nucleus of an atom.   The force between a proton or an alpha-particle and another nucleus is a repulsive central force.   In the most important cases, the force $F(r)$ is inversely proportional to r^2. This case will be treated in the next section.   Other forms of the function $F(r)$ occur occasionally; for example, in some problems involving the structure and interactions of nuclei, complex atoms, and molecules.   In this section, we present the general method of attack on the problem of a particle moving under the action of a central force.

Since in all these examples, neither of the two interacting particles is actually fastened to a fixed position, the problem we are solving, like most problems in physics, represents an idealization of the actual problem, valid when one of the particles can be regarded as practically at rest at the origin.   This will be the case if one of the particles is much heavier than the other.   Since the forces acting on the two particles have the same magnitude by Newton's third law, the acceleration of the heavy one will be much smaller than that of the lighter one, and the motion of the heavy particle can be neglected in comparison with the motion of the lighter one. We shall discover later, in Section 4–7, that, with a slight modification, our solution can be made to yield an exact solution to the problem of the motion of two interacting particles, even when their masses are equal.

We may note that the vector angular momentum of a particle under the action of a central force is constant, since the torque is

$$\mathbf{N} = \mathbf{r} \times \mathbf{F} = (\mathbf{r} \times \mathbf{n})F(r) = 0. \qquad (3\text{–}201)$$

Therefore, by Eq. (3–144),

$$\frac{d\mathbf{L}}{dt} = 0. \qquad (3\text{–}202)$$

As a consequence, the angular momentum about any axis through the center of force is constant. It is because many physical forces are central forces that the concept of angular momentum is of importance.

In solving for the motion of a particle acted on by a central force, we first show that the path of the particle lies in a single plane containing the center of force. To show this, let the position $\mathbf{r}_0$ and velocity $\mathbf{v}_0$ be given at any initial time t_0, and choose the x-axis through the initial position $\mathbf{r}_0$ of the particle, and the z-axis perpendicular to the initial velocity $\mathbf{v}_0$. Then we have initially:

$$x_0 = |\mathbf{r}_0|, \quad y_0 = z_0 = 0, \qquad (3\text{–}203)$$
$$v_{x_0} = \mathbf{v}_0 \cdot \mathbf{i}, \quad v_{y_0} = \mathbf{v}_0 \cdot \mathbf{j}, \quad v_{z_0} = 0. \qquad (3\text{–}204)$$

The equations of motion in rectangular coordinates are, by Eqs. (3–199),

$$m\ddot{x} = \frac{x}{r}F(r), \quad m\ddot{y} = \frac{y}{r}F(r), \quad m\ddot{z} = \frac{z}{r}F(r). \qquad (3\text{–}205)$$

A solution of the z-equation which satisfies the initial conditions on z_0 and v_{z_0} is

$$z(t) = 0. \qquad (3\text{–}206)$$

Hence the motion takes place entirely in the xy-plane. We can see physically that if the force on a particle is always toward the origin, the particle can never acquire any component of velocity out of the plane in which it is initially moving. We can also regard this result as a consequence of the conservation of angular momentum. By Eq. (3–202), the vector $\mathbf{L} = m(\mathbf{r} \times \mathbf{v})$ is constant; therefore both $\mathbf{r}$ and $\mathbf{v}$ must always lie in a fixed plane perpendicular to $\mathbf{L}$.

We have now reduced the problem to one of motion in a plane with two differential equations and four initial conditions remaining to be satisfied. If we choose polar coordinates r, θ in the plane of the motion, the equations of motion in the r and θ directions are, by Eqs. (3–80) and (3–198),

$$m\ddot{r} - mr\dot{\theta}^2 = F(r), \qquad (3\text{–}207)$$
$$mr\ddot{\theta} + 2m\dot{r}\dot{\theta} = 0. \qquad (3\text{–}208)$$

Multiplying Eq. (3–208) by r, as in the derivation of the (plane) angular momentum theorem, we have

$$\frac{d}{dt}(mr^2\dot{\theta}) = \frac{dL}{dt} = 0. \qquad (3\text{–}209)$$

This equation expresses the conservation of angular momentum about the origin and is a consequence also of Eq. (3–202) above. It may be integrated to give the angular momentum integral of the equations of motion:

$$mr^2\dot\theta = L = \text{a constant.} \qquad (3\text{–}210)$$

The constant L is to be evaluated from the initial conditions. Another integral of Eqs. (3–207) and (3–208), since the force is conservative, is

$$T + V = \tfrac{1}{2}m\dot r^2 + \tfrac{1}{2}mr^2\dot\theta^2 + V(r) = E, \qquad (3\text{–}211)$$

where $V(r)$ is given by Eq. (3–200) and E is the energy constant, to be evaluated from the initial conditions. If we substitute for $\dot\theta$ from Eq. (3–210), the energy becomes

$$\tfrac{1}{2}m\dot r^2 + \frac{L^2}{2mr^2} + V(r) = E. \qquad (3\text{–}212)$$

We can solve for $\dot r$:

$$\dot r = \sqrt{\frac{2}{m}\left(E - V(r) - \frac{L^2}{2mr^2}\right)^{\frac{1}{2}}}. \qquad (3\text{–}213)$$

Therefore

$$\int_{r_0}^{r} \frac{dr}{\left(E - V(r) - \dfrac{L^2}{2mr^2}\right)^{\frac{1}{2}}} = \sqrt{\frac{2}{m}}\,t. \qquad (3\text{–}214)$$

The integral is to be evaluated and the resulting equation solved for $r(t)$. We then obtain $\theta(t)$ from Eq. (3–210):

$$\theta = \theta_0 + \int_0^t \frac{L}{mr^2}\,dt. \qquad (3\text{–}215)$$

We thus obtain the solution of Eqs. (3–207) and (3–208) in terms of the four constants L, E, r_0, θ_0, which can be evaluated when the initial position and velocity in the plane are given.

It will be noted that our treatment based on Eq. (3–212) is analogous to our treatment of the one-dimensional problem based on the energy integral [Eq. (2–44)]. The coordinate r here plays the role of x, and the $\dot\theta$ term in the kinetic energy, when $\dot\theta$ is eliminated by Eq. (3–210), plays the role of an addition to the potential energy. We may bring out this analogy further by substituting from Eq. (3–210) into Eq. (3–207):

$$m\ddot r - \frac{L^2}{mr^3} = F(r). \qquad (3\text{–}216)$$

If we transpose the term $-L^2/mr^3$ to the right side, we obtain

$$m\ddot r = F(r) + \frac{L^2}{mr^3}. \qquad (3\text{–}217)$$

This equation has exactly the form of an equation of motion in one dimension for a particle subject to the actual force $F(r)$ plus a "centrifugal force" L^2/mr^3. The centrifugal force is not really a force at all but a part of the mass times acceleration, transposed to the right side of the equation in order to reduce the equation for r to an equation of the same form as for one-dimensional motion. We may call it a "fictitious force." If we treat Eq. (3–217) as a problem in one-dimensional motion, the effective "potential energy" corresponding to the "force" on the right is

$$'V'(r) = -\int F(r)\, dr - \int \frac{L^2}{mr^3}\, dr$$

$$= V(r) + \frac{L^2}{2mr^2}. \qquad (3\text{–}218)$$

The second term in $'V'$ is the "potential energy" associated with the "centrifugal force." The resulting energy integral is just Eq. (3–212). The reason why we have been able to obtain a complete solution to our problem based on only two integrals, or constants of the motion (L and E), is that the equations of motion do not contain the coordinate θ, so that the constancy of L is sufficient to enable us to eliminate θ entirely from Eq. (3–207) and to reduce the problem to an equivalent problem in one-dimensional motion.

The integral in Eq. (3–214) sometimes turns out rather difficult to evaluate in practice, and the resulting equation difficult to solve for $r(t)$. It is sometimes easier to find the path of the particle in space than to find its motion as a function of time. We can describe the path of the particle by giving $r(\theta)$. The resulting equation is somewhat simpler if we make the substitution

$$u = \frac{1}{r}, \quad r = \frac{1}{u}. \qquad (3\text{–}219)$$

Then we have, using Eq. (3–210),

$$\dot{r} = -\frac{1}{u^2}\frac{du}{d\theta}\,\dot{\theta} = -r^2\dot{\theta}\,\frac{du}{d\theta}$$

$$= -\frac{L}{m}\frac{du}{d\theta}, \qquad (3\text{–}220)$$

$$\ddot{r} = -\frac{L}{m}\frac{d^2u}{d\theta^2}\,\dot{\theta} = -\frac{L^2u^2}{m^2}\frac{d^2u}{d\theta^2}. \qquad (3\text{–}221)$$

Substituting for r and $\ddot{r}$ in Eq. (3–217), and multiplying by $-m/(L^2u^2)$, we have a differential equation for the path or orbit in terms of $u(\theta)$:

$$\frac{d^2u}{d\theta^2} = -u - \frac{m}{L^2u^2}\,F\!\left(\frac{1}{u}\right). \qquad (3\text{–}222)$$

In case $L = 0$, Eq. (3–222) blows up, but we see from Eq. (3–210) that in this case θ is constant, and the path is a straight line through the origin.

Even in cases where the explicit solutions of Eqs. (3–214) and (3–215), or Eq. (3–222), are difficult to carry through, we can obtain qualitative information about the r motion from the effective potential 'V' given by Eq. (3–218), just as in the one-dimensional case discussed in Section 2–5. By plotting 'V'(r), we can decide for any total energy E whether the motion in r is periodic or aperiodic, we can locate the turning points, and we can describe roughly how the velocity $\dot{r}$ varies during the motion. If 'V'(r) has a minimum at a point r_0, then for energy E slightly greater than 'V'(r_0), r may execute small, approximately harmonic oscillations about r_0 with angular frequency given by

$$\omega^2 = \frac{1}{m}\left(\frac{d^2\,'V'}{dr^2}\right)_{r_0}. \tag{3–223}$$

[See the discussion in Section 2–7 concerning Eq. (2–87).] We must remember, of course, that at the same time the particle is revolving around the center of force with an angular velocity

$$\dot{\theta} = \frac{L}{mr^2}. \tag{3–224}$$

The rate of revolution decreases as r increases. When the r motion is periodic, the period of the r motion is not, in general, the same as the period of revolution, so that the orbit may not be closed, although it is confined to a finite region of space. (See Fig. 3–34.) In cases where the r motion is not periodic, then $\dot{\theta} \to 0$ as $r \to \infty$, and the particle may or may not perform one or more complete revolutions as it moves toward $r = \infty$, depending on how rapidly r increases. In the event the motion is periodic, that is, when the particle moves in a closed orbit, the period of orbital motion is related to the area of the orbit. This can be seen as follows. The area swept out by the radius from the origin to the particle when the particle moves through a small angle $d\theta$ is approximately (Fig. 3–35),

$$dS = \tfrac{1}{2}r^2\,d\theta. \tag{3–225}$$

Hence the rate at which area is swept out by the radius is, by Eq. (3–210),

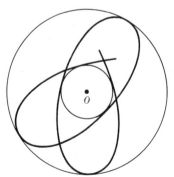

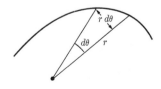

FIG. 3–34.   An aperiodic bounded orbit.

FIG. 3–35.   Area swept out by radius vector.

$$\frac{dS}{dt} = \tfrac{1}{2}r^2\dot{\theta} = \frac{L}{2m}. \tag{3-226}$$

This result is true for any particle moving under the action of a central force. If the motion is periodic, then, integrating over a complete period τ of the motion, we have for the area of the orbit

$$S = \frac{L\tau}{2m}. \tag{3-227}$$

If the orbit is known, the period of revolution can be calculated from this formula.

3-14 The central force inversely proportional to the square of the distance.

The most important problem in three-dimensional motion is that of a mass moving under the action of a central force inversely proportional to the square of the distance from the center:

$$\mathbf{F} = \frac{K}{r^2}\,\mathbf{n}, \tag{3-228}$$

for which the potential energy is

$$V(r) = \frac{K}{r}, \tag{3-229}$$

where the standard radius r_s is taken to be infinite in order to avoid an additional constant term in $V(r)$. As an example, the gravitational force (Section 1-5) between two masses m_1 and m_2 a distance r apart is given by Eq. (3-228) with

$$K = -Gm_1m_2, \quad G = 6.658 \times 10^{-8} \text{ dyne-gm}^{-2}\text{-cm}^2, \tag{3-230}$$

where K is negative, since the gravitational force is attractive. Another example is the electrostatic force between two electric charges q_1 and q_2 a distance r apart, given by Eq. (3-228) with

$$K = q_1q_2, \tag{3-231}$$

where the charges are in electrostatic units, and the force is in dynes. The electrostatic force is repulsive when q_1 and q_2 have the same sign, otherwise attractive. Historically, the first problems to which Newton's mechanics was applied were problems involving the motion of the planets under the gravitational attraction of the sun, and the motion of satellites around the planets. The success of the theory in accounting for such motions was responsible for its initial acceptance.

We first determine the nature of the orbits given by the inverse square law of force. In Fig. 3-36 is plotted the effective potential

$$'V'(r) = \frac{K}{r} + \frac{L^2}{2mr^2}. \tag{3-232}$$

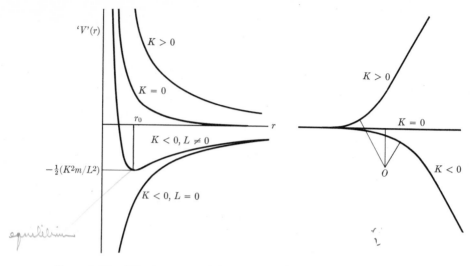

FIG. 3–36. Effective potential for central inverse square law of force.

FIG. 3–37. Sketch of unbounded inverse square law orbits.

For a repulsive force $(K > 0)$, there are no periodic motions in r; only positive total energies E are possible, and the particle comes in from $r = \infty$ to a turning point and travels out to infinity again. For a given energy and angular momentum, the turning point occurs at a larger value of r than for $K = 0$ (no force), for which the orbit would be a straight line. For an attractive force $(K < 0)$ with $L \neq 0$, the motion is also unbounded if $E > 0$, but in this case the turning point occurs at a smaller value of r than for $K = 0$. Hence the orbits are as indicated in Fig. 3–37. The light lines in Fig. 3–37 represent the turning point radius or perihelion distance measured from the point of closest approach of the particle to the attracting or repelling center. For $K < 0$, and $-\frac{1}{2}K^2m/L^2 < E < 0$, the coordinate r oscillates between two turning points. For $E = -\frac{1}{2}K^2m/L^2$, the particle moves in a circle of radius $r_0 = L^2/(-Km)$. Computation shows (see problem 26 at the end of this chapter) that the period of small oscillations in r is the same as the period of revolution, so that for E near $-\frac{1}{2}K^2m/L^2$, the orbit is a closed curve with the origin slightly off center. We shall show later that the orbit is, in fact, an ellipse for all negative values of E if $L \neq 0$. If $L = 0$, the problem reduces to the one-dimensional motion of a falling body, discussed in Section 2–6.

To evaluate the integrals in Eqs. (3–214) and (3–215) for the inverse square law of force is rather laborious. We shall find that we can obtain all the essential information about the motion more simply by starting from Eq. (3–222) for the orbit. Equation (3–222) for the orbit becomes, in this case,

$$\frac{d^2u}{d\theta^2} + u = -\frac{mK}{L^2}. \tag{3-233}$$

This equation has the same form as that of a harmonic oscillator (of unit frequency) subject to a constant force, where θ here plays the role of t. The homogeneous equation and its general solution are

$$\frac{d^2u}{d\theta^2} + u = 0, \tag{3-234}$$

$$u = A\cos(\theta - \theta_0), \tag{3-235}$$

where A, θ_0 are arbitrary constants. An obvious particular solution of the inhomogeneous equation (3-233) is the constant solution

$$u = -\frac{mK}{L^2}. \tag{3-236}$$

Hence the general solution of Eq. (3-233) is

$$u = \frac{1}{r} = -\frac{mK}{L^2} + A\cos(\theta - \theta_0). \tag{3-237}$$

This is the equation of a conic section (ellipse, parabola, or hyperbola) with focus at $r = 0$, as we shall presently show. The constant θ_0 determines the orientation of the orbit in the plane. The constant A, which may be taken as positive (since θ_0 is arbitrary), determines the turning points of the r motion, which are given by

$$\frac{1}{r_1} = -\frac{mK}{L^2} + A, \quad \frac{1}{r_2} = -\frac{mK}{L^2} - A. \tag{3-238}$$

If $A > -mK/L^2$ (as it necessarily is for $K > 0$), then there is only one turning point, r_1, since r cannot be negative. We cannot have $A < mK/L^2$, since r could then not be positive for any value of θ. For a given E, the turning points are solutions of the equation

$$'V'(r) = \frac{K}{r} + \frac{L^2}{2mr^2} = E. \tag{3-239}$$

The solutions are

$$\frac{1}{r_1} = -\frac{mK}{L^2} + \left[\left(\frac{mK}{L^2}\right)^2 + \frac{2mE}{L^2}\right]^{\frac{1}{2}},$$

$$\frac{1}{r_2} = -\frac{mK}{L^2} - \left[\left(\frac{mK}{L^2}\right)^2 + \frac{2mE}{L^2}\right]^{\frac{1}{2}}. \tag{3-240}$$

Comparing Eq. (3-238) with Eq. (3-240), we see that the value of A in terms of the energy and angular momentum is given by

$$A^2 = \frac{m^2K^2}{L^4} + \frac{2mE}{L^2}. \tag{3-241}$$

The orbit is now determined in terms of the initial conditions.

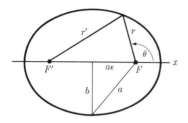

FIG. 3–38.   Geometry of the ellipse.

An ellipse is defined as the curve traced by a particle moving so that the sum of its distances from two fixed points F, F' is constant.* The points F, F' are called the *foci* of the ellipse. Using the notation indicated in Fig. 3–38, we have

$$r' + r = 2a, \qquad (3\text{--}242)$$

where a is half the largest diameter (major axis) of the ellipse. In terms of polar coordinates with center at the focus F and with the negative x-axis through the focus F', the cosine law gives

$$r'^2 = r^2 + 4a^2\epsilon^2 + 4ra\epsilon \cos\theta, \qquad (3\text{--}243)$$

where $a\epsilon$ is the distance from the center of the ellipse to the focus. ϵ is called the *eccentricity* of the ellipse. If $\epsilon = 0$, the foci coincide and the ellipse is a circle. As $\epsilon \to 1$, the ellipse degenerates into a parabola or straight line segment, depending on whether the focus F' recedes to infinity or remains a finite distance from F. Substituting r' from Eq. (3–242) in Eq. (3–243), we find

$$r = \frac{a(1 - \epsilon^2)}{1 + \epsilon \cos\theta}. \qquad (3\text{--}244)$$

This is the equation of an ellipse in polar coordinates with the origin at one focus. If b is half the smallest diameter (minor axis), we have, from Fig. 3–38,

$$b = a(1 - \epsilon^2)^{\frac{1}{2}}. \qquad (3\text{--}245)$$

The area of the ellipse can be obtained in a straightforward way by integration:

$$S = \pi ab. \qquad (3\text{--}246)$$

A hyperbola is defined as the curve traced by a particle moving so that the difference of its distances from two fixed foci F, F' is constant (Fig. 3–39). A hyperbola has two branches defined by

$$
\begin{aligned}
r' - r &= 2a \quad (+ \text{ branch}), \\
r' - r &= -2a \quad (- \text{ branch}).
\end{aligned}
\qquad (3\text{--}247)
$$

We shall call the branch which encircles F the $+$ branch (left branch in the figure), and the branch which avoids F, the $-$ branch (right branch in the figure). Equation (3–243) holds also for the hyperbola, but the eccen-

---

*For a more detailed treatment of conic sections, see W. F. Osgood and W. C. Graustein, *Plane and Solid Analytic Geometry*. New York: Macmillan, 1938. (Chapters 6, 7, 8, 10.)

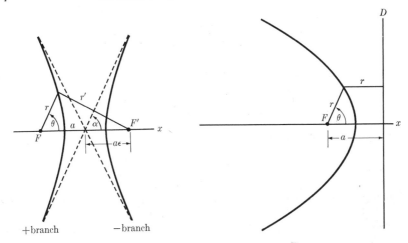

FIG. 3–39. Geometry of the hyperbola.   FIG. 3–40. Geometry of the parabola.

tricity ϵ is now greater than one.   The equation of the hyperbola becomes in polar coordinates:

$$r = \frac{a(\epsilon^2 - 1)}{\pm 1 + \epsilon \cos \theta}. \tag{3-248}$$

(The $+$ sign refers to the $+$ branch, the $-$ sign to the $-$ branch.)   The asymptotes of the hyperbola (dotted lines in Fig. 3–39) make an angle α with the axis through the foci, where α is the value of θ for which r is infinite:

$$\cos \alpha = \pm \frac{1}{\epsilon}. \tag{3-249}$$

A parabola is the curve traced by a particle moving so that its distance from a fixed line D (the *directrix*) equals its distance from a fixed focus F. From Fig. 3–40, we have

$$r = \frac{a}{1 + \cos \theta}, \tag{3-250}$$

where a is the distance from the focus F to the directrix D.

We can write the equations for all three conic sections in the standard form

$$\frac{1}{r} = B + A \cos \theta, \tag{3-251}$$

where A is positive, and B and A are given as follows:

$B > A$, ellipse,

$$B = \frac{1}{a(1 - \epsilon^2)}, \qquad A = \frac{\epsilon}{a(1 - \epsilon^2)}; \tag{3-252}$$

$B = A$, parabola,

$$B = \frac{1}{a}, \quad A = \frac{1}{a}; \tag{3-253}$$

$0 < B < A$, hyperbola, $+$ branch,

$$B = \frac{1}{a(\epsilon^2 - 1)}, \quad A = \frac{\epsilon}{a(\epsilon^2 - 1)}; \tag{3-254}$$

$-A < B < 0$, hyperbola, $-$ branch,

$$B = -\frac{1}{a(\epsilon^2 - 1)}, \quad A = \frac{\epsilon}{a(\epsilon^2 - 1)}. \tag{3-255}$$

The case $B < -A$ cannot occur, since r would then not be positive for any value of θ. If we allow an arbitrary orientation of the curve with respect to the x-axis, then Eq. (3–251) becomes

$$\frac{1}{r} = B + A \cos (\theta - \theta_0), \tag{3-256}$$

where θ_0 is the angle between the x-axis and the line from the origin to the perihelion (point of closest approach of the curve to the origin). It will be noted that in all cases

$$\epsilon = \frac{A}{|B|}. \tag{3-257}$$

For an ellipse or hyperbola,

$$a = \left| \frac{B}{A^2 - B^2} \right|. \tag{3-258}$$

Equation (3–237) for the orbit of a particle under an inverse square law force has the form of Eq. (3–256) for a conic section, with [if we use Eq. (3–241)]

$$B = -\frac{mK}{L^2},$$

$$A = \left(B^2 + \frac{2mE}{L^2} \right)^{\frac{1}{2}}. \tag{3-259}$$

The eccentricity of the orbit, by Eq. (3–257), is

$$\epsilon = \left(1 + \frac{2EL^2}{mK^2} \right)^{\frac{1}{2}}. \tag{3-260}$$

For an attractive force ($K < 0$), the orbit is an ellipse, parabola, or hyperbola, depending on whether $E < 0$, $E = 0$, or $E > 0$; if a hyperbola, it is the $+$ branch. For a repulsive force ($K > 0$), we must have $E > 0$, and the orbit can only be the $-$ branch of a hyperbola. These results agree with our preliminary qualitative discussion. For elliptic and hyperbolic orbits, the semimajor axis a is given by

$$a = \left| \frac{K}{2E} \right|. \tag{3-261}$$

It is curious that this relation does not involve the eccentricity or the angular momentum; the energy E depends only on the semimajor axis a, and vice versa.   Equations (3–260) and (3–261) may be obtained directly from Eq. (3–239) for the turning points of the r motion.   If we solve this equation for r, we obtain the turning points

$$r_{1,2} = \frac{K}{2E} \pm \left[\left(\frac{K}{2E}\right)^2 + \frac{L^2}{2mE} \right]^{\frac{1}{2}}. \qquad (3\text{–}262)$$

The maximum and minimum radii for an ellipse are

$$r_{1,2} = a(1 \pm \epsilon), \qquad (3\text{–}263)$$

and the minimum radius for a hyperbola is

$$r_1 = a(\epsilon \mp 1), \qquad (3\text{–}264)$$

where the upper sign is for the $+$ branch and the lower sign for the $-$ branch.   Comparing Eqs. (3–263) and (3–264) with Eq. (3–262), we can read off the values of a and ϵ.   Thus if we know that the path is an ellipse or hyperbola, we can find the size and shape from Eq. (3–239), which follows from the simple energy method of treatment, without going through the exact solution of the equation for the orbit.   This is a useful point to remember.

3–15 Elliptic orbits. The Kepler problem.   Early in the seventeenth century, before Newton's discovery of the laws of motion, Kepler announced the following three laws describing the motion of the planets, deduced from the extensive and accurate observations of planetary motions by Tycho Brahe:

1. The planets move in ellipses with the sun at one focus.
2. Areas swept out by the radius vector from the sun to a planet in equal times are equal.
3. The square of the period of revolution is proportional to the cube of the semimajor axis.

The second law is expressed by our Eq. (3–226), and is a consequence of the conservation of angular momentum; it shows that the force acting on the planet is a central force.   The first law follows, as we have shown, from the fact that the force is inversely proportional to the square of the distance.   The third law follows from the fact that the gravitational force is proportional to the mass of the planet, as we now show.

In the case of an elliptical orbit, we can find the period of the motion from Eqs. (3–227) and (3–246):

$$\tau = \frac{2m}{L} \pi ab = \frac{2m}{L} \pi a^2 (1 - \epsilon^2)^{\frac{1}{2}} = \left(\frac{\pi^2 K^2 m}{2|E|^3}\right)^{\frac{1}{2}}, \qquad (3\text{–}265)$$

or, using Eq. (3–261),

$$\tau^2 = 4\pi^2 a^3 \left| \frac{m}{K} \right|. \tag{3–266}$$

In the case of a small body of mass m moving under the gravitational attraction [Eq. (3–230)] of a large body of mass M, this becomes

$$\tau^2 = \frac{4\pi^2}{MG} a^3. \tag{3–267}$$

The coefficient of a^3 is now a constant for all planets, in agreement with Kepler's third law. Equation (3–267) allows us to "weigh" the sun, if we know the value of G, by measuring the period and major axis of any planetary orbit. This has already been worked out in Chapter 1, problem 9, for a circular orbit. Equation (3–267) now shows that the result applies also to elliptical orbits if the semimajor axis is substituted for the radius.

We have shown that Kepler's laws follow from Newton's laws of motion and the law of gravitation. The converse problem, to deduce the law of force from Kepler's laws and the law of motion is an easier problem, and a very important one historically, for it was in this way that Newton deduced the law of gravitation. We expect that the motions of the planets should show slight deviations from Kepler's laws, in view of the fact that the central force problem which was solved in the last section represents an idealization of the actual physical problem. In the first place, as pointed out in Section 3–13, we have assumed that the sun is stationary, whereas actually it must wobble slightly due to the attraction of the planets going around it. This effect is very small, even in the case of the largest planets, and can be corrected for by the methods explained later in Section 4–7. In the second place, a given planet, say the earth, is acted on by the gravitational pull of the other planets, as well as by the sun. Since the masses of even the heaviest planets are only a few percent of the mass of the sun, this will produce small but measurable deviations from Kepler's laws. The expected deviations can be calculated, and they agree with the very precise astronomical observations. In fact, the planets Neptune and Pluto were discovered as a result of their effects on the orbits of the other planets. Observations of the planet Uranus for about sixty years after its discovery in 1781 showed unexplained deviations from the predicted orbit, even after corrections were made for the gravitational effects of the other known planets. By a careful and elaborate mathematical analysis of the data, Adams and Leverrier were able to show that the deviations could be accounted for by assuming an unknown planet beyond Uranus, and they calculated the position of the unknown planet. The planet Neptune was promptly discovered in the predicted place.

The orbits of the comets, which are occasionally observed to move in around the sun and out again, are, at least in some cases, very elongated ellipses. It is not at present known whether any of the comets come from beyond the solar system, in which case they would, at least initially, have parabolic or hyperbolic orbits. Even those comets whose orbits are known to be elliptical have rather irregular periods due to the perturbing gravitational pull of the larger planets near which they occasionally pass. Between close encounters with the larger planets, a comet will follow fairly closely a path given by Eq. (3–256), but during each such encounter, its motion will be disturbed, so that afterwards the constants A, B, and θ_0 will have values different from those before the encounter.

As noted in Section 3–13, we expect in general that the bounded orbits arising from an attractive central force $F(r)$ will not be closed (Fig. 3–34). Closed orbits (except for circular orbits) arise only where the period of radial oscillations is equal to, or is an exact rational multiple of, the period of revolution. Only for certain special forms of the function $F(r)$, of which the inverse square law is one, will the orbits be closed. Any change in the inverse square law, either a change in the exponent of r or an addition to $F(r)$ of a term not inversely proportional to r^2, will be expected to lead to orbits that are not closed. However, if the change is very small, then the orbits ought to be approximately elliptical. The period of revolution will then be only slightly greater or slightly less than the period of radial oscillations, and the orbit will be approximately an ellipse whose major axis rotates slowly about the center of force. As a matter of fact, a slow precession of the major axis of the orbit of the planet Mercury has been observed, with an angular velocity of 41 seconds of arc per century, over and above the perturbations accounted for by the gravitational effects of the other planets. It was once thought that this could be accounted for by the gravitational effect of dust in the solar system, but it can be shown that the amount of dust is far too small to account for the effect. It is now fairly certain that the effect is due to slight corrections to Newton's theory of planetary motion required by the theory of relativity.[*]

The problem of the motion of electrons around the nucleus of an atom would be the same as that of the motion of planets around the sun, if Newtonian mechanics were applicable. Actually, the motion of electrons must be calculated from the laws of quantum mechanics. Before the discovery of quantum mechanics, Bohr was able to give a fair account of the behavior of atoms by assuming that the electrons revolve in orbits given by Newtonian mechanics. Bohr's theory is still useful as a rough picture of atomic structure.[†]

---

[*] A. Einstein and L. Infeld, *The Evolution of Physics*. New York: Simon and Schuster, 1938. (Page 253.) For a mathematical discussion, see R. C. Tolman, *Relativity, Thermodynamics, and Cosmology*. Oxford: Oxford University Press, 1934. (Section 83.)

[†] M. Born, *Atomic Physics*, tr. by John Dougall. New York: Stechert, 1936. (Chapter 5.)

3–16 Hyperbolic orbits. The Rutherford problem. Scattering cross section. The hyperbolic orbits are of interest in connection with the motion of particles around the sun which may come from or escape to outer space, and also in connection with the collisions of two charged particles. If a light particle of charge q_1 encounters a heavy particle of charge q_2 at rest, the light particle will follow a hyperbolic trajectory past the heavy particle, according to the results obtained in Section 3–14. In the case of collisions of atomic particles, the region in which the trajectory bends from one asymptote to the other is very small (a few Angstrom units or less), and what is observed is the deflection angle $\Theta = \pi - 2\alpha$ (Fig. 3–41) between the paths of the incident particle before and after the collision. Figure 3–41 is drawn for the case of a repelling center of force at F, but the figure may also be taken to represent the case of an attracting center at F'. By Eqs. (3–249) and (3–260),

$$\tan \frac{\Theta}{2} = \cot \alpha = (\epsilon^2 - 1)^{-\frac{1}{2}} = \left(\frac{mK^2}{2EL^2}\right)^{\frac{1}{2}}. \tag{3–268}$$

Let the particle have an initial speed v_0, and let it be traveling in such a direction that, if undeflected, it would pass a distance s from the center of force (F). The distance s is called the *impact parameter* for the collision. We can readily compute the energy and angular momentum in terms of the speed and impact parameter:

$$E = \tfrac{1}{2}mv_0^2, \tag{3–269}$$
$$L = mv_0s. \tag{3–270}$$

Substituting in Eq. (3–268), we have for the scattering angle Θ:

$$\tan \frac{\Theta}{2} = \frac{|K|}{msv_0^2}. \tag{3–271}$$

If a light particle of charge q_1 collides with a heavy particle of charge q_2, this is, by Eq. (3–231),

$$\tan \frac{\Theta}{2} = \frac{|q_1q_2|}{msv_0^2}. \tag{3–272}$$

In a typical scattering experiment, a stream of charged particles may be shot in a definite direction through a thin foil. Many of the particles emerge from the foil in a different direction, after being deflected or scattered through an angle Θ by a collision with a particle within the foil. To put Eq. (3–272) in a form in which it can be compared with experiment, we must eliminate the impact parameter s, which cannot be determined experimentally. In the experiment, the fraction of incident particles scattered through various angles Θ is observed. It is customary to express the results in terms of a *cross section* defined as follows. If N incident particles strike a thin foil containing n scattering centers per unit area, the

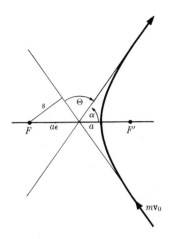

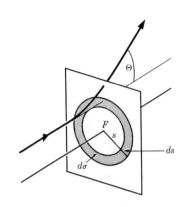

FIG. 3–41. A hyperbolic orbit.   FIG. 3–42.   Cross section for scattering.

average number dN of particles scattered through an angle between Θ and $\Theta + d\Theta$ is given in terms of the cross section $d\sigma$ by the formula

$$\frac{dN}{N} = n \, d\sigma. \qquad (3\text{–}273)$$

$d\sigma$ is called the cross section for scattering through an angle between Θ and $\Theta + d\Theta$, and can be thought of as the effective area surrounding the scattering center which the incident particle must hit in order to be scattered through an angle between Θ and $\Theta + d\Theta$.   For if there is a "target area" $d\sigma$ around each scattering center, then the total target area in a unit area is $n \, d\sigma$.   If N particles strike one unit area, the average number striking the target area is $Nn \, d\sigma$, and this, according to Eq. (3–273), is just dN, the number of particles scattered through an angle between Θ and $\Theta + d\Theta$.

Now consider an incident particle approaching a scattering center F as in Figs. 3–41 and 3–42.   If the impact parameter is between s and $s + ds$, the particle will be scattered through an angle between Θ and $\Theta + d\Theta$, where Θ is given by Eq. (3–272), and $d\Theta$ is given by the differential of Eq. (3–272):

$$\frac{1}{2 \cos^2 \dfrac{\Theta}{2}} \, d\Theta = - \frac{|q_1 q_2|}{ms^2 v_0^2} \, ds. \qquad (3\text{–}274)$$

The area of the ring around F of inner radius s, outer radius $s + ds$, at which the incident particle must be aimed in order to be scattered through an angle between Θ and $\Theta + d\Theta$, is

$$d\sigma = 2\pi s \, ds. \qquad (3\text{–}275)$$

Substituting for s from Eq. (3–272), and for ds from Eq. (3–274) (omitting the negative sign), we obtain

$$d\sigma = \left(\frac{q_1 q_2}{2mv_0^2}\right)^2 \frac{2\pi \sin \Theta}{\sin^4 \dfrac{\Theta}{2}} \, d\Theta. \tag{3–276}$$

This formula can be compared with $d\sigma$ determined experimentally as given by Eq. (3–273). Formula (3–276) was deduced by Rutherford and used in interpreting his experiments on the scattering of alpha-particles by thin metal foils. He was able to show that the formula agrees with his experiments with $q_1 = 2e$ (charge on alpha-particle),* and $q_2 = Ze$ (charge on atomic nucleus), so long as the perihelion distance ($a + a\epsilon$ in Fig. 3–41) is larger than about 10^{-12} cm, which shows that the positive charge on the atom must be concentrated within a region of radius less than 10^{-12} cm. This was the origin of the nuclear theory of the atom. The perihelion distance can be computed from formula (3–262) or by using the conservation laws for energy and angular momentum, and is given by

$$r_1 = \frac{q_1 q_2}{2E}\left[1 + \left(1 + \frac{2EL^2}{mq_1^2 q_2^2}\right)^{\frac{1}{2}}\right]. \tag{3–277}$$

The smallest perihelion distance for incident particles of a given energy occurs when $L = 0$ ($s = 0$), and has the value

$$r_{1\,\text{min}} = \frac{q_1 q_2}{E}. \tag{3–278}$$

Hence if there is a deviation from Coulomb's law of force when the alpha-particle grazes or penetrates the nucleus, it should show up first as a deviation from Rutherford's law [Eq. (3–276)] at large angles of deflection Θ, and should show up when the energy E is large enough so that

$$E > \frac{q_1 q_2}{r_0}, \tag{3–279}$$

where r_0 is the radius of the nucleus. The earliest measurements of nuclear radii were made in this way by Rutherford, and turn out to be of the order of 10^{-12} cm.

The above calculation of the cross section is strictly correct only when the alpha-particle impinges on a nucleus much heavier than itself, since the scattering center is assumed to remain fixed. This restriction can be removed by methods to be discussed in Section 4–8. Alpha-particles also collide with electrons, but the electron is so light that it cannot appreciably deflect the alpha-particle. The collision of an alpha-particle with a nucleus should really be treated by the methods of quantum mechanics. The con-

---

* e here stands for the magnitude of the electronic charge.

cept of a definite trajectory with a definite impact parameter s is no longer valid in quantum mechanics.   The concept of cross section is still valid in quantum mechanics, however, as it should be, since it is defined in terms of experimentally determined quantities.   The final result for the scattering cross section turns out the same as our formula (3–276).*   It is a fortunate coincidence in the history of physics that classical mechanics gives the right answer to this problem.

3–17 Motion of a particle in an electromagnetic field.   The laws determining the electric and magnetic fields due to various arrangements of electric charges and currents are the subject matter of electromagnetic theory.   The determination of the motions of charged particles under given electric and magnetic forces is a problem in mechanics.   The electric force on a particle of charge q located at a point $\mathbf{r}$ is

$$\mathbf{F} = q\mathbf{E}(\mathbf{r}), \tag{3–280}$$

where $\mathbf{E}(\mathbf{r})$ is the electric field intensity at the point $\mathbf{r}$.   The electric field intensity may be a function of time as well as of position in space.   The force exerted by a magnetic field on a charged particle at a point $\mathbf{r}$ depends on the velocity $\mathbf{v}$ of the particle, and is given in terms of the magnetic induction $\mathbf{B}(\mathbf{r})$ by the equation:†

$$\mathbf{F} = \frac{q}{c}\mathbf{v} \times \mathbf{B}(\mathbf{r}), \tag{3–281}$$

where $c = 3 \times 10^{10}$ cm/sec is the velocity of light, and all quantities are in gaussian units, i.e., q is in electrostatic units, $\mathbf{B}$ in electromagnetic units (gauss), and $\mathbf{v}$ and $\mathbf{F}$ are in cgs units.   In mks units, the equation reads

$$\mathbf{F} = q\mathbf{v} \times \mathbf{B}(\mathbf{r}). \tag{3–282}$$

Equation (3–280) holds for either gaussian or mks units.   We shall base our discussion on Eq. (3–281) (gaussian units), but the results are readily transcribed into mks units by omitting c wherever it occurs.   The total electromagnetic force acting on a particle due to an electric field intensity $\mathbf{E}$ and a magnetic induction $\mathbf{B}$ is

$$\mathbf{F} = q\mathbf{E} + \frac{q}{c}\mathbf{v} \times \mathbf{B}. \tag{3–283}$$

If an electric charge moves near the north pole of a magnet, the magnet will exert a force on the charge given by Eq. (3–281); and by Newton's third law the charge should exert an equal and opposite force on

---

* D. Bohm, *Quantum Theory.*   New York: Prentice-Hall, 1951.   (Page 537.)

† G. P. Harnwell, *Principles of Electricity and Electromagnetism*, 2nd ed.   New York: McGraw-Hill, 1949.   (Page 302.)

the magnet. This is indeed found to be the case, at least when the velocity of the particle is small compared with the speed of light, if the magnetic field due to the moving charge is calculated and the force on the magnet computed. However, since the magnetic induction **B** is directed radially away from the pole, and the force **F** is perpendicular to **B**, the forces on the charge and on the pole are not directed along the line joining them, as in the case of a central force. Newton's third law is sometimes stated in the "strong" form in which action and reaction are not only equal and opposite, but are directed along the line joining the interacting particles. For magnetic forces, the law holds only in the "weak" form in which nothing is said about the directions of the two forces except that they are opposite. This is true not only of the forces between magnets and moving charges, but also of the magnetic forces exerted by moving charges on one another.

If the magnetic field is constant in time, then the electric field intensity can be shown to satisfy the equation

$$\nabla \times \mathbf{E} = 0. \tag{3-284}$$

The proof of this statement belongs to electromagnetic theory and need not concern us here.* We note, however, that this implies that for static electric and magnetic fields, the electric force on a charged particle is conservative. We can therefore define an electric potential

$$\phi(\mathbf{r}) = -\int_{\mathbf{r}_s}^{\mathbf{r}} \mathbf{E} \cdot d\mathbf{r}, \tag{3-285}$$

such that

$$\mathbf{E} = -\nabla \phi. \tag{3-286}$$

Since **E** is the force per unit charge, ϕ will be the potential energy per unit charge associated with the electric force:

$$V(\mathbf{r}) = q\phi(\mathbf{r}). \tag{3-287}$$

Furthermore, since the magnetic force is perpendicular to the velocity, it can do no work on a charged particle. Consequently, the law of conservation of energy holds for a particle in a static electromagnetic field:

$$T + q\phi = E, \tag{3-288}$$

where E is a constant.

A great variety of problems of practical and theoretical interest arise involving the motion of charged particles in electric and magnetic fields. In general, special methods of attack must be devised for each type of problem. We shall discuss two special problems which are of interest both for the results obtained and for the methods of obtaining those results.

---

* Harnwell, *loc. cit.* (Page 340.)

We first consider the motion of a particle of mass m, charge q, in a uniform constant magnetic field.   Let the z-axis be chosen in the direction of the field, so that

$$\mathbf{B}(\mathbf{r},t) = B\mathbf{k}, \tag{3–289}$$

where B is a constant.   The equations of motion are then, by Eq. (3–281),

$$m\ddot{x} = \frac{qB}{c}\dot{y}, \quad m\ddot{y} = -\frac{qB}{c}\dot{x}, \quad m\ddot{z} = 0. \tag{3–290}$$

According to the last equation, the z-component of velocity is constant, and we shall consider the case when $v_z = 0$, and the motion is entirely in the xy-plane.   The first two equations are not hard to solve, but we can avoid solving them directly by making use of the energy integral, which in this case reads

$$\tfrac{1}{2}mv^2 = E. \tag{3–291}$$

The force is given by:

$$\mathbf{F} = \frac{qB}{c}\mathbf{v} \times \mathbf{k}, \tag{3–292}$$

$$F = \frac{qBv}{c}. \tag{3–293}$$

The force, and consequently the acceleration, is therefore of constant magnitude and perpendicular to the velocity.   A particle moving with constant speed v and constant acceleration a perpendicular to its direction of motion moves in a circle of radius r given by Eq. (3–80):

$$a = r\dot{\theta}^2 = \frac{v^2}{r} = \frac{F}{m}. \tag{3–294}$$

We substitute for F from Eq. (3–293) and solve for r:

$$r = \frac{cmv}{qB}. \tag{3–295}$$

The product Br is therefore proportional to the momentum and inversely proportional to the charge.

This result has many practical applications.   If a cloud chamber is placed in a uniform magnetic field, one can measure the momentum of a charged particle by measuring the radius of curvature of its track.   The same principle is used in a beta-ray spectrometer to measure the momentum of a fast electron by the curvature of its path in a magnetic field.   In a mass spectrometer, a particle is accelerated through a known difference of electric potential, so that, by Eq. (3–288), its kinetic energy is

$$\tfrac{1}{2}mv^2 = q(\phi_0 - \phi_1). \tag{3–296}$$

It is then passed through a uniform magnetic field B.   If q is known, and r,B, $(\phi_0 - \phi_1)$ are measured, we can eliminate v between Eqs. (3–295) and (3–296), and solve for the mass:

$$m = \frac{qB^2r^2}{2c^2(\phi_0 - \phi_1)}. \tag{3–297}$$

There are many variations of this basic idea. The historic experiments of J. J. Thomson which demonstrated the existence of the electron were essentially of this type, and by them Thomson succeeded in showing that the path traveled by a cathode ray is that which would be followed by a stream of charged particles, all with the same ratio q/m. In a cyclotron, charged particles travel in circles in a uniform magnetic field, and receive increments in energy twice per revolution by passing through an alternating electric field. The radius r of the circles therefore increases, according to Eq. (3–295), until a maximum radius is reached, at which radius the particles emerge in a beam of definite energy determined by Eq. (3–295). The frequency ν of the alternating electric field must be the same as the frequency ν of revolution of the particles, which is given by

$$v = 2\pi r\nu. \tag{3–298}$$

Combining this equation with Eq. (3–295), we have

$$\nu = \frac{qB}{2\pi mc}. \tag{3–299}$$

Thus if B is constant, ν is independent of r, and this is the fundamental principle on which the operation of the cyclotron is based.* In the betatron, electrons travel in circles, and the magnetic field within the circle is made to increase. Since B is changing with time, $\nabla \times \mathbf{E}$ is no longer zero; the changing magnetic flux induces a voltage around the circle such that a net amount of work is done on the electrons by the electric field as they travel around the circle. The betatron is so designed that the increase of B at the electron orbit is proportional to the increase of mv, so that r remains constant.

Finally, we consider a particle of mass m, charge q, moving in a uniform constant electric field intensity $\mathbf{E}$ and a uniform constant magnetic induction $\mathbf{B}$. Again let the z-axis be chosen in the direction of $\mathbf{B}$, and let the y-axis be chosen so that $\mathbf{E}$ is parallel to the yz-plane:

$$\mathbf{B} = B\mathbf{k}, \quad \mathbf{E} = E_y\mathbf{j} + E_z\mathbf{k}, \tag{3–300}$$

where B, E_y, E_z are constants. The equations of motion, by Eq. (3–283), are

$$m\ddot{x} = \frac{qB}{c}\,\dot{y}, \tag{3–301}$$

$$m\ddot{y} = -\frac{qB}{c}\,\dot{x} + qE_y, \tag{3–302}$$

$$m\ddot{z} = qE_z. \tag{3–303}$$

The z-component of the motion is uniformly accelerated:

$$z = z_0 + \dot{z}_0 t + \frac{1}{2}\frac{qE_z}{m}\,t^2. \tag{3–304}$$

---

* According to the theory of relativity, the mass of a particle increases with velocity at velocities near the speed of light, and consequently the cyclotron cannot accelerate particles to such speeds unless ν is reduced or B is increased as the particle velocity increases. [It turns out that Eq. (3–295) still holds in relativity theory.]

To solve the x and y equations, we differentiate Eq. (3–301) and substitute in Eq. (3–302) in order to eliminate $\ddot{y}$:

$$\frac{m^2c}{qB}\,\dddot{x} = -\frac{qB}{c}\,\dot{x} + qE_y. \tag{3–305}$$

By making the substitutions

$$\omega = \frac{qB}{mc}, \tag{3–306}$$

$$a = \frac{qE_y}{m}, \tag{3–307}$$

we can write Eq. (3–305) in the form

$$\frac{d^2\dot{x}}{dt^2} + \omega^2\dot{x} = a\omega. \tag{3–308}$$

This equation has the same form as the equation for a harmonic oscillator with angular frequency ω subject to a constant applied "force" $a\omega$, except that $\dot{x}$ appears in place of the coordinate. The corresponding oscillator problem was considered in Chapter 2, problem 21. The solution in this case will be

$$\dot{x} = \frac{a}{\omega} + A_x \cos(\omega t + \theta_x), \tag{3–309}$$

where A_x and θ_x are arbitrary constants to be determined. By eliminating $\ddot{x}$ from Eqs. (3–301) and (3–302), in a similar way, we obtain a solution for $\dot{y}$:

$$\dot{y} = A_y \cos(\omega t + \theta_y). \tag{3–310}$$

We get x and y by integrating Eqs. (3–309) and (3–310):

$$x = C_x + \frac{at}{\omega} + \frac{A_x}{\omega} \sin(\omega t + \theta_x), \tag{3–311}$$

$$y = C_y + \frac{A_y}{\omega} \sin(\omega t + \theta_y). \tag{3–312}$$

Now a difficulty arises, for we have six constants A_x, A_y, θ_x, θ_y, C_x, and C_y to be determined, and only four initial values $x_0, y_0, \dot{x}_0, \dot{y}_0$, to determine them. The trouble is that we obtained the solutions (3–311) and (3–312) by differentiating the original equations, and differentiating an equation may introduce new solutions that do not satisfy the original equation. Consider, for example, the very simple equation

$$x = 3.$$

Differentiating, we get

$$\dot{x} = 0,$$

whose solution is

$$x = C.$$

Now only for one particular value of the constant C will this satisfy the original equation. Let us substitute Eqs. (3–311) and (3–312) or, equivalently, Eqs. (3–309) and (3–310) into the original Eqs. (3–301) and (3–302), using Eqs. (3–306) and (3–307):

$$-\frac{qB}{c} A_x \sin(\omega t + \theta_x) = \frac{qB}{c} A_y \cos(\omega t + \theta_y), \qquad (3\text{–}313)$$

$$-\frac{qB}{c} A_y \sin(\omega t + \theta_y) = -\frac{qB}{c} A_x \cos(\omega t + \theta_x). \qquad (3\text{–}314)$$

These two equations will hold only if A_x, A_y, θ_x, and θ_y are chosen so that

$$A_x = A_y, \qquad (3\text{–}315)$$
$$\sin(\omega t + \theta_x) = -\cos(\omega t + \theta_y), \qquad (3\text{–}316)$$
$$\cos(\omega t + \theta_x) = \sin(\omega t + \theta_y). \qquad (3\text{–}317)$$

The latter two equations are satisfied if

$$\theta_y = \theta_x + \frac{\pi}{2}. \qquad (3\text{–}318)$$

Let us set

$$A_x = A_y = \omega A, \qquad (3\text{–}319)$$
$$\theta_x = \theta, \qquad (3\text{–}320)$$
$$\theta_y = \theta + \frac{\pi}{2}. \qquad (3\text{–}321)$$

Then Eqs. (3–311) and (3–312) become

$$x = C_x + A \sin(\omega t + \theta) + \frac{at}{\omega}, \qquad (3\text{–}322)$$
$$y = C_y + A \cos(\omega t + \theta). \qquad (3\text{–}323)$$

There are now only four constants, A, θ, C_x, C_y, to be determined by the initial values $x_0, y_0, \dot{x}_0, \dot{y}_0$. The z motion is, of course, given by Eq. (3–304). If $E_y = 0$, the xy motion is in a circle of radius A with angular velocity ω about the point (C_x, C_y); this is the motion considered in the previous example. The effect of E_y is to add to this uniform circular motion a uniform translation in the *x-direction!* The resulting path in the xy-plane will be a cycloid having loops, cusps, or ripples, depending on the initial conditions and on the magnitude of E_y (Fig. 3–43). This problem is of interest in connection with the design of magnetrons.

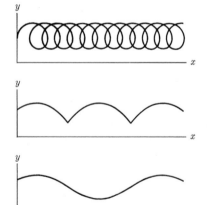

Fig. 3–43. Orbits in the xy-plane of a charged particle subject to a magnetic field in the z-direction and an electric field in the y-direction.

PROBLEMS

1. Prove, on the basis of the geometric definitions of the operations of vector algebra, the following equations. In many cases a diagram will suffice. (a) Eq. (3–7), (b) Eq. (3–17), (c) Eq. (3–26), (d) Eq. (3–27), (e) Eq. (3–35). [Part (e) is difficult.]

2. Prove, on the basis of the algebraic definitions of the operations of vector algebra in terms of components, the following equations: (a) Eq. (3–8), (b) Eq. (3–17), (c) Eq. (3–27), (d) Eq. (3–34), (e) Eq. (3–35).

3. Derive Eq. (3–32) by direct calculation, using Eq. (3–10) to represent $\mathbf{A}$ and $\mathbf{B}$, and making use of Eqs. (3–25) to (3–31).

4. (a) Prove that $\mathbf{A} \cdot (\mathbf{B} \times \mathbf{C})$ is the volume of the parallelepiped whose edges are $\mathbf{A}, \mathbf{B}, \mathbf{C}$, with positive or negative sign according to whether a right-hand screw rotated from $\mathbf{A}$ toward $\mathbf{B}$ would advance along $\mathbf{C}$ in the positive or negative direction. $\mathbf{A}, \mathbf{B}, \mathbf{C}$ are any three vectors not lying in a single plane. (b) Use this result to prove Eq. (3–34) geometrically. Verify that the right and left members of Eq. (3–34) are equal in sign as well as in magnitude.

5. Prove the following inequalities. Give a geometric and an algebraic proof (in terms of components) for each:

(a) $\qquad\qquad |\mathbf{A} + \mathbf{B}| \le |\mathbf{A}| + |\mathbf{B}|$.

(b) $\qquad\qquad |\mathbf{A} \cdot \mathbf{B}| \le |\mathbf{A}|\,|\mathbf{B}|$.

(c) $\qquad\qquad |\mathbf{A} \times \mathbf{B}| \le |\mathbf{A}|\,|\mathbf{B}|$.

6. (a) Obtain a formula analogous to Eq. (3–40) for the magnitude of the sum of three forces $\mathbf{F}_1, \mathbf{F}_2, \mathbf{F}_3$, in terms of F_1, F_2, F_3, and the angles $\theta_{12}, \theta_{23}, \theta_{31}$ between pairs of forces. [Use the suggestions following Eq. (3–40).]

(b) Obtain a formula in the same terms for the angle α_1, between the total force and the component force $\mathbf{F}_1$.

7. Prove Eqs. (3–54) and (3–55) from the definition (3–52) of vector differentiation.

8. Prove Eqs. (3–56) and (3–57) from the algebraic definition (3–53) of vector differentiation.

9. Give suitable definitions, analogous to Eqs. (3–52) and (3–53), for the integral of a vector function $\mathbf{A}(t)$ with respect to a scalar t:

$$\int_{t_1}^{t_2} \mathbf{A}(t)\, dt.$$

Write a set of equations like Eqs. (3–54)–(3–57) expressing the algebraic properties you would expect such an integral to have. Prove that on the basis of either definition

$$\frac{d}{dt} \int_0^t \mathbf{A}(t)\, dt = \mathbf{A}(t).$$

10. A 45° isosceles right triangle ABC has a hypotenuse AB of length $4a$. A particle is acted on by a force attracting it toward a point O on the hypotenuse a distance a from the point A. The force is equal in magnitude to k/r^2, where r is the distance of the particle from the point O. Calculate the work done by this force when the particle moves from A to C to B along the two legs of the triangle. Make the calculation by both methods, that based on Eq. (3–61) and that based on Eq. (3–63).

11. Plane parabolic coordinates f,h are defined in terms of Cartesian coordinates x,y by the equations

$$x = f - h, \quad y = 2(fh)^{\frac{1}{2}},$$

where f and h are never negative. Find f and h in terms of x and y. Let unit vectors $\mathbf{f},\mathbf{h}$ be defined in the directions of increasing f and h respectively. That is, $\mathbf{f}$ is a unit vector in the direction in which a point would move if its f-coordinate increases slightly while its h-coordinate remains constant. Show that $\mathbf{f}$ and $\mathbf{h}$ are perpendicular at every point. [*Hint:* $\mathbf{f} = (\mathbf{i}\,dx + \mathbf{j}\,dy)[(dx)^2 + (dy)^2]^{-\frac{1}{2}}$, when $df > 0, dh = 0$. Why?]

Show that $\mathbf{f}$ and $\mathbf{h}$ are functions of f,h, and find their derivatives with respect to f and h. Show that $\mathbf{r} = f^{\frac{1}{2}}(f + h)^{\frac{1}{2}}\mathbf{f} + h^{\frac{1}{2}}(f + h)^{\frac{1}{2}}\mathbf{h}$. Find the components of velocity and acceleration in parabolic coordinates.

12. A particle moves along the parabola

$$y^2 = 4f_0^2 - 4f_0 x,$$

where f_0 is a constant. Its speed v is constant. Find its velocity and acceleration components in rectangular and in polar coordinates. Show that the equation of the parabola in polar coordinates is

$$r \cos^2 \frac{\theta}{2} = f_0.$$

What is the equation of this parabola in parabolic coordinates (problem 11)?

13. A particle moves with varying speed along an arbitrary curve lying in the xy-plane. The position of the particle is to be specified by the distance s the particle has traveled along the curve from some fixed point on the curve. Let $\boldsymbol{\tau}(s)$ be a unit vector tangent to the curve at the point s in the direction of increasing s. Show that

$$\frac{d\boldsymbol{\tau}}{ds} = \frac{\boldsymbol{\nu}}{r},$$

where $\boldsymbol{\nu}(s)$ is a unit vector normal to the curve at the point s, and $r(s)$ is the radius of curvature at the point s, defined as the distance from the curve to the point of intersection of two nearby normals.* Hence derive the following formulas for the velocity and acceleration of the particle:

$$\mathbf{v} = \dot{s}\boldsymbol{\tau}, \quad \mathbf{a} = \ddot{s}\boldsymbol{\tau} + \frac{\dot{s}^2}{r}\boldsymbol{\nu}.$$

14. Using the properties of the vector symbol ∇, derive the vector identities:

$$\text{curl (curl } \mathbf{A}) = \text{grad (div } \mathbf{A}) - \nabla^2\mathbf{A},$$
$$u \text{ grad } v = \text{grad } (uv) - v \text{ grad } u.$$

Then write out the x-components of each side of these equations and prove by direct calculation that they are equal in each case. (One must be very careful, in using the first identity in curvilinear coordinates, to take proper account of the dependence of the unit vectors on the coordinates.)

15. Calculate curl $\mathbf{A}$ in cylindrical coordinates.

16. Give a suitable definition of the angular momentum of a particle about an axis in space. Taking the specified axis as the z-axis, express the angular momen-

---

* W. F. Osgood, *Introduction to the Calculus*. New York: Macmillan, 1937. (Page 259.)

tum in terms of cylindrical coordinates. If the force acting on the particle has cylindrical components F_z, F_ρ, F_φ, prove that the time rate of change of angular momentum about the z-axis is equal to the torque about that axis.

17. A moving particle of mass m is located by spherical coordinates $r(t), \theta(t), \varphi(t)$. The force acting on it has spherical components F_r, F_θ, F_φ. Calculate the spherical components of the angular momentum vector and of the torque vector about the origin, and verify by direct calculation that the equation

$$\frac{d\mathbf{L}}{dt} = \mathbf{N}$$

follows from Newton's equation of motion.

18. Solve for the next term beyond those given in Eqs. (3–177) and (3–178).

19. A projectile is to be fired from the origin in the xz-plane (z-axis vertical) with muzzle velocity v_0 to hit a target at the point $x = x_0, z = 0$. (a) Neglecting air resistance, find the correct angle of elevation of the gun. Show that, in general, there are two such angles unless the target is at or beyond the maximum range. (b) Find the first order correction to the angle of elevation due to air resistance.

20. A projectile is fired from the origin with initial velocity $\mathbf{v}_0 = (v_{x_0}, v_{y_0}, v_{z_0})$. The wind velocity is $\mathbf{v}_w = w\mathbf{j}$. Solve the equations of motion (3–180) for x, y, z as functions of t. Find the point x_1, y_1 at which the projectile will return to the horizontal plane, keeping only first order terms in b. Show that if air resistance and wind velocity are neglected in aiming the gun, air resistance alone will cause the projectile to fall short of its target a fraction $4bv_{z_0}/3mg$ of the target distance, and that the wind causes an additional miss in the y-coordinate of amount $2bwv_{z_0}^2/(mg^2)$.

21. Determine which of the following forces are conservative, and find the potential energy for those which are:

(a) $F_x = 6z^3y - 20x^3y^2, \quad F_y = 6xz^3 - 10x^4y, \quad F_z = 18xz^2y$.
(b) $F_x = 18yz^3 - 20x^3y^2, \quad F_y = 18xz^3 - 10x^4y, \quad F_z = 6xyz^2$.
(c) $\mathbf{F} = \mathbf{i}F_x(x) + \mathbf{j}F_y(y) + \mathbf{k}F_z(z)$.

22. Find the components of force for the following potential energy functions:

(a) $V = axy^2z^3$.
(b) $V = \frac{1}{2}kr^2$.
(c) $V = \frac{1}{2}k_xx^2 + \frac{1}{2}k_yy^2 + \frac{1}{2}k_zz^2$.

23. Find the force on the electron in the hydrogen molecule ion for which the potential is

$$V = -\frac{e^2}{r_1} - \frac{e^2}{r_2},$$

where r_1 is the distance from the electron to the point $y = 0, x = -a$, and r_2 is the distance from the electron to the point $y = 0, x = a$.

24. Show that $\mathbf{F} = \mathbf{n}F(r)$ (where $\mathbf{n}$ is a unit vector directed away from the origin) is a conservative force by showing by direct calculation that the integral

$$\int_{r_1}^{r_2} \mathbf{F} \cdot d\mathbf{r}$$

along any path between $\mathbf{r}_1$ and $\mathbf{r}_2$ depends only on r_1 and r_2. (*Hint:* Express $\mathbf{F}$ and $d\mathbf{r}$ in spherical coordinates.)

25. The potential energy for an isotropic harmonic oscillator is

$$V = \frac{1}{2}kr^2.$$

Plot the effective potential energy for the r-motion when a particle of mass m moves with this potential energy and with angular momentum L about the origin.   Discuss the types of motion that are possible, giving as complete a description as is possible without carrying out the solution.   Find the frequency of revolution for circular motion and the frequency of small radial oscillations about this circular motion.   Hence describe the nature of the orbits which differ slightly from circular orbits.

26. Find the frequency of small radial oscillations about steady circular motion for the effective potential given by Eq. (3–232) for an attractive inverse square law force, and show that it is equal to the frequency of revolution.

27. Find $r(t), \theta(t)$ for the orbit of the particle in problem 25.   Compare with the orbits found in Section 3–10 for the three-dimensional harmonic oscillator.

28. A particle of mass m moves under the action of a central force whose potential is

$$V(r) = Kr^4, \quad K > 0.$$

For what energy and angular momentum will the orbit be a circle of radius a about the origin?   What is the period of this circular motion?   If the particle is slightly disturbed from this circular motion, what will be the period of small radial oscillations about $r = a$?

29. According to Yukawa's theory of nuclear forces, the attractive force between a neutron and a proton has the potential

$$V(r) = \frac{Ke^{-\alpha r}}{r}, \quad K < 0.$$

(a) Find the force, and compare it with an inverse square law of force.   (b) Discuss the types of motion which can occur if a particle of mass m moves under such a force.   (c) Discuss how. the motions will be expected to differ from the corresponding types of motion for an inverse square law of force.   (d) Find L and E for motion in a circle of radius a.   (e) Find the period of circular motion and the period of small radial oscillations.   (f) Show that the nearly circular orbits are almost closed when a is very small.

30. (a) Discuss by the method of the effective potential the types of motion to be expected for an attractive central force inversely proportional to the cube of the radius:

$$F(r) = -\frac{K}{r^3}, \quad K > 0.$$

(b) Find the ranges of energy and angular momentum for each type of motion. (c) Solve the orbital equation (3–222), and show that the solution is one of the forms:

$$\frac{1}{r} = A \cos [\beta(\theta - \theta_0)], \tag{1}$$

$$\frac{1}{r} = A \cosh [\beta(\theta - \theta_0)], \tag{2}$$

$$\frac{1}{r} = A \sinh [\beta(\theta - \theta_0)], \tag{3}$$

$$\frac{1}{r} = A (\theta - \theta_0). \tag{4}$$

(d) For what values of L and E does each of the above types of motion occur? Express the constants A and β in terms of E and L for each case.   (e) Sketch a typical orbit of each type.

31. (a) Discuss the types of motion that can occur for a central force

$$F(r) = -\frac{K}{r^2} + \frac{K'}{r^3}.$$

Assume that $K > 0$, and consider both signs for K'.

(b) Solve the orbital equation, and show that the bounded orbits have the form (if $L^2 > - mK'$)

$$r = \frac{a(1 - \epsilon^2)}{1 + \epsilon \cos \alpha\theta}.$$

(c) Show that this is a precessing ellipse, determine the angular velocity of precession, and state whether the precession is in the same or in the opposite direction to the orbital angular velocity.

32. A comet is observed a distance of 1.00×10^8 kilometers from the sun, traveling toward the sun with a velocity of 51.6 kilometers per second at an angle of 45° with the radius from the sun. Work out an equation for the orbit of the comet in polar coordinates with origin at the sun and x-axis through the observed position of the comet. (The mass of the sun is 2.00×10^{30} kg.)

33. It will be shown in Chapter 6 (problem 3) that the effect of a uniform distribution of dust of density ρ about the sun is to add to the gravitational attraction of the sun on a planet of mass m an additional attractive central force

$$F' = -mkr,$$

where

$$k = \frac{4\pi}{3} \rho G.$$

(a) If the mass of the sun is M, find the angular velocity of revolution of the planet in a circular orbit of radius r_0, and find the angular frequency of small radial oscillations. Hence show that if F' is much less than the attraction due to the sun, a nearly circular orbit will be approximately an ellipse whose major axis precesses slowly with angular velocity

$$\omega_p = 2\pi\rho \left(\frac{r_0^3 G}{M}\right)^{\frac{1}{2}}.$$

(b) Does the axis precess in the same or in the opposite direction to the orbital angular velocity? Look up M and the radius of the orbit of Mercury, and calculate the density of dust required to cause a precession of 41 seconds of arc per century.

34. It can be shown that the orbit given by the special theory of relativity for a particle of mass m moving under a potential energy $V(r)$ is the same as the orbit which the particle would follow according to Newtonian mechanics if the potential energy were

$$V(r) - \frac{[E - V(r)]^2}{2mc^2},$$

where E is the energy (kinetic plus potential), and c is the speed of light. Discuss the nature of the orbits for an inverse square law of force according to the theory of relativity. Show by comparing the orbital angular velocity with the frequency of radial oscillations for nearly circular motion that the nearly circular orbits, when the relativistic correction is small, are precessing ellipses, and calculate the angular velocity of precession.

35. A particle of mass m moves in an elliptical orbit of major axis $2a$, eccentricity ϵ, in such a way that the radius to the particle from the center of the ellipse sweeps out area at a constant rate

$$\frac{dS}{dt} = C,$$

and with period τ independent of a and ϵ. (a) Write out the equation of the ellipse in polar coordinates with origin at the center of the ellipse. (b) Show that the force on the particle is a central force, and find $F(r)$ in terms of m,τ.

36. Show that for a repulsive central force inversely proportional to the cube of the radius,

$$F(r) = \frac{K}{r^3}, \quad K > 0,$$

the orbits are of the form (1) given in problem 30, and express β in terms of K,E,L, and the mass m of the incident particle. Show that the cross section for scattering through an angle between Θ and $\Theta + d\Theta$ for a particle subject to this force is

$$d\sigma = \frac{2\pi^3 K}{m v_0^2} \frac{\pi - \Theta}{\Theta^2(2\pi - \Theta)^2} d\Theta.$$

37. A particle of charge q in a cylindrical magnetron moves in a uniform magnetic field

$$\mathbf{B} = B\mathbf{k},$$

and an electric field, directed radially outward or inward from a central wire along the z-axis,

$$\mathbf{E} = \frac{a}{\rho}\mathbf{h},$$

where ρ is the distance from the z-axis, and $\mathbf{h}$ is a unit vector directed radially outward from the z-axis. The constants a and B may be either positive or negative. (a) Set up the equations of motion in cylindrical coordinates. (b) Show that the quantity

$$m\rho^2\dot{\varphi} + \frac{qB}{2c}\rho^2 = K$$

is a constant of the motion. (c) Using this result, give a qualitative discussion, based on the energy integral, of the types of motion that can occur. Consider all cases, including all values of a, B, K, and E. (c) Under what conditions can circular motion about the axis occur? (d) What is the frequency of small radial oscillations about this circular motion?

CHAPTER 4

THE MOTION OF A SYSTEM OF PARTICLES

4–1 Conservation of linear momentum. Center of mass. We consider in this chapter the behavior of mechanical systems containing two or more particles acted upon by *internal* forces exerted by the particles upon one another, and by *external* forces exerted upon particles of the system by agents not belonging to the system. We assume the particles to be point masses each specified by its position (x,y,z) in space, like the single particle whose motion was studied in the preceding chapter.

Let the system we are studying contain N particles, and let them be numbered $1,2,\ldots,N$. The masses of the particles we designate by $m_1, m_2, \ldots, m_N$. The total force acting on the kth particle will be the sum of the internal forces exerted on particle k by all the other $(N-1)$ particles in the system, plus any external force which may be applied to particle k. Let the sum of the internal forces on particle k be $\mathbf{F}_k^i$, and let the total external force on particle k be $\mathbf{F}_k^e$. Then the equation of motion of the kth particle will be

$$m_k\ddot{\mathbf{r}}_k = \mathbf{F}_k^e + \mathbf{F}_k^i, \quad k = 1,2,\ldots,N. \tag{4-1}$$

The N equations obtained by letting k in Eqs. (4–1) run over the numbers $1,\ldots,N$ are the equations of motion of our system. Since each of these N equations is itself a vector equation, we have in general a set of $3N$ simultaneous second order differential equations to be solved. The solution will be a set of functions $\mathbf{r}_k(t)$ specifying the motion of each particle in the system. The solution will depend on $6N$ "arbitrary" constants specifying the initial position and velocity of each particle. The problem of solving the set of equations (4–1) is very difficult, except in certain special cases, and no general methods are available for attacking the N-body problem, even in the case where the forces between the bodies are central forces. The two-body problem can often be solved, as we shall see, and some general theorems are available when the internal forces satisfy certain conditions.

If $\mathbf{p}_k = m_k\mathbf{v}_k$ is the linear momentum of the kth particle, we can write Eqs. (4–1) in the form

$$\frac{d\mathbf{p}_k}{dt} = \mathbf{F}_k^e + \mathbf{F}_k^i, \quad k = 1,\ldots,N. \tag{4-2}$$

Summing the right and left sides of these equations over all the particles, we have

$$\sum_{k=1}^{N} \frac{d\mathbf{p}_k}{dt} = \frac{d}{dt}\sum_{k=1}^{N} \mathbf{p}_k = \sum_{k=1}^{N} \mathbf{F}_k^e + \sum_{k=1}^{N} \mathbf{F}_k^i. \tag{4-3}$$

We designate by $\mathbf{P}$ the total linear momentum of the particles, and by $\mathbf{F}$ the total external force:

$$\mathbf{P} = \sum_{k=1}^{N} \mathbf{p}_k = \sum_{k=1}^{N} m_k \mathbf{v}_k, \tag{4-4}$$

$$\mathbf{F} = \sum_{k=1}^{N} \mathbf{F}_k^e. \tag{4-5}$$

We now make the assumption, to be justified below, that the sum of the internal forces acting on all the particles is zero:

$$\sum_{k=1}^{N} \mathbf{F}_k^i = \mathbf{0}. \tag{4-6}$$

When Eqs. (4–4), (4–5), and (4–6) are substituted in Eq. (4–3), it becomes

$$\frac{d\mathbf{P}}{dt} = \mathbf{F}. \tag{4-7}$$

This is the momentum theorem for a system of particles. It states that the time rate of change of the total linear momentum is equal to the total external force. An immediate corollary is the conservation theorem for linear momentum, which states that the total momentum $\mathbf{P}$ is constant when no external forces act.

We now try to justify the assumption (4–6). Our first proof is based on Newton's third law. We assume that the force $\mathbf{F}_k^i$ acting on particle k due to all the other particles can be represented as a sum of separate forces due to each of the other particles:

$$\mathbf{F}_k^i = \sum_{l \neq k} \mathbf{F}_{l \rightarrow k}^i, \tag{4-8}$$

where $\mathbf{F}_{l \rightarrow k}^i$ is the force on particle k due to particle l. According to Newton's third law, the force exerted by particle l on particle k is equal and opposite to that exerted by k on l:

$$\mathbf{F}_{k \rightarrow l}^i = -\mathbf{F}_{l \rightarrow k}^i. \tag{4-9}$$

Equation (4–9) expresses Newton's third law in what we may call the weak form; that is, it says that the forces are equal and opposite, but does not imply that the forces act along the line joining the two particles. If we now consider the sum in Eq. (4–6), we have

$$\sum_{k=1}^{N} \mathbf{F}_k^i = \sum_{k=1}^{N} \sum_{l \neq k} \mathbf{F}_{l \rightarrow k}^i. \tag{4-10}$$

The sum on the right is over all forces acting between all pairs of particles in the system. Since for each pair or particles k,l, two forces $\mathbf{F}_{k \rightarrow l}^i$ and $\mathbf{F}_{l \rightarrow k}^i$ appear in the total sum, and by Eq. (4–9) the sum of each such pair is zero, the total sum on the right in Eq. (4–10) vanishes, and Eq. (4–6) is proved.

Thus Newton's third law, in the form (4–9), is sufficient to guarantee the conservation of linear momentum for a system of particles, and it was for this purpose that the law was introduced. The law of conservation of momentum has, however, a more general validity than Newton's third law, as we shall see later. We can derive assumption (4–6) on the basis of a somewhat weaker assumption than Newton's third law. We do not need to assume that the particles interact in pairs. We assume only that the internal forces are such that they would do no net work if every particle in the system should be displaced the same small distance δr from its position at any particular instant. An imagined motion of all the particles in the system is called a *virtual displacement*. The motion described, in which every particle moves the same small distance δr, is called a *small virtual translation* of the system. We assume, then, that in any small virtual translation δr of the entire system, the internal forces would do no net work. From the point of view of the general idea of conservation of energy, this assumption amounts to little more than assuming that space is homogeneous. If we move the system to a slightly different position in space without otherwise disturbing it, the internal state of the system should be unaffected, hence in particular the distribution of various kinds of energy within it should remain the same and no net work can have been done by the internal forces. Let us use this idea to prove Eq. (4–6). The work done by the force $\mathbf{F}_k^i$ in a small virtual translation δr is

$$\delta W_k = \mathbf{F}_k^i \cdot \delta\mathbf{r}. \tag{4–11}$$

The total work done by all the internal forces is

$$\delta W = \sum_{k=1}^{N} \delta W_k = \delta\mathbf{r} \cdot \left(\sum_{k=1}^{N} \mathbf{F}_k^i \right), \tag{4–12}$$

where we have factored out δr from the sum, since it is the same for all particles. Assuming that $\delta W = 0$, we have

$$\delta\mathbf{r} \cdot \left(\sum_{k=1}^{N} \mathbf{F}_k^i \right) = 0. \tag{4–13}$$

Since Eq. (4–13) must hold for any δr, Eq. (4–6) follows.

We can put Eq. (4–7) in an illuminating form by introducing the concept of center of mass of the system of particles. The vector $\mathbf{R}$ which locates the center of mass is defined by the equation

$$M\mathbf{R} = \sum_{k=1}^{N} m_k\mathbf{r}_k, \tag{4–14}$$

where M is the total mass:

$$M = \sum_{k=1}^{N} m_k. \tag{4–15}$$

The coordinates of the center of mass are given by the components of Eq. (4–14):

$$X = \frac{1}{M} \sum_{k=1}^{N} m_k x_k, \quad Y = \frac{1}{M} \sum_{k=1}^{N} m_k y_k, \quad Z = \frac{1}{M} \sum_{k=1}^{N} m_k z_k. \quad (4\text{–}16)$$

The total momentum defined by Eq. (4–4) is, in terms of the center of mass,

$$\mathbf{P} = \sum_{k=1}^{N} m_k \dot{\mathbf{r}}_k = M\dot{\mathbf{R}}, \quad (4\text{–}17)$$

so that Eq. (4–7) can be written

$$M\ddot{\mathbf{R}} = \mathbf{F}. \quad (4\text{–}18)$$

This equation has the same form as the equation of motion of a particle of mass M acted on by a force $\mathbf{F}$. We thus have the important theorem that [when Eq. (4–6) holds] *the center of mass of a system of particles moves like a single particle, whose mass is the total mass of the system, acted on by a force equal to the total external force acting on the system.*

4–2 Conservation of angular momentum. Let us calculate the time rate of change of the total angular momentum of a system of N particles about a point Q not necessarily fixed in space. The vector angular momentum of particle k about a point Q, not necessarily the origin, is to be defined according to Eq. (3–142):

$$\mathbf{L}_{kQ} = (\mathbf{r}_k - \mathbf{r}_Q) \times \mathbf{p}_k, \quad (4\text{–}19)$$

where $\mathbf{r}_Q$ is the position vector of the point Q, and $(\mathbf{r}_k - \mathbf{r}_Q)$ is the vector from Q to particle k. Taking the cross product of $(\mathbf{r}_k - \mathbf{r}_Q)$ with the equation of motion (4–2) for particle k, as in the derivation of Eq. (3–144), we obtain

$$(\mathbf{r}_k - \mathbf{r}_Q) \times \frac{d\mathbf{p}_k}{dt} = (\mathbf{r}_k - \mathbf{r}_Q) \times \mathbf{F}_k^e + (\mathbf{r}_k - \mathbf{r}_Q) \times \mathbf{F}_k^i. \quad (4\text{–}20)$$

We now differentiate Eq. (4–19):

$$\frac{d\mathbf{L}_{kQ}}{dt} = (\mathbf{r}_k - \mathbf{r}_Q) \times \frac{d\mathbf{p}_k}{dt} + \dot{\mathbf{r}}_k \times \mathbf{p}_k - \dot{\mathbf{r}}_Q \times \mathbf{p}_k. \quad (4\text{–}21)$$

The second term on the right vanishes, since $\mathbf{p}_k$ is parallel to $\dot{\mathbf{r}}_k$. Therefore, by Eq. (4–20),

$$\frac{d\mathbf{L}_{kQ}}{dt} = (\mathbf{r}_k - \mathbf{r}_Q) \times \mathbf{F}_k^e + (\mathbf{r}_k - \mathbf{r}_Q) \times \mathbf{F}_k^i - \dot{\mathbf{r}}_Q \times \mathbf{p}_k. \quad (4\text{–}22)$$

The total angular momentum and total external torque about the point Q are defined as follows:

$$\mathbf{L}_Q = \sum_{k=1}^{N} \mathbf{L}_{kQ}, \quad (4\text{–}23)$$

$$\mathbf{N}_Q = \sum_{k=1}^{N} (\mathbf{r}_k - \mathbf{r}_Q) \times \mathbf{F}_k^e. \tag{4–24}$$

Summed over all particles, Eq. (4–22) becomes, if we use Eq. (4–4),

$$\frac{d\mathbf{L}_Q}{dt} = \mathbf{N}_Q + \sum_{k=1}^{N} (\mathbf{r}_k - \mathbf{r}_Q) \times \mathbf{F}_k^i - \dot{\mathbf{r}}_Q \times \mathbf{P}. \tag{4–25}$$

The last term will vanish if the point Q is at rest, or if its velocity is in the same direction as the velocity of the center of mass. We shall restrict the discussion to moments about a point Q satisfying this condition:

$$\dot{\mathbf{r}}_Q \times \dot{\mathbf{R}} = 0. \tag{4–26}$$

The most important applications will be to cases where Q is at rest, or where Q is the center of mass. If we also assume that the total internal torque vanishes:

$$\sum_{k=1}^{N} (\mathbf{r}_k - \mathbf{r}_Q) \times \mathbf{F}_k^i = 0, \tag{4–27}$$

then Eq. (4–25) becomes

$$\frac{d\mathbf{L}_Q}{dt} = \mathbf{N}_Q. \tag{4–28}$$

This is the angular momentum theorem for a system of particles. An immediate corollary is the conservation theorem for angular momentum, which states that the total angular momentum of a system of particles is constant if there is no external torque on the system.

In order to prove Eq. (4–27) from Newton's third law, we need to assume a stronger version of the law than that needed in the preceding section, namely, that the force $\mathbf{F}_{k \to l}^i$ is not only equal and opposite to $\mathbf{F}_{l \to k}^i$, but that these forces act along the line joining the two particles, that is, the two particles can only attract or repel each other. We shall assume, as in the previous section, that $\mathbf{F}_k^i$ is the sum of forces due to each of the other particles:

$$\sum_{k=1}^{N} (\mathbf{r}_k - \mathbf{r}_Q) \times \mathbf{F}_k^i = \sum_{k=1}^{N} \sum_{l \neq k} (\mathbf{r}_k - \mathbf{r}_Q) \times \mathbf{F}_{l \to k}^i$$

$$= \sum_{k=1}^{N} \sum_{l=1}^{k-1} [(\mathbf{r}_k - \mathbf{r}_Q) \times \mathbf{F}_{l \to k}^i + (\mathbf{r}_l - \mathbf{r}_Q) \times \mathbf{F}_{k \to l}^i]. \tag{4–29}$$

In the second step, the sum of torques has been rearranged as a sum of pairs of torques due to pairs of forces which, according to Newton's third law, are equal and opposite [Eq. (4–9)], so that

$$\sum_{k=1}^{N} (\mathbf{r}_k - \mathbf{r}_Q) \times \mathbf{F}_k^i = \sum_{k=1}^{N} \sum_{l=1}^{k-1} [(\mathbf{r}_k - \mathbf{r}_Q) - (\mathbf{r}_l - \mathbf{r}_Q)] \times \mathbf{F}_{l \to k}^i$$

$$= \sum_{k=1}^{N} \sum_{l=1}^{k-1} (\mathbf{r}_k - \mathbf{r}_l) \times \mathbf{F}_{l \to k}^i. \tag{4–30}$$

The vector $(\mathbf{r}_k - \mathbf{r}_l)$ has the direction of the line joining particle l with particle k. If $\mathbf{F}_{l \to k}^i$ acts along this line, the cross product in Eq. (4–30) vanishes. Hence if we assume Newton's third law in the strong form, then assumption (4–27) can be proved.

Alternatively, by assuming that no net work is done by the internal forces in a small virtual rotation about any axis through the point Q, we can show that the component of total internal torque in any direction is zero, and hence justify Eq. (4–27).

As an application of Eq. (4–28), we consider the action of a gyroscope or top. A gyroscope is a rigid system of particles symmetrical about an axis and rotating about that axis. The reader can convince himself that when the gyroscope is rotating about a fixed axis, the angular momentum vector of the gyroscope about a point Q on the axis of rotation is directed along the axis of rotation, as in Fig. 4–1. The symmetry about the axis guarantees that any component of the angular momentum $\mathbf{L}_k$ of particle k that is perpendicular to the axis, will be compensated by an equal and opposite component due to the diametrically opposite particle. Let us choose the point Q where the gyroscope axis rests on its support. If now a force $\mathbf{F}$ is applied downward on the gyroscope axis (e.g., the force of gravity), the torque $(\mathbf{r} \times \mathbf{F})$ due to $\mathbf{F}$ will be directed perpendicular to $\mathbf{r}$ and to $\mathbf{L}$, as shown in Fig. 4–1. By Eq. (4–28) the vector $d\mathbf{L}/dt$ is in the same direction, as shown in the figure, and the vector $\mathbf{L}$ tends to precess around the figure in a cone under the action of the force $\mathbf{F}$. Now the statement that $\mathbf{L}$ is directed along the gyroscope axis is strictly true only if the gyroscope is simply rotating about its axis. If the gyroscope axis itself is changing its direction, then this latter motion will contribute an additional component of angular momentum. If, however, the gyroscope is spinning very rapidly, then the component of angular momentum along its axis will be much greater than the component due to the motion of the

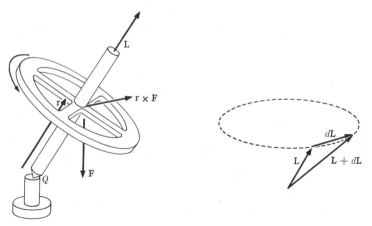

FIG. 4–1. Motion of a simple gyroscope.

axis, and **L** will be very nearly parallel to the gyroscope axis. Therefore the gyroscope axis must also precess around the vertical, remaining essentially parallel to **L**. A careful analysis of the off-axis components of **L** shows that, if the gyroscope axis is initially stationary in a certain direction and is released, it will wobble slightly down and up as it precesses around the vertical. The gyroscope does not "resist any change in its direction," as is sometimes asserted, for the rate of change in its angular momentum is always equal to the applied torque, just as the rate of change of linear momentum is always equal to the applied force. We can make the gyroscope turn in any direction we please by applying the appropriate torque. The importance of the gyroscope as a directional stabilizer arises from the fact that the angular momentum vector **L** remains constant when no torque is applied. The changes in direction of a well-made gyroscope are small because the applied torques are small and **L** is very large, so that a small $d\mathbf{L}$ gives no appreciable change in direction. Furthermore, a gyroscope only changes direction while a torque is applied; if it shifts slightly due to occasional small frictional torques in its mountings, it stops shifting when the torque stops. A large nonrotating mass, if mounted like a gyroscope, would acquire only small angular velocities due to frictional torques, but once set in motion by a small torque, it would continue to rotate, and the change in position might eventually become large.

4–3 Conservation of energy. In many cases, the total force acting on any particle in a system of particles depends only on the positions of the particles in the system:

$$\mathbf{F}_k = \mathbf{F}_k(\mathbf{r}_1, \mathbf{r}_2, \ldots, \mathbf{r}_N), \quad k = 1, 2, \ldots, N. \tag{4–31}$$

The external force $\mathbf{F}_k^e$, for example, might depend on the position $\mathbf{r}_k$ of particle k, and the internal force $\mathbf{F}_k^i$ might depend on the positions of the other particles relative to particle k. It may be that a potential function $V(\mathbf{r}_1, \mathbf{r}_2, \ldots, \mathbf{r}_N)$ exists such that

$$F_{kx} = -\frac{\partial V}{\partial x_k}, \quad F_{ky} = -\frac{\partial V}{\partial y_k}, \quad F_{kz} = -\frac{\partial V}{\partial z_k}, \quad k = 1, \ldots, N. \tag{4–32}$$

Conditions to be satisfied by the force functions $\mathbf{F}_k(\mathbf{r}_1, \ldots, \mathbf{r}_k)$ in order for a potential V to exist can be worked out, analogous to the condition (3–189) for a single particle. The result is rather unwieldy and of little practical importance, and we omit this development here. If a potential energy exists, we can derive a conservation of energy theorem as follows. By Eq. (4–32), the equations of motion of the kth particle are

$$m_k \frac{dv_{kx}}{dt} = -\frac{\partial V}{\partial x_k}, \quad m_k \frac{dv_{ky}}{dt} = -\frac{\partial V}{\partial y_k}, \quad m_k \frac{dv_{kz}}{dt} = -\frac{\partial V}{\partial z_k}. \tag{4–33}$$

Multiplying Eqs. (4–33) by v_{kx}, v_{ky}, v_{kz}, respectively, and adding, we have for each k:

$$\frac{d}{dt}\left(\tfrac{1}{2}m_k v_k^2\right) + \frac{\partial V}{\partial x_k}\frac{dx_k}{dt} + \frac{\partial V}{\partial y_k}\frac{dy_k}{dt} + \frac{\partial V}{\partial z_k}\frac{dz_k}{dt} = 0, \quad k = 1, \ldots, N. \quad (4\text{–}34)$$

This is to be summed over all values of k:

$$\frac{d}{dt}\sum_{k=1}^{N}\left(\tfrac{1}{2}m_k v_k^2\right) + \sum_{k=1}^{N}\left(\frac{\partial V}{\partial x_k}\frac{dx_k}{dt} + \frac{\partial V}{\partial y_k}\frac{dy_k}{dt} + \frac{\partial V}{\partial z_k}\frac{dz_k}{dt}\right) = 0. \quad (4\text{–}35)$$

The second term in Eq. (4–35) is dV/dt:

$$\frac{dV}{dt} = \sum_{k=1}^{N}\left(\frac{\partial V}{\partial x_k}\frac{dx_k}{dt} + \frac{\partial V}{\partial y_k}\frac{dy_k}{dt} + \frac{\partial V}{\partial z_k}\frac{dz_k}{dt}\right), \quad (4\text{–}36)$$

and the first term is the time derivative of the total kinetic energy

$$T = \sum_{k=1}^{N}\tfrac{1}{2}m_k v_k^2. \quad (4\text{–}37)$$

Consequently, Eq. (4–35) can be written

$$\frac{d}{dt}(T + V) = 0. \quad (4\text{–}38)$$

Hence we again have a conservation of energy theorem,

$$T + V = E, \quad (4\text{–}39)$$

where E is constant. If the internal forces are derivable from a potential energy function V, as in Eq. (4–32), but the external forces are not, the energy theorem will be

$$\frac{d}{dt}(T + V) = \sum_{k=1}^{N}\mathbf{F}_k^e \cdot \mathbf{v}_k. \quad (4\text{–}40)$$

Suppose the internal force acting on any particle k can be regarded as the sum of forces due to each of the other particles, where the force $\mathbf{F}_{l \to k}^i$ on k due to l depends only on the relative position $(\mathbf{r}_k - \mathbf{r}_l)$ of particle k with respect to particle l:

$$\mathbf{F}_k^i = \sum_{l \ne k}\mathbf{F}_{l \to k}^i(\mathbf{r}_k - \mathbf{r}_l). \quad (4\text{–}41)$$

It may be that the vector function $\mathbf{F}_{l \to k}^i(\mathbf{r}_k - \mathbf{r}_l)$ is such that we can define a potential energy function

$$V_{kl}(\mathbf{r}_{kl}) = -\int_{\mathbf{r}_s}^{\mathbf{r}_{kl}}\mathbf{F}_{l \to k}^i(\mathbf{r}_{kl}) \cdot d\mathbf{r}_{kl}, \quad (4\text{–}42)$$

where

$$\mathbf{r}_{kl} = \mathbf{r}_k - \mathbf{r}_l. \quad (4\text{–}43)$$

This will be true if $\mathbf{F}^t_{l \to k}$ is a conservative force in the sense of Chapter 3, that is, if

$$\text{curl } \mathbf{F}^t_{l \to k} = \mathbf{0}, \tag{4-44}$$

where the derivatives are with respect to x_{kl}, y_{kl}, z_{kl}. The gravitational and electrostatic forces between pairs of particles are examples of conservative forces. If $\mathbf{F}^t_{l \to k}$ is conservative, so that V_{kl} can be defined, then[*]

$$\mathbf{F}^t_{l \to k} = -\mathbf{i} \frac{\partial V_{kl}}{\partial x_{kl}} - \mathbf{j} \frac{\partial V_{kl}}{\partial y_{kl}} - \mathbf{k} \frac{\partial V_{kl}}{\partial z_{kl}}$$

$$= -\mathbf{i} \frac{\partial V_{kl}}{\partial x_k} - \mathbf{j} \frac{\partial V_{kl}}{\partial y_k} - \mathbf{k} \frac{\partial V_{kl}}{\partial z_k}. \tag{4-45}$$

If Newton's third law (weak form) holds, then

$$\mathbf{F}^t_{k \to l} = -\mathbf{F}^t_{l \to k} = \mathbf{i} \frac{\partial V_{kl}}{\partial x_{kl}} + \mathbf{j} \frac{\partial V_{kl}}{\partial y_{kl}} + \mathbf{k} \frac{\partial V_{kl}}{\partial z_{kl}}$$

$$= -\mathbf{i} \frac{\partial V_{kl}}{\partial x_l} - \mathbf{j} \frac{\partial V_{kl}}{\partial y_l} - \mathbf{k} \frac{\partial V_{kl}}{\partial z_l}. \tag{4-46}$$

Thus V_{kl} will also serve as the potential energy function for the force $\mathbf{F}^t_{k \to l}$. We can now define the total internal potential energy V^i for the system of particles as the sum of V_{kl} over all the pairs of particles:

$$V^i(\mathbf{r}_1, \ldots, \mathbf{r}_N) = \sum_{k=1}^{N} \sum_{l=1}^{k-1} V_{kl}(\mathbf{r}_k - \mathbf{r}_l). \tag{4-47}$$

It follows from Eqs. (4-41), (4-45), and (4-46), that the internal forces are given by

$$\mathbf{F}^t_k = -\mathbf{i} \frac{\partial V^i}{\partial x_k} - \mathbf{j} \frac{\partial V^i}{\partial y_k} - \mathbf{k} \frac{\partial V^i}{\partial z_k}, \quad k = 1, \ldots, N. \tag{4-48}$$

In particular, if the forces between pairs of particles are central forces, the potential energy $V_{kl}(\mathbf{r}_{kl})$ for each pair of particles depends only on the distance r_{kl} between them, and is given by Eq. (3-200); the internal forces of the system are then conservative, and Eq. (4-48) holds. The energy theorem (4-40) will be valid for such a system of particles. If the external forces are also conservative, their potential energy can be added to V^i, and the total energy is constant.

If there is internal friction, as is often the case, the internal frictional forces depend on the relative velocities of the particles, and the conservation law of potential plus kinetic energy no longer holds.

4-4 Critique of the conservation laws. We may divide the phenomena to which the laws of mechanics have been applied into three major classes. The motions of celestial bodies — stars, satellites, planets — are described

---

[*] Note that $V(\mathbf{r}_{kl}) = V(x_{kl}, y_{kl}, z_{kl}) = V(x_k - x_l,\ y_k - y_l,\ z_k - z_l)$, so that $\partial V/\partial x_k = \partial V/\partial x_{kl} = -\partial V/\partial x_l$, etc.

with extremely great precision by the laws of classical mechanics. It was in this field that the theory had many of its important early successes. The motions of the bodies in the solar system can be predicted with great accuracy for periods of thousands of years. The theory of relativity predicts a few slight deviations from the classically predicted motion, but these are too small to be observed except in the case of the orbit of Mercury, where relativity and observation agree in showing a slow precession of the axis of the elliptical orbit around the sun at an angular velocity of about 0.01 degree per century.

The motion of terrestrial bodies of macroscopic and microscopic size constitutes the second major division of phenomena. Motions in this class are properly described by Newtonian mechanics, without any significant corrections, but the laws of force are usually very complicated, and often not precisely known, so that the beautifully precise calculations of celestial mechanics cannot be duplicated here.

The third class of phenomena is the motion of "atomic" particles: molecules, atoms, electrons, nuclei, protons, neutrons, etc. Early attempts to describe the motions of such particles were based on classical mechanics, and many phenomena in this class can be understood and predicted on this basis. However, the finer details of the behavior of atomic particles can only be properly described in terms of quantum mechanics and, for high velocities, relativistic quantum mechanics must be introduced. We might add a fourth class of phenomena, having to do with the intrinsic structure of the elementary particles themselves (protons, neutrons, electrons, etc.). Even quantum mechanics fails to describe such phenomena correctly, and physics is now struggling to produce a new theory which will describe this class of phenomena.

The conservation law for linear momentum holds for systems of celestial bodies, as well as for bodies of macroscopic and microscopic size. The gravitational and mechanical forces acting between such bodies satisfy Newton's third law, at least to a high degree of precision. Linear momentum is also conserved in most interactions of particles of atomic size, except when high velocities or rapid accelerations are involved. The electrostatic forces between electric charges at rest satisfy Newton's third law, but when the charges are in motion, their electric fields propagate with the velocity of light, so that if two charges are in rapid relative motion, the forces between them may not at any instant be exactly equal and opposite. If a fast electron moves past a stationary proton, the proton "sees" the electron always a little behind its actual position at any instant, and the force on the proton is determined, not by where the electron is, but by where it was a moment earlier. When electric charges accelerate, they may emit electromagnetic radiation and lose momentum in so doing. It turns out that the law of conservation of momentum can be preserved also in such cases, but only by associating momentum with the electromagnetic field as well as with moving particles.   Such a redefinition of momentum goes beyond the original limits of Newtonian mechanics.

Celestial bodies and bodies of macroscopic or microscopic size are obviously not really particles, since they have a structure which for many purposes is not adequately represented by merely giving to the body three position coordinates x,y,z.   Nevertheless, the motion of such bodies, in problems where their structure can be neglected, is correctly represented by the law of motion of a single particle,

$$m\ddot{\mathbf{r}} = \mathbf{F}. \tag{4–49}$$

This is often justified by regarding the macroscopic body as a system of smaller particles satisfying Newton's third law.   For such a system, the linear momentum theorem holds, and can be written in the form of Eq. (4–18), which has the same form as Eq. (4–49).   This is a very convenient way of justifying the application of Eq. (4–49) to bodies of macroscopic or astronomical size, provided our conscience is not troubled by the fact that according to modern ideas it does not make sense.   If the particles of which the larger body is composed are taken as atoms and molecules, then in the first place Newton's third law does not invariably hold for such particles, and in the second place we should apply quantum mechanics, not classical mechanics, to their motion.   The momentum theorem (4–18) can be derived for bodies made up of atoms by using the laws of electrodynamics and quantum mechanics, but this lies outside the scope of Newtonian mechanics.   Hence, for the present, we must take the law of motion (4–49), as applied to macroscopic and astronomical bodies, as a fundamental postulate in itself, whose justification is based on experimental grounds or on the results of deeper theories.   The theorems proved in Section 4–1 show that this postulate gives a consistent theory of mechanics in the sense that if, from bodies satisfying this postulate, we construct a composite body, the latter body will also satisfy the postulate.

The law of conservation of angular momentum, as formulated in Section 4–2 for a system of particles, holds for systems of celestial bodies (regarded as particles) and for systems of bodies of macroscopic size whenever effects due to rotation of the individual bodies can be neglected. When rotations of the individual bodies enter into the motion, then a conservation law for angular momentum still holds, provided we include the angular momentum associated with such rotations; the bodies are then no longer regarded as particles of the simple type considered in the preceding sections whose motions are completely described simply by specifying the function $\mathbf{r}(t)$ for each particle.   The total angular momentum of the solar system is very nearly constant, even if the sun, planets, and satellites are regarded as simple particles whose rotations can be neglected. Tidal forces, however, convert some rotational angular momentum into orbital angular momentum of the planets and satellites, and so rotational angular momentum must be included if the law of conservation of angular momentum is to hold precisely here.   Some change in angular momentum occurs due to friction with interplanetary dust and rocks, but the effect is too small to be observed, and could in any case be included by adding the angular momentum of the interplanetary matter to the total.

The law of conservation of total angular momentum, including rotation, of astronomical and terrestrial bodies can be justified by regarding each body as a system of smaller particles whose mutual forces satisfy Newton's third law (strong form).   The argument of Section 4–2 then gives the law of conservation of total angular momentum, the rotational angular momentum of a body appearing as ordinary orbital angular momentum ($\mathbf{r} \times \mathbf{p}$) of the particles of which it is composed.   This argument is subject to the same criticism as applied above to the case of linear momentum.   If the "particles" of which a body is composed are atoms and molecules, then Newton's third law does not always hold, particularly in its strong form; moreover, the laws of quantum mechanics apply to such particles; and in addition atoms and molecules also possess rotational angular momentum which must be taken into account.   Even the elementary particles — electrons, protons, neutrons, etc. — possess an intrinsic angular momentum which is not associated with their orbital motion.   This angular momentum is called *spin* angular momentum from its analogy with the intrinsic angular momentum of rotation of a macroscopic body, and must be included if the total is to satisfy a conservation law.   Thus we never arrive at the ideal simple particle of Newtonian mechanics, described by its position $\mathbf{r}(t)$ alone. We are left with the choice of accepting the conservation law of angular momentum as a basic postulate, or appealing for its justification to theories which go beyond classical mechanics.

The gravitational forces acting between astronomical bodies are conservative, so that the principle of conservation of mechanical energy holds very accurately in astronomy.   In principle, there is a small loss of mechanical energy in the solar system due to friction with interplanetary dust and rocks, but the effect is too small to produce any observable effects on planetary motion, even with the high precision with which astronomical events are predicted and observed.   There is also a very gradual but measurable loss of rotational energy of planets and satellites due to tidal friction.   For terrestrial bodies of macroscopic or microscopic size, friction usually plays an important part, and only in certain special cases where friction may be neglected can the principle of conservation of energy in the form (4–39) or even (4–40) be applied.   However, it was discovered by Joule that we can associate energy with heat in such a way that the law of conservation of energy of a system of bodies still applies to the total kinetic plus potential plus heat energy.   If we regard a body as composed of atoms and molecules, its heat energy turns out to be kinetic and potential energy of random motion of its atoms and molecules.   The electromagnetic forces on moving charged particles are not conservative, and an electromagnetic energy must be associated with the electromagnetic field in order to preserve the conservation law of energy. Such extensions of the concept of energy to include heat and electromagnetic energy are, of course, outside the domain of mechanics. When the definition of energy is suitably extended to include not only kinetic energy, but energy associated with the electromagnetic fields and any other force fields which may act, then a law of conservation of energy holds quite generally, in classical, relativistic, and quantum physics.

The conservation laws of energy, momentum, and angular momentum are the cornerstones of present-day physics, being generally valid in all physical theories. It seems at present an idle exercise to attempt to prove them for material bodies within the framework of classical mechanics by appealing to an outmoded picture of matter as made up of simple Newtonian particles exerting central forces upon one another. The conservation laws are in a sense not laws at all, but postulates which we insist must hold in any physical theory. If, for example, for moving charged particles, we find that the total energy, defined as $(T + V)$, is not constant, we do not abandon the law, but change its meaning by redefining energy to include electromagnetic energy in such a way as to preserve the law. We prefer always to look for quantities which are conserved, and agree to apply the names "total energy," "total momentum," "total angular momentum" only to such quantities. The conservation of these quantities is then not a physical fact, but a consequence of our determination to define them in this way. It is, of course, a statement of physical fact, which may or may not be true, to assert that such definitions of energy, momentum, and angular momentum can always be found. So far this assertion has proved true.

4-5 Rockets, conveyor belts, and planets. There are many problems that can be solved by appropriate applications of the conservation laws of linear momentum, angular momentum, and energy. In solving such problems, it is necessary to decide which conservation laws are appropriate. The conservation laws of linear and angular momentum or, rather, the theorems (4-7) and (4-28) of which they are corollaries, are always applicable to any physical system provided all external forces and torques are taken into account, and application of one or the other is appropriate whenever the external forces or torques are known. The law of conservation of kinetic plus potential energy is applicable only when there is no conversion of mechanical energy into other forms of energy. We cannot use the law of conservation of energy when there is friction, for example, unless there is a way to determine the amount of heat energy produced.

The conservation laws of energy, momentum, and angular momentum refer always to a definite fixed system of particles. In applying the conservation laws, care must be taken to decide just how much is included in the system to which they are to be applied, and to include all the energy and momentum of this system in writing down the equations. One may choose the system arbitrarily, including and excluding whatever particles may be convenient, but if any forces act from outside the system on particles in the system, these must be taken into account.

A typical problem in which the law of conservation of linear momentum is applicable is the conveyor belt problem. Material is dropped continuously from a hopper onto a moving belt, and it is required to find the force F required to keep the belt moving at constant velocity v (Fig. 4–2). Let the rate at which mass is dropped on the belt be dm/dt. If m is the mass of material on the belt, and M is the mass of the belt (which really does not figure in the problem), the total momentum of the system, belt plus material on the belt and in the hopper, is

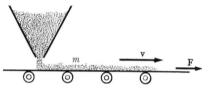

Fig. 4–2. A conveyor belt.

$$P = (m + M)v. \quad (4\text{–}50)$$

We assume that the hopper is at rest; otherwise the momentum of the hopper and its contents must be included in Eq. (4–50). The linear momentum theorem requires that

$$F = \frac{dP}{dt} = v\,\frac{dm}{dt}. \quad (4\text{–}51)$$

This gives the force applied to the belt. The power supplied by the force is

$$Fv = v^2\,\frac{dm}{dt} = \frac{d}{dt}\,(mv^2) = \frac{d}{dt}\,[(m + M)v^2]. \quad (4\text{–}52)$$

This is twice the rate at which the kinetic energy is increasing, so that the conservation theorem of mechanical energy (4–40) does not apply here. Where is the excess half of the power going?

The equation of motion of a rocket can be obtained from the law of conservation of momentum. Let the mass of the rocket at any given instant be M, and let its speed be $\mathbf{v}$ relative to some fixed coordinate system. If material is shot out of the rocket motor with an exhaust velocity $\mathbf{u}$ relative to the rocket, the velocity of the exhaust relative to the fixed coordinate system is $\mathbf{v} + \mathbf{u}$. If an external force $\mathbf{F}$ also acts on the rocket, then the linear momentum theorem reads in this case:

$$\frac{d}{dt}\,(M\mathbf{v}) - (\mathbf{v} + \mathbf{u})\,\frac{dM}{dt} = \mathbf{F}. \quad (4\text{–}53)$$

The first term is the time rate of change of momentum of the rocket. The second term represents the rate at which momentum is appearing in the rocket exhaust, where $-(dM/dt)$ is the rate at which matter is being exhausted. The conservation law applies to a definite fixed system of particles. If we fix our attention on the rocket at any moment, we must remember that at a time dt later this system will comprise the rocket plus the material exhausted from the rocket during that time, and both must be considered in computing the change in momentum. The equation can be rewritten:

$$M \frac{d\mathbf{v}}{dt} = \mathbf{u} \frac{dM}{dt} + \mathbf{F}. \tag{4–54}$$

The first term on the right is called the thrust of the rocket motor. Since dM/dt is negative, the thrust is opposite in direction to the exhaust velocity. The force $\mathbf{F}$ may represent air resistance, or a gravitational force. Let us solve this equation for the special case where there is no external force:

$$M \frac{d\mathbf{v}}{dt} = \mathbf{u} \frac{dM}{dt}. \tag{4–55}$$

We multiply by dt/M and integrate, assuming that $\mathbf{u}$ is constant:

$$\mathbf{v} - \mathbf{v}_0 = -\mathbf{u} \ln \frac{M_0}{M}. \tag{4–56}$$

The change of speed in any interval of time depends only on the exhaust velocity and on the fraction of mass exhausted during that time interval. This result is independent of any assumption as to the rate at which mass is exhausted.

Problems in which the law of conservation of angular momentum is useful turn up frequently in astronomy. The angular momentum of the galaxy of stars, or of the solar system, remains constant during the course of its development provided no material is ejected from the system. The effect of lunar tides is gradually to slow down the rotation of the earth. As the angular momentum of the rotating earth decreases, the angular momentum of the moon must increase. The magnitude of the (orbital) angular momentum of the moon is

$$L = mr^2\omega, \tag{4–57}$$

where m is the mass, ω is the angular velocity, and r is the radius of the orbit of the moon. We can equate the mass times the centripetal acceleration to the gravitational force, to obtain the relation

$$mr\omega^2 = \frac{GMm}{r^2}, \tag{4–58}$$

where M is the mass of the earth. Solving this equation for ω and substituting in Eq. (4–57), we obtain

$$L = (GMm^2r)^{\frac{1}{2}}. \tag{4–59}$$

Therefore, as the moon's angular momentum increases, it moves farther away from the earth. (In attempting to determine the rate of recession of the moon by equating the change of L to the change of the earth's rotational angular momentum, it would be necessary to determine how much of the slowing down of the earth's rotation by tidal friction is due to the moon and how much to the sun. The angular momentum of the moon plus the rotational angular momentum of the earth is not constant because of the tidal friction due to the sun. The total angular momentum of the earth-moon system about the sun is very nearly constant except for the very small effect of tides raised on the sun by the earth.)

4–6 Collision problems. Many questions concerning collisions of particles can be answered by applying the conservation laws. Since the conservation laws are valid also in quantum mechanics,* results obtained with their use are valid for particles of atomic and subatomic size, as well as for macroscopic particles. In most collision problems, the colliding particles are moving at constant velocity, free of any force, for some time before and after the collision, while during the collision they are under the action of the forces which they exert on one another. If the mutual forces during the collision satisfy Newton's third law, then the total linear momentum of the particles is the same before and after the collision. If Newton's third law holds in the strong form, the total angular momentum is conserved also. If the forces are conservative, kinetic energy is conserved (since the potential energy before and after the collision is the same). In any case, the conservation laws are always valid if we take into account all the energy, momentum, and angular momentum, including that associated with any radiation which may be emitted and including any energy which is converted from kinetic energy into other forms, or vice versa.

We consider first a collision between two particles, 1 and 2, in which the total kinetic energy and linear momentum are known to be conserved. Such a collision is said to be *elastic*. If we designate by subscripts 1 and 2 the two particles, and by subscripts I and F the values of kinetic energy and momentum before and after the collision respectively, the conservation laws require

$$\mathbf{p}_{1I} + \mathbf{p}_{2I} = \mathbf{p}_{1F} + \mathbf{p}_{2F}, \qquad (4\text{--}60)$$

$$T_{1I} + T_{2I} = T_{1F} + T_{2F}. \qquad (4\text{--}61)$$

Equation (4–61) can be rewritten in terms of the momenta and masses of the particles:

$$\frac{p_{1I}^2}{2m_1} + \frac{p_{2I}^2}{2m_2} = \frac{p_{1F}^2}{2m_1} + \frac{p_{2F}^2}{2m_2}. \qquad (4\text{--}62)$$

---

* P. A. M. Dirac, *The Principles of Quantum Mechanics*, 3rd ed. Oxford: Oxford University Press, 1947. (Page 115.)

To specify any momentum vector **p**, we must specify three quantities, which may be either its three components along any set of axes, or its magnitude and direction (the latter specified perhaps by spherical angles θ,φ). Thus Eqs. (4–60) and (4–62) represent four equations involving the ratio of the two masses and twelve quantities required to specify the momenta involved. If nine of these quantities are given, the equations can be solved for the remaining four. In a typical case, we might be given the masses and initial momenta of the two particles, and the final direction of motion of one of the particles, say particle 1. We could then find the final momentum **p**$_{2F}$ of particle 2, and the magnitude of the final momentum **p**$_{1F}$ (or equivalently, the energy) of particle 1. In many important cases, the mass of one of the particles is unknown, and can be computed from Eqs. (4–60) and (4–62) if enough is known about the momenta and energies before and after the collision. Note that the initial conditions alone are not enough to determine the outcome of the collision from Eqs. (4–60) and (4–62); we must know something about the motion after the collision. The initial conditions alone would determine the outcome if we could solve the equations of motion of the system.

Consider a collision of a particle of mass m_1, momentum **p**$_{1I}$, with a particle of mass m_2 at rest. This is a common case. (There is actually no loss of generality in this problem, since, as we pointed out in Section 1–4 and will show in Section 7–1, if m_2 is initially moving with a uniform velocity **v**$_{2I}$, Newton's laws are equally applicable in a coordinate system moving with uniform velocity $-$**v**$_{2I}$, in which m_2 is initially at rest.) Let m_1 be "scattered" through an angle ϑ_1, that is, let ϑ_1 be the angle between its final and its initial direction of motion (Fig. 4–3). The momentum **p**$_{2F}$ must lie in the same plane as **p**$_{1I}$ and **p**$_{1F}$, since there is no component of momentum perpendicular to this plane before the collision, and there must be none after. Let **p**$_{2F}$ make an angle ϑ_2 with the direction of **p**$_{1I}$. We write out Eq. (4–60) in components along and perpendicular to **p**$_{1I}$:

$$p_{1I} = p_{1F} \cos \vartheta_1 + p_{2F} \cos \vartheta_2, \qquad (4\text{–}63)$$
$$0 = p_{1F} \sin\vartheta_1 - p_{2F} \sin \vartheta_2. \qquad (4\text{–}64)$$

Equation (4–62) becomes, in the present case,

$$\frac{p_{1I}^2 - p_{1F}^2}{m_1} = \frac{p_{2F}^2}{m_2}. \qquad (4\text{–}65)$$

If two of the quantities

$$(p_{1F}/p_{1I}, p_{2F}/p_{1I}, \vartheta_1, \vartheta_2, m_1/m_2)$$

are known, the remaining three can be found. If the masses, the initial momentum p_{1I}, and the angle ϑ_1

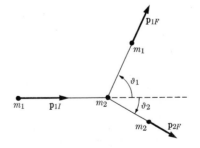

Fig. 4–3. Collision of particle m_1 with particle m_2 at rest.

are known, for example, we can solve for $p_{1F}, p_{2F}, \vartheta_2$ as follows. Transposing the first term on the right to the left side in Eqs. (4–63) and (4–64), squaring, and adding, we eliminate ϑ_2:

$$p_{1I}^2 + p_{1F}^2 - 2p_{1I}p_{1F} \cos \vartheta_1 = p_{2F}^2. \qquad (4\text{–}66)$$

After substituting this in Eq. (4–65), we can solve for p_{1F}:

$$\frac{p_{1F}}{p_{1I}} = \frac{m_1}{m_1 + m_2} \cos \vartheta_1 \pm \left[\left(\frac{m_1}{m_1 + m_2} \right)^2 \cos^2 \vartheta_1 + \frac{m_2 - m_1}{m_1 + m_2} \right]^{\frac{1}{2}}, \quad (4\text{–}67)$$

and p_{2F} can now be found from Eq. (4–66), and ϑ_2 from Eq. (4–63). If $m_1 > m_2$, the quantity under the radical is zero for $\vartheta_1 = \vartheta_m$, where ϑ_m is given by

$$\cos^2 \vartheta_m = 1 - \frac{m_2^2}{m_1^2}, \quad 0 \le \vartheta_m \le \frac{\pi}{2}. \qquad (4\text{–}68)$$

If $\vartheta_1 > \vartheta_m$ (and $\vartheta_1 \le \pi$), then p_{1F}/p_{1I} is either imaginary or negative, neither of which is allowable physically, so that ϑ_m represents the maximum angle through which m_1 can be scattered. If $m_1 \gg m_2$, this angle is very small, as we know from experience. For $\vartheta_1 < \vartheta_m$, there are two values of p_{1F}/p_{1I}, the larger corresponding to a glancing collision, the smaller to a more nearly head-on collision; ϑ_2 will be different for these two cases. The case $\vartheta_1 = 0$ may represent either no collision at all ($p_{1F} = p_{1I}$) or a head-on collision. In the latter case,

$$\frac{p_{1F}}{p_{1I}} = \frac{m_1 - m_2}{m_1 + m_2},$$
$$\vartheta_2 = 0, \qquad (4\text{–}69)$$
$$\frac{p_{2F}}{p_{1I}} = \frac{2m_2}{m_1 + m_2}.$$

If $m_1 = m_2$, Eqs. (4–67), (4–66), and (4–64) reduce to

$$\frac{p_{1F}}{p_{1I}} = \cos \vartheta_1,$$
$$\frac{p_{2F}}{p_{1I}} = \sin \vartheta_1, \qquad (4\text{–}70)$$
$$\vartheta_2 = \left(\frac{\pi}{2} - \vartheta_1 \right).$$

ϑ_1 now varies from $\vartheta_1 = 0$ for no collision to $\vartheta_1 = \pi/2$ for a head-on collision in which the entire momentum is transferred to particle 2. (Actually, ϑ_1 is undefined if $p_{1F} = 0$, but $\vartheta_1 \to \pi/2$ and $p_{1F} \to 0$ as the collision approaches a head-on collision.) If $m_1 < m_2$, all values of ϑ_1 from 0 to π are possible, and give a positive value for p_{1F}/p_{1I} if the plus sign is chosen in Eq. (4–67). The minus sign cannot be chosen, since it leads to a negative value for p_{1F}/p_{1I}.   If $\vartheta_1 = 0$, then $p_{1F} = p_{1I}$; this is the case when there is no collision.   The case $\vartheta_1 = \pi$ corresponds to a head-on collision, for which

$$
\begin{aligned}
\frac{p_{1F}}{p_{1I}} &= \frac{m_2 - m_1}{m_1 + m_2}, \quad \vartheta_1 = \pi, \\
\frac{p_{2F}}{p_{1I}} &= \frac{2m_2}{m_1 + m_2}, \quad \vartheta_2 = 0.
\end{aligned}
\tag{4-71}
$$

If m_1 is unknown, but either p_{1I} or T_{1I} can be measured or calculated, observation of the final momentum of particle 2 (whose mass is assumed known) is sufficient to determine m_1.   As an example, if $T_{1I} = p_{1I}^2/2m_1$ is known, and T_{2F} is measured for a head-on collision, m_1 is given by Eq. (4-69) or (4-71):

$$
\frac{m_1}{m_2} = \frac{2T_{1I}}{T_{2F}} - 1 \pm \left[\left(\frac{2T_{1I}}{T_{2F}} - 1 \right)^2 - 1 \right]^{\frac{1}{2}}.
\tag{4-72}
$$

We thus determine m_1 to within one of two possible values.   If results for a collision with another particle of different mass m_2, or for a different scattering angle, are known, m_1 is determined uniquely.   Essentially this method was used by Chadwick to establish the existence of the neutron.*   Unknown neutral particles created in a nuclear reaction were allowed to impinge on matter containing various nuclei of known masses.   The energies of two kinds of nuclei of different masses m_2, m_2' projected forward by head-on collisions were measured.   By writing Eq. (4-72) for both cases, the unknown energy T_{1I} could be eliminated, and the mass m_1 was found to be practically equal to that of the proton.

We have seen that if we know the initial momenta of two colliding particles of known masses, and the angle of scattering ϑ_1 (or ϑ_2), all other quantities involved in the collision can be calculated from the conservation laws.   To predict the angles of scattering, we must know not only the initial momenta and the initial trajectories, but also the law of force between the particles.   An example is the collision of two particles acted on by a central inverse square law of force, to be treated in Section 4-8.   Such predictions can be made for collisions of macroscopic or astronomical bodies under suitable assumptions as to the law of force.   For atomic particles, which obey quantum mechanics, this cannot be done, although we can predict the probabilities of observing various angles ϑ_1 (or ϑ_2) for given initial conditions; that is, we can predict cross sections.   In all cases where energy is conserved, the relationships between energies, momenta, and angles of scattering developed above are valid except at particle velocities comparable with the velocity of light.   In the latter case, Eqs. (4-60), (4-61), (4-63), and (4-64) are still valid, but the relativistic relationships between mass, momentum, and energy must be used, instead of Eq. (4-62).

---

* J. Chadwick, *Nature*, **129**, 312 (1932).

We quote without proof the relation between mass, momentum, and energy as given by the theory of relativity:*

$$\frac{p^2}{2m} = T + \frac{T^2}{2mc^2},$$ (4–73)

where c is the speed of light, and m is the rest mass of the particle, that is, the mass when the particle is at rest. The relativistic relations between kinetic energy, momentum, and velocity are

$$T = mc^2 \left(\frac{1}{\sqrt{1 - \dfrac{v^2}{c^2}}} - 1 \right),$$ (4–74)

$$\mathbf{p} = \frac{m\mathbf{v}}{\sqrt{1 - \dfrac{v^2}{c^2}}},$$ (4–75)

which reduce to the classical relations (2–5) and (3–127), when $v \ll c$. Unless v is nearly equal to c, the second term on the right in Eq. (4–73) is much smaller than the first, and this equation reduces to the classical one. With the help of Eq. (4–73), the conservation laws can be applied to collisions involving velocities near the speed of light.

Atoms, molecules, and nuclei possess internal potential and kinetic energy associated with the motion of their parts, and may absorb or release energy on collision. Such inelastic collisions between atomic particles are said to be of the *first kind*, or *endoergic*, if kinetic energy of translational motion is absorbed, and of the *second kind*, or *exoergic*, if kinetic energy is released in the process. It may also happen that in an atomic or nuclear collision, the final particles after the collision are not the same as the initial particles before collision. For example, a proton may collide with a nucleus and be absorbed while a neutron is released and flies away. There are a great many possible types of such processes. Two particles may collide and stick together to form a single particle or, conversely, a single particle may suddenly break up into two particles which fly apart. Two particles may collide and form

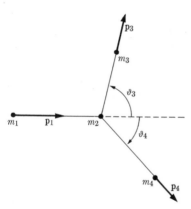

Fig. 4–4. Collision of m_1 with m_2 at rest, resulting in the production of m_3 and m_4.

* P. G. Bergmann, *Introduction to the Theory of Relativity*. New York: Prentice-Hall, 1946. (Chapter 6.)

two other particles which fly apart. Or three or more particles may be formed in the process and fly apart after the collision. In all these cases, the law of conservation of momentum holds, and the law of conservation of energy also if we take into account the internal energy of the atoms and molecules. We consider here a case in which a particle of mass m_1 collides with a particle of mass m_2 at rest (Fig. 4–4). Particles of masses m_3 and m_4 leave the scene of the collision at angles ϑ_3 and ϑ_4 with respect to the original direction of motion of m_1. Let kinetic energy Q be absorbed in the process ($Q > 0$ for an endoergic collision; $Q = 0$ for an elastic collision; $Q < 0$ for an exoergic collision). Then, applying the conservation laws of energy and momentum, we write

$$p_1 = p_3 \cos \vartheta_3 + p_4 \cos \vartheta_4, \tag{4–76}$$

$$0 = p_3 \sin \vartheta_3 - p_4 \sin \vartheta_4, \tag{4–77}$$

$$T_1 = T_3 + T_4 + Q. \tag{4–78}$$

Since kinetic energy can be expressed in terms of momentum, if the masses are known, we may find any three of the quantities $p_1, p_3, p_4, \vartheta_3, \vartheta_4, Q$ in terms of the other three. In many cases p_1 is known, p_3 and ϑ_3 are measured, and it is desired to calculate Q. By eliminating ϑ_4 from Eqs. (4–76) and (4–77), as in the previous example, we obtain

$$p_4^2 = p_1^2 + p_3^2 - 2p_1 p_3 \cos \vartheta_3. \tag{4–79}$$

This may now be substituted in Eq. (4–78) to give Q in terms of known quantities:

$$Q = T_1 - T_3 - T_4 = \frac{p_1^2}{2m_1} - \frac{p_3^2}{2m_3} - \frac{p_1^2 + p_3^2 - 2p_1 p_3 \cos \vartheta_3}{2m_4}, \tag{4–80}$$

or

$$Q = T_1 \left(1 - \frac{m_1}{m_4} \right) - T_3 \left(1 + \frac{m_3}{m_4} \right) + 2 \left(\frac{m_1 m_3 T_1 T_3}{m_4^2} \right)^{\frac{1}{2}} \cos \vartheta_3. \tag{4–81}$$

Every step up to the substitution for T_1, T_3, and T_4 is valid also for particles moving at velocities of the order of the velocity of light. At high velocities, the relativistic relation (4–73) between T and p should be used in the last step. Equation (4–81) is useful in obtaining Q for a nuclear reaction in which an incident particle m_1 of known energy collides with a nucleus m_2, with the result that a particle m_3 is emitted whose energy and direction of motion can be observed. Equation (4–81) allows us to determine Q from these known quantities, taking into account the effect of the slight recoil of the residual nucleus m_4, which is usually difficult to observe directly.

Collisions of inert macroscopic bodies are always inelastic and endoergic, kinetic energy being converted to heat by frictional forces during the impact. Kinetic energy of translation may also be converted into kinetic energy of rotation, and conversely. (Exchanges of rotational energy are included in Q in the previous analysis.) Such collisions range from the nearly elastic collisions of hard steel balls, to which the above analysis of elastic collisions applies when rotation is not involved, to completely inelastic collisions in which the two bodies stick together after the collision. Let us consider a completely inelastic collision in which a bullet of mass m_1, velocity $\mathbf{v}_1$ strikes and sticks in an object of mass m_2 at rest. Let the velocity of the two after the collision be $\mathbf{v}_2$. Evidently the conservation of momentum implies that $\mathbf{v}_2$ be in the same direction as $\mathbf{v}_1$, and we have:

$$m_1\mathbf{v}_1 = (m_1 + m_2)\mathbf{v}_2. \tag{4-82}$$

The velocity after the collision is

$$\mathbf{v}_2 = \frac{m_1}{m_1 + m_2}\mathbf{v}_1. \tag{4-83}$$

Energy is not conserved in such a collision. The amount of energy converted into heat is

$$Q = \tfrac{1}{2}m_1v_1^2 - \tfrac{1}{2}(m_1 + m_2)v_2^2 = \tfrac{1}{2}m_1v_1^2\left(\frac{m_2}{m_1 + m_2}\right). \tag{4-84}$$

In a head-on collision of two bodies in which rotation is not involved, it has been found experimentally that the ratio of relative velocity after impact to relative velocity before impact is a constant for any two bodies. Let bodies m_1, m_2, traveling with initial velocities v_{1I}, v_{2I} along the x-axis, collide and rebound along the same axis with velocities v_{1F}, v_{2F}. Then the experimental result is expressed by the equation

$$v_{2F} - v_{1F} = e(v_{1I} - v_{2I}), \tag{4-85}$$

where the constant e is called the *coefficient of restitution*, and has a value between 0 and 1. If $e = 1$, the collision is perfectly elastic; if $e = 0$, it is completely inelastic. Conservation of momentum yields, in any case,

$$m_1v_{1I} + m_2v_{2I} = m_1v_{1F} + m_2v_{2F}. \tag{4-86}$$

Equations (4-85) and (4-86) enable us to find the final velocities v_{1F} and v_{2F} for a head-on collision when the initial velocities are known.

4-7 The two-body problem. We consider in this section the motion of a system of two particles acted on by internal forces satisfying Newton's third law (weak form), and by no external forces, or by external forces satisfying a rather specialized condition to be introduced later. We shall find that this problem can be separated into two single-particle problems. The motion of the center of mass is governed by an equation (4-18) of the same form as that for a single particle. In addition, we shall find that the motion of either particle, with respect to the other as origin, is the same as the motion with respect to a fixed origin, of a single particle of suitably chosen mass acted on by the same internal force. This result will allow application of the results of Section 3-14 to cases where the motion of the attracting center cannot be neglected.

Let the two particles have masses m_1 and m_2, and let them be acted on by external forces $\mathbf{F}_1^e, \mathbf{F}_2^e$, and internal forces $\mathbf{F}_1^i, \mathbf{F}_2^i$ exerted by each particle on the other, and satisfying Newton's third law:

$$\mathbf{F}_1^i = -\mathbf{F}_2^i. \tag{4-87}$$

The equations of motion for the system are then

$$m_1\ddot{\mathbf{r}}_1 = \mathbf{F}_1^i + \mathbf{F}_1^e, \tag{4-88}$$
$$m_2\ddot{\mathbf{r}}_2 = \mathbf{F}_2^i + \mathbf{F}_2^e. \tag{4-89}$$

We now introduce a change of coordinates:

$$\mathbf{R} = \frac{m_1\mathbf{r}_1 + m_2\mathbf{r}_2}{m_1 + m_2}, \tag{4-90}$$

$$\mathbf{r} = \mathbf{r}_1 - \mathbf{r}_2. \tag{4-91}$$

The inverse transformation is

$$\mathbf{r}_1 = \mathbf{R} + \frac{m_2}{m_1 + m_2}\mathbf{r}, \tag{4-92}$$

$$\mathbf{r}_2 = \mathbf{R} - \frac{m_1}{m_1 + m_2}\mathbf{r}, \tag{4-93}$$

where $\mathbf{R}$ is the coordinate of the center of mass, and $\mathbf{r}$ is the relative coordinate of m_1 with respect to m_2. (See Fig. 4–5.) Adding Eqs. (4–88) and (4–89) and using Eq. (4–87), we obtain the equation of motion for $\mathbf{R}$:

$$(m_1 + m_2)\ddot{\mathbf{R}} = \mathbf{F}_1^e + \mathbf{F}_2^e. \tag{4-94}$$

Multiplying Eq. (4–89) by m_1, and subtracting from Eq. (4–88) multiplied by m_2, using Eq. (4–87), we obtain the equation of motion for $\mathbf{r}$:

$$m_1 m_2 \ddot{\mathbf{r}} = (m_1 + m_2)\mathbf{F}_1^i + m_1 m_2 \left(\frac{\mathbf{F}_1^e}{m_1} - \frac{\mathbf{F}_2^e}{m_2}\right). \tag{4-95}$$

We now assume that

$$\frac{\mathbf{F}_1^e}{m_1} = \frac{\mathbf{F}_2^e}{m_2}, \tag{4-96}$$

and introduce the abbreviations

$$M = m_1 + m_2, \tag{4-97}$$

$$\mu = \frac{m_1 m_2}{m_1 + m_2}, \tag{4-98}$$

$$\mathbf{F} = \mathbf{F}_1^e + \mathbf{F}_2^e. \tag{4-99}$$

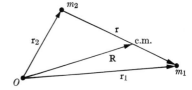

Fig. 4–5. Coordinates for the two-body problem.

Equations (4–94) and (4–95) then take the form of single-particle equations of motion:

$$M\ddot{\mathbf{R}} = \mathbf{F}, \tag{4-100}$$

$$\mu\ddot{\mathbf{r}} = \mathbf{F}_1^i. \tag{4-101}$$

Equation (4–100) is the familiar equation for the motion of the center of mass.   Equation (4–101) is the equation of motion for a particle of mass μ acted on by the internal force $\mathbf{F}_1^i$ which particle 2 exerts on particle 1. Thus the motion of particle 1 as viewed from particle 2 is the same as if particle 2 were fixed and particle 1 had a mass μ (μ is called the *reduced mass*).   If one particle is much heavier than the other, μ is slightly less than the mass of the lighter particle.   If the particles are of equal mass, μ is half the mass of either.   We may now apply the results of Section 3–14 to any two-body problem in which the two particles exert an inverse square law attraction or repulsion on each other, provided the external forces are either zero or are proportional to the masses, as required by Eq. (4–96).

Equation (4–96) is satisfied if the external forces are gravitational forces exerted by masses whose distances from the two bodies m_1 and m_2 are much greater than the distance r from m_1 to m_2.   As an example, the motion of the earth-moon system can be treated, to a good approximation, by the method of this section, since the moon is much closer to the earth than either is to the sun (or to the other planets).   Atomic particles are acted on by electrical forces proportional to their charges, and hence Eq. (4–96) holds ordinarily only if the external forces are zero.   There is also the less important case where the two particles have the same ratio of charge to mass, and are acted on by external forces due to distant charges.   We may remark here that although Eqs. (4–88) and (4–89) are not the correct equations for describing the motions of atomic particles, the introduction of the coordinates $\mathbf{R}, \mathbf{r}$, and the reduction of the two-body problem to two one-body problems can be carried out in the quantum mechanical treatment in a way exactly analogous to the above classical treatment, under the same assumptions about the forces.

It is worth remarking that the kinetic energy of the two-body system can be separated into two parts, one associated with each of the two one-body problems into which we have separated the two-body problem.   The center of mass velocity and the relative velocity are, according to Eqs. (4–90)–(4–93), related to the particle velocities by

$$\mathbf{V} = \dot{\mathbf{R}} = \frac{m_1 \mathbf{v}_1 + m_2 \mathbf{v}_2}{m_1 + m_2}, \tag{4–102}$$

$$\mathbf{v} = \dot{\mathbf{r}} = \mathbf{v}_1 - \mathbf{v}_2, \tag{4–103}$$

or

$$\mathbf{v}_1 = \mathbf{V} + \frac{\mu}{m_1} \mathbf{v}, \tag{4–104}$$

$$\mathbf{v}_2 = \mathbf{V} - \frac{\mu}{m_2} \mathbf{v}. \tag{4–105}$$

The total kinetic energy is

$$\begin{aligned} T &= \tfrac{1}{2} m_1 v_1^2 + \tfrac{1}{2} m_2 v_2^2 \\ &= \tfrac{1}{2} M V^2 + \tfrac{1}{2} \mu v^2. \end{aligned} \tag{4–106}$$

The angular momentum can similarly be separated into two parts:

$$\mathbf{L} = m_1(\mathbf{r}_1 \times \mathbf{v}_1) + m_2(\mathbf{r}_2 \times \mathbf{v}_2)$$
$$= M(\mathbf{R} \times \mathbf{V}) + \mu(\mathbf{r} \times \mathbf{v}). \tag{4–107}$$

The total linear momentum is, however, just

$$\mathbf{P} = m_1\mathbf{v}_1 + m_2\mathbf{v}_2 = M\mathbf{V}. \tag{4–108}$$

There is no term $\mu\mathbf{v}$ in the total linear momentum.

4–8 Center of mass coordinates. Rutherford scattering by a charged particle of finite mass.   By making use of the results of the preceding section, we can solve a two-body scattering problem completely, if we know the interaction force between the two particles, by solving the one-body equation of motion for the coordinate $\mathbf{r}$.   The result, however, is not in a very convenient form for application.   The solution $\mathbf{r}(t)$ describes the motion of particle 1 with respect to particle 2 as origin.   Since particle 2 itself will be moving along some orbit, this is not usually a very convenient way of interpreting the motion.   It would be better to describe the motion of both particles by means of coordinates $\mathbf{r}_1(t),\mathbf{r}_2(t)$ referred to some fixed origin.   Usually one of the particles is initially at rest; we shall take it to be particle 2, and call it the *target* particle.   Particle 1, approaching the target with an initial velocity $\mathbf{v}_{1I}$, we shall call the *incident* particle. The two particles are to be located by vectors $\mathbf{r}_1$ and $\mathbf{r}_2$ relative to an origin with respect to which the target particle is initially at rest.   We shall call the coordinates $\mathbf{r}_1,\mathbf{r}_2$ the *laboratory coordinate system.*

The translation from the coordinates $\mathbf{R},\mathbf{r}$ to laboratory coordinates is most conveniently carried out in two steps.   We first introduce a *center-of-mass coordinate system* in which the particles are located by vectors $\mathbf{r}_1^i,\mathbf{r}_2^i$ with respect to the center of mass as origin:

$$\mathbf{r}_1^i = \mathbf{r}_1 - \mathbf{R},$$
$$\mathbf{r}_2^i = \mathbf{r}_2 - \mathbf{R} \tag{4–109}$$

and, conversely,

$$\mathbf{r}_1 = \mathbf{r}_1^i + \mathbf{R},$$
$$\mathbf{r}_2 = \mathbf{r}_2^i + \mathbf{R}. \tag{4–110}$$

The relation between the center-of-mass coordinates and the relative coordinate $\mathbf{r}$ is obtained from Eqs. (4–92) and (4–93):

$$\mathbf{r}_1^i = \frac{m_2}{m_1 + m_2}\mathbf{r} = \frac{\mu}{m_1}\mathbf{r}.$$
$$\mathbf{r}_2^i = -\frac{m_1}{m_1 + m_2}\mathbf{r} = -\frac{\mu}{m_2}\mathbf{r}. \tag{4–111}$$

The position vectors of the particles relative to the center of mass are constant multiples of the relative coordinate $\mathbf{r}$.   The center of mass has the

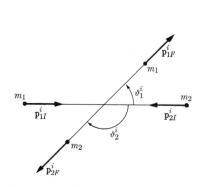

FIG. 4-6. Two-particle collision in center of mass coordinates.

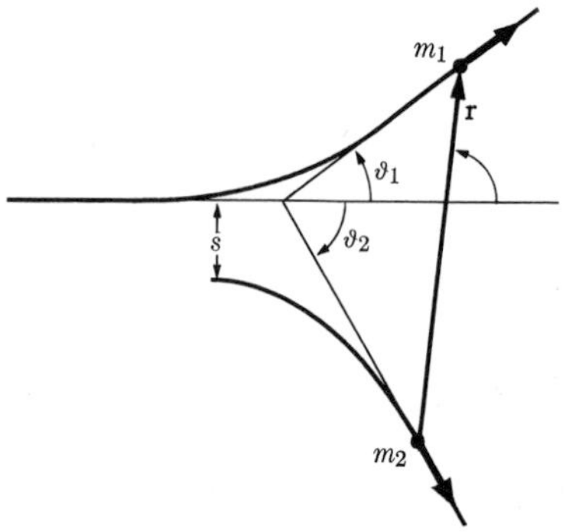

FIG. 4-7. Orbits for two-body collision in the laboratory system.

advantage over particle 2, as an origin of coordinates, in that it moves with uniform velocity, in collision problems where no external forces are assumed to act.

In the center-of-mass coordinate system the total linear momentum is zero, and the momenta $\mathbf{p}_1^i$ and $\mathbf{p}_2^i$ of the two particles are always equal and opposite. The scattering angles ϑ_1^i and ϑ_2^i between the two final directions of motion and the initial direction of motion of particle 1 are the supplements of each other, as shown in Fig. 4-6.

We now determine the relation between the scattering angle Θ in the equivalent one-body problem and the scattering angle ϑ_1 in the laboratory coordinate system (Fig. 4-7). The velocity of the incident particle in the center-of-mass system is related to the relative velocity in the one-body problem, according to Eq. (4-111), by

$$\mathbf{v}_1^i = \frac{\mu}{m_1}\,\mathbf{v}. \qquad (4\text{-}112)$$

Since these two velocities are always parallel, the angle of scattering ϑ_1^i of the incident particle in the center-of-mass system is equal to the angle of scattering Θ in the one-body problem. The incident particle velocities in the center-of-mass and laboratory systems are related by [Eq. (4-110)]

$$\mathbf{v}_1 = \mathbf{v}_1^i + \mathbf{V}, \qquad (4\text{-}113)$$

where the constant velocity of the center of mass can be expressed in terms of the initial velocity in the laboratory system by Eq. (4-102):

$$\mathbf{V} = \frac{m_1}{m_1 + m_2}\,\mathbf{v}_{1I} = \frac{\mu}{m_2}\,\mathbf{v}_{1I}. \qquad (4\text{-}114)$$

The relation expressed by Eq. (4-113) is shown in Fig. 4-8, from which the relation between $\vartheta_1^i = \Theta$ and ϑ_1 can be determined:

$$\tan \vartheta_1 = \frac{v_{1F}^i \sin \Theta}{v_{1F}^i \cos \Theta + V}, \quad (4\text{--}115)$$

or, with the help of Eqs. (4–112) and (4–114),

$$\tan \vartheta_1 = \frac{\sin \Theta}{\cos \Theta + \dfrac{m_1 v_I}{m_2 v_F}}, \quad (4\text{--}116)$$

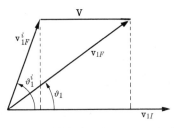

Fig. 4–8. Relation between velocities in laboratory and center of mass coordinate systems.

where v_I and v_F are the initial and final relative speeds, and we have substituted v_I for v_{1I}, since initially the relative velocity is just the velocity of the incident particle. If the collision is elastic, the initial and final speeds are the same and Eq. (4–116) reduces to:

$$\tan \vartheta_1 = \frac{\sin \Theta}{\cos \Theta + \dfrac{m_1}{m_2}}. \quad (4\text{--}117)$$

A similar relation for ϑ_2 can be worked out.

If the incident particle is much heavier than the target particle, then ϑ_1 will be very small, no matter what value Θ may have. This corresponds to the result obtained in Section 4–6, that ϑ_1 can never be larger than ϑ_m given by Eq. (4–68), if $m_1 > m_2$. If $m_1 = m_2$, then Eq. (4–117) is easily solved for ϑ_1:

$$\tan \vartheta_1 = \frac{\sin \Theta}{\cos \Theta + 1} = \frac{2 \sin \dfrac{\Theta}{2} \cos \dfrac{\Theta}{2}}{2 \cos^2 \dfrac{\Theta}{2}} = \tan \frac{\Theta}{2},$$

$$\vartheta_1 = \tfrac{1}{2}\Theta. \quad (4\text{--}118)$$

Since Θ may always have any value between 0 and π without violating the conservation laws in the center-of-mass system, the maximum value of ϑ_1 in this case is $\pi/2$, in agreement with the corresponding result of Section 4–6. If the target mass m_2 is much larger than the incident mass m_1, then $\tan \vartheta_1 \doteq \tan \Theta$; this justifies rigorously our application to this case of Eq. (3–276) for the Rutherford cross section, deduced in Chapter 3 for the one-body scattering problem with an inverse square law force.

According to the above developments, Eq. (3–276) applies also to the two-body problem for any ratio m_1/m_2 of incident mass to target mass, but Θ must be interpreted as the angle of scattering in terms of relative coordinates, or else in terms of center-of-mass coordinates. That is, $d\sigma$ in Eq. (3–276) is the cross section for a scattering process in which the relative velocity **v** after the collision makes an angle between Θ and $\Theta + d\Theta$ with the initial velocity. Since it is the laboratory scattering angle ϑ_1

that is ordinarily measured, we must substitute for Θ and $d\Theta$ in Eq. (3–276) their values in terms of ϑ_1 and $d\vartheta_1$ as determined from Eq. (4–117). This is most easily done in case $m_1 = m_2$, when, by Eq. (4–118), the Rutherford scattering cross section [Eq. (3–276)] becomes

$$d\sigma = \left(\frac{q_1 q_2}{2\mu v_0^2}\right)^2 \frac{4 \cos \vartheta_1}{\sin^4 \vartheta_1} 2\pi \sin \vartheta_1 \, d\vartheta_1. \qquad (4\text{–}119)$$

4–9 The N-body problem. It would be very satisfactory if we could arrive at a general method of solving the problem of any number of particles moving under the forces which they exert on one another, analogous to the method given in Section 4–7 by which the two-body problem was reduced to two separate one-body problems. Unfortunately no such general method is available for systems of more than two particles. This does not mean that such problems cannot be solved. The extremely accurate calculations of the motions of the planets represent a solution of a problem involving the gravitational interactions of a considerable number of bodies. However, these solutions are not general solutions of the equations of motion, like the system of orbits we have obtained for the two-body case, but are numerical solutions obtained by elaborate calculations for specified initial conditions and holding over certain periods of time. Even the three-body problem admits of no general reduction, say, to three one-body problems, or to any other manageable set of equations.

However, we can partially separate the problem of the motion of a system of particles into two problems: first, to find the motion of the center of mass, and second, to find the internal motion of the system, that is, the motion of its particles relative to the center of mass. Let us define the internal coordinate vector $\mathbf{r}_k^i$ of the kth particle as the vector from the center of mass to the kth particle (Fig. 4–9):

$$\mathbf{r}_k^i = \mathbf{r}_k - \mathbf{R}, \quad k = 1, \ldots, N, \qquad (4\text{–}120)$$
$$\mathbf{r}_k = \mathbf{R} + \mathbf{r}_k^i, \quad k = 1, \ldots, N. \qquad (4\text{–}121)$$

In view of the definition (4–14) of the center of mass, the internal coordinates $\mathbf{r}_k^i$ satisfy the equation

$$\sum_{k=1}^{N} m_k \mathbf{r}_k^i = 0. \qquad (4\text{–}122)$$

We define the center-of-mass velocity and the internal velocities:

$$\mathbf{V} = \dot{\mathbf{R}}, \qquad (4\text{–}123)$$
$$\mathbf{v}_k^i = \dot{\mathbf{r}}_k^i = \mathbf{v}_k - \mathbf{V}. \qquad (4\text{–}124)$$

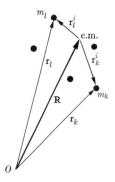

FIG. 4–9. Center of mass and internal coordinates of a system of particles.

The total internal momentum of a system of particles (i.e., the momentum relative to the center of mass) vanishes by Eq. (4–122):

$$\sum_{k=1}^{N} m_k \mathbf{v}_k^i = \mathbf{0}. \tag{4–125}$$

We first show that the total kinetic energy, momentum, and angular momentum can each be split up into a part depending on the total mass M and the motion of the center of mass, and an internal part depending only on the internal coordinates and velocities. The total kinetic energy of the system of particles is

$$T = \sum_{k=1}^{N} \tfrac{1}{2} m_k v_k^2. \tag{4–126}$$

By substituting for $\mathbf{v}_k$ from Eq. (4–124), and making use of Eq. (4–125), we can split T into two parts:

$$\begin{aligned} T &= \sum_{k=1}^{N} \tfrac{1}{2} m_k (V^2 + 2\mathbf{V} \cdot \mathbf{v}_k^i + v_k^{i2}) \\ &= \sum_{k=1}^{N} \tfrac{1}{2} m_k V^2 + \sum_{k=1}^{N} \tfrac{1}{2} m_k v_k^{i2} + \sum_{k=1}^{N} m_k \mathbf{V} \cdot \mathbf{v}_k^i \\ &= \tfrac{1}{2} M V^2 + \sum_{k=1}^{N} \tfrac{1}{2} m_k v_k^{i2} + \mathbf{V} \cdot \sum_{k=1}^{N} m_k \mathbf{v}_k^i \\ &= \tfrac{1}{2} M V^2 + \sum_{k=1}^{N} \tfrac{1}{2} m_k v_k^{i2}. \end{aligned} \tag{4–127}$$

The total linear momentum is, if we make use of Eqs. (4–124) and (4–125),

$$\begin{aligned} \mathbf{P} &= \sum_{k=1}^{N} m_k \mathbf{v}_k \\ &= \sum_{k=1}^{N} m_k \mathbf{V} + \sum_{k=1}^{N} m_k \mathbf{v}_k^i \\ &= M\mathbf{V}. \end{aligned} \tag{4–128}$$

The internal linear momentum is zero.

The total angular momentum about the origin is, if we use Eqs. (4–121), (4–122), (4–124), and (4–125),

$$\begin{aligned} \mathbf{L} &= \sum_{k=1}^{N} m_k (\mathbf{r}_k \times \mathbf{v}_k) \\ &= \sum_{k=1}^{N} m_k (\mathbf{R} \times \mathbf{V} + \mathbf{r}_k^i \times \mathbf{V} + \mathbf{R} \times \mathbf{v}_k^i + \mathbf{r}_k^i \times \mathbf{v}_k^i) \\ &= \sum_{k=1}^{N} m_k (\mathbf{R} \times \mathbf{V}) + \left(\sum_{k=1}^{N} m_k \mathbf{r}_k^i \right) \times \mathbf{V} + \mathbf{R} \times \left(\sum_{k=1}^{N} m_k \mathbf{v}_k^i \right) + \sum_{k=1}^{N} m_k (\mathbf{r}_k^i \times \mathbf{v}_k^i) \\ &= M(\mathbf{R} \times \mathbf{V}) + \sum_{k=1}^{N} m_k (\mathbf{r}_k^i \times \mathbf{v}_k^i). \end{aligned} \tag{4–129}$$

Notice that the internal angular momentum depends only on the internal coordinates and velocities and is independent of the origin about which $\mathbf{L}$ is being computed (and from which the vector $\mathbf{R}$ is drawn).

The position of particle k with respect to particle l is specified by the vector

$$\mathbf{r}_k - \mathbf{r}_l = \mathbf{r}_k^i - \mathbf{r}_l^i. \tag{4-130}$$

The relative positions of the particles with respect to one another depend only on the internal coordinates $\mathbf{r}_k^i$, and likewise the relative velocities, so that the internal forces $\mathbf{F}_k^i$ will be expected to depend only on the internal coordinates $\mathbf{r}_k^i$, and possibly on the internal velocities. If there is a potential energy associated with the internal forces, it likewise will depend only on the internal coordinates.

Although the forces, energy, momentum, and angular momentum can each be split into two parts, a part associated with the motion of the center of mass and an internal part depending only on the internal coordinates and velocities, it must not be supposed that the internal motion and the center-of-mass motion are two completely separate problems. The motion of the center of mass, as governed by Eq. (4-18), is a separate one-body problem, *when the external force* $\mathbf{F}$ *is given*. However, in most cases $\mathbf{F}$ will depend to some extent on the internal motion of the system. The internal equations of motion contain the external forces except in special cases and, furthermore, they also depend on the motion of the center of mass. If we substitute Eqs. (4-121) in Eqs. (4-1), and rearrange, we have

$$m_k\ddot{\mathbf{r}}_k^i = \mathbf{F}_k^i + \mathbf{F}_k^e - m_k\ddot{\mathbf{R}}. \tag{4-131}$$

There are many cases, however, in which a group of particles forms a system which seems to have some identity of its own, independent of other particles and systems of particles. An atomic nucleus, made up of neutrons and protons, is an example, as is an atom, made up of nucleus and electrons, or a molecule, composed of nuclei and electrons, or the collection of particles which make up a baseball. In all such cases, it turns out that the internal forces are much stronger than the external ones, and the acceleration $\ddot{\mathbf{R}}$ is small, so that the internal equations of motion (4-131) depend essentially only on the internal forces, and their solutions represent internal motions which are nearly independent of the external forces and of the motion of the system as a whole. The system viewed externally then behaves like a single particle with coordinate vector $\mathbf{R}$, mass M, acted on by the (external) force $\mathbf{F}$, but a particle which has, in addition to its "orbital" energy, momentum, and angular momentum, associated with the motion of its center of mass, an intrinsic or internal energy and angular momentum associated with its internal motion. The orbital and intrinsic parts of the energy, momentum, and angular momentum can be identified in Eqs. (4-127), (4-128), and (4-129). The internal angular momentum is usually called *spin* and is independent of the position or velocity of the center of mass relative to the origin about which the total angular momentum is to be computed. So long as the external forces are small, this approximate representation of the system as a single particle is valid. Whenever the external forces are strong enough to affect appreciably the internal motion, the separation into problems of internal and of orbital motions breaks down and the system begins to lose its individuality. Some of the central problems at the frontiers of present-day physical theories are concerned with bridging the gap between a loose collection of particles and a system with sufficient individuality to be treated as a single particle.

4-10 Two coupled harmonic oscillators. A very commonly occurring type of mechanical system is one in which several harmonic oscillators interact with one another. As a typical example of such a system, consider the mechanical system shown in Fig. 4-10, consisting of two masses m_1, m_2 fastened to fixed supports by springs whose elastic constants are k_1, k_2, and connected by a third spring of elastic constant k_3. We suppose the masses are free to move only along the x-axis; they may, for example, slide along a rail. If spring k_3 were not present, the two masses would vibrate independently in simple harmonic motion with angular frequencies (neglecting damping)

$$\omega_{10}^0 = \sqrt{\frac{k_1}{m_1}}, \quad \omega_{20}^0 = \sqrt{\frac{k_2}{m_2}}. \tag{4-132}$$

We wish to investigate the effect of coupling these two oscillators together by means of the spring k_3. We describe the positions of the two masses by specifying the distances x_1 and x_2 that the springs k_1 and k_2 have been stretched from their equilibrium positions. We assume for simplicity that when springs k_1 and k_2 are relaxed ($x_1 = x_2 = 0$), spring k_3 is also relaxed. The amount by which spring k_3 is compressed is then ($x_1 + x_2$). The equations of motion for the masses m_1, m_2 (neglecting friction) are

$$m_1\ddot{x}_1 = -k_1x_1 - k_3(x_1 + x_2), \tag{4-133}$$
$$m_2\ddot{x}_2 = -k_2x_2 - k_3(x_1 + x_2). \tag{4-134}$$

We rewrite these in the form

$$m_1\ddot{x}_1 + k_1'x_1 + k_3x_2 = 0, \tag{4-135}$$
$$m_2\ddot{x}_2 + k_2'x_2 + k_3x_1 = 0, \tag{4-136}$$

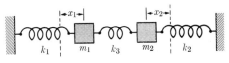

FIG. 4-10. A simple model of two coupled harmonic oscillators.

where

$$k_1' = k_1 + k_3, \qquad (4\text{--}137)$$
$$k_2' = k_2 + k_3. \qquad (4\text{--}138)$$

We have two second order linear differential equations to solve simultaneously. If the third terms were not present, the equations would be independent of one another, and we would have independent harmonic vibrations of x_1 and x_2 at frequencies

$$\omega_{10} = \sqrt{\frac{k_1'}{m_1}}, \qquad (4\text{--}139)$$

$$\omega_{20} = \sqrt{\frac{k_2'}{m_2}}. \qquad (4\text{--}140)$$

These are the frequencies with which each mass would vibrate if the other were held fixed. Thus the first effect of the coupling spring is simply to change the frequency of independent vibration of each mass, due to the fact that each mass is now held in position by two springs instead of one. The third terms in Eqs. (4–135) and (4–136) give rise to a coupling between the motions of the two masses, so that they no longer move independently.

We may solve Eqs. (4–135), (4–136) by an extension of the method of Section 2–8 applicable to any set of simultaneous linear differential equations with constant coefficients. We assume that

$$x_1 = C_1 e^{pt}, \qquad (4\text{--}141)$$
$$x_2 = C_2 e^{pt}, \qquad (4\text{--}142)$$

where C_1, C_2 are constants. Note that the same time dependence is assumed for both x_1 and x_2, in order that the factor e^{pt} will cancel out when we substitute in Eqs. (4–135) and (4–136):

$$(m_1 p^2 + k_1')C_1 + k_3 C_2 = 0, \qquad (4\text{--}143)$$
$$(m_2 p^2 + k_2')C_2 + k_3 C_1 = 0. \qquad (4\text{--}144)$$

We now have two algebraic equations in the three unknown quantities C_1, C_2, p. We note that either Eq. (4–143) or (4–144) can be solved for the ratio C_2/C_1:

$$\frac{C_2}{C_1} = -\frac{m_1 p^2 + k_1'}{k_3} = -\frac{k_3}{m_2 p^2 + k_2'}. \qquad (4\text{--}145)$$

The two values of C_2/C_1 must be equal, and we have an equation for p:

$$\frac{m_1 p^2 + k_1'}{k_3} = \frac{k_3}{m_2 p^2 + k_2'}, \qquad (4\text{--}146)$$

which may be rearranged as a quadratic equation in p^2, called the *secular equation:*

$$m_1 m_2 p^4 + (m_2 k_1' + m_1 k_2')p^2 + (k_1' k_2' - k_3^2) = 0, \qquad (4\text{--}147)$$

whose solutions are

$$p^2 = -\tfrac{1}{2}\left(\frac{k_1'}{m_1} + \frac{k_2'}{m_2}\right) \pm \left[\tfrac{1}{4}\left(\frac{k_1'}{m_1} + \frac{k_2'}{m_2}\right)^2 - \frac{k_1'k_2'}{m_1m_2} + \frac{k_3^2}{m_1m_2}\right]^{\frac{1}{2}}$$
$$= -\tfrac{1}{2}(\omega_{10}^2 + \omega_{20}^2) \pm \left[\tfrac{1}{4}(\omega_{10}^2 - \omega_{20}^2)^2 + \frac{k_3^2}{m_1m_2}\right]^{\frac{1}{2}}. \qquad (4\text{-}148)$$

It is not hard to show that the quantity in brackets is less than the square of the first term, so that we have two negative solutions for p^2. If we assume that $\omega_{10} \geq \omega_{20}$, the solutions for p^2 are

$$\begin{aligned} p^2 &= -\omega_1^2 = -(\omega_{10}^2 + \tfrac{1}{2}\Delta\omega^2), \\ p^2 &= -\omega_2^2 = -(\omega_{20}^2 - \tfrac{1}{2}\Delta\omega^2), \end{aligned} \qquad (4\text{-}149)$$

where

$$\Delta\omega^2 = (\omega_{10}^2 - \omega_{20}^2)\left[\left(1 + \frac{4\kappa^4}{(\omega_{10}^2 - \omega_{20}^2)^2}\right)^{\frac{1}{2}} - 1\right], \qquad (4\text{-}150)$$

with the abbreviation

$$\kappa^2 = \frac{k_3}{\sqrt{m_1m_2}}, \qquad (4\text{-}151)$$

where κ is the coupling constant. If $\omega_{10} = \omega_{20}$, Eq. (4-150) reduces to

$$\Delta\omega^2 = 2\kappa^2. \qquad (4\text{-}152)$$

The four solutions for p are

$$p = \pm i\omega_1, \quad \pm i\omega_2. \qquad (4\text{-}153)$$

If $p^2 = -\omega_1^2$, Eq. (4-145) can be written

$$\frac{C_2}{C_1} = \frac{m_1}{k_3}(\omega_1^2 - \omega_{10}^2) = \frac{\Delta\omega^2}{2\kappa^2}\sqrt{\frac{m_1}{m_2}}, \qquad (4\text{-}154)$$

and if $p^2 = -\omega_2^2$, it can be written

$$\frac{C_1}{C_2} = \frac{m_2}{k_3}(\omega_2^2 - \omega_{20}^2) = -\frac{\Delta\omega^2}{2\kappa^2}\sqrt{\frac{m_2}{m_1}}. \qquad (4\text{-}155)$$

By substituting from Eq. (4-153) in Eqs. (4-141), (4-142), we get four solutions of Eqs. (4-135) and (4-136) provided the ratio C_2/C_1 is chosen according to Eq. (4-154) or (4-155). Each of these solutions involves one arbitrary constant (C_1 or C_2). Since the equations (4-135), (4-136) are linear, the sum of these four solutions will also be a solution, and is in fact the general solution, for it will contain four arbitrary constants (say C_1, C_1', C_2, C_2'):

$$x_1 = C_1e^{i\omega_1 t} + C_1'e^{-i\omega_1 t} - \frac{\Delta\omega^2}{2\kappa^2}\sqrt{\frac{m_2}{m_1}}C_2e^{i\omega_2 t} - \frac{\Delta\omega^2}{2\kappa^2}\sqrt{\frac{m_2}{m_1}}C_2'e^{-i\omega_2 t}, \qquad (4\text{-}156)$$

$$x_2 = \frac{\Delta\omega^2}{2\kappa^2}\sqrt{\frac{m_1}{m_2}}C_1e^{i\omega_1 t} + \frac{\Delta\omega^2}{2\kappa^2}\sqrt{\frac{m_1}{m_2}}C_1'e^{-i\omega_1 t} + C_2e^{i\omega_2 t} + C_2'e^{-i\omega_2 t}. \qquad (4\text{-}157)$$

In order to make x_1 and x_2 real, we choose

$$C_1 = \tfrac{1}{2}A_1 e^{i\theta_1}, \quad C_1' = \tfrac{1}{2}A_1 e^{-i\theta_1}, \tag{4-158}$$
$$C_2 = \tfrac{1}{2}A_2 e^{i\theta_2}, \quad C_2' = \tfrac{1}{2}A_2 e^{-i\theta_2}, \tag{4-159}$$

so that

$$x_1 = A_1 \cos(\omega_1 t + \theta_1) - \frac{\Delta\omega^2}{2\kappa^2} \sqrt{\frac{m_2}{m_1}} A_2 \cos(\omega_2 t + \theta_2), \tag{4-160}$$

$$x_2 = \frac{\Delta\omega^2}{2\kappa^2} \sqrt{\frac{m_1}{m_2}} A_1 \cos(\omega_1 t + \theta_1) + A_2 \cos(\omega_2 t + \theta_2). \tag{4-161}$$

This is the general solution, involving the four arbitrary constants $A_1, A_2, \theta_1, \theta_2$. We see that the motion of each coordinate is a superposition of two harmonic vibrations at frequencies ω_1 and ω_2. The oscillation frequencies are the same for both coordinates, but the relative amplitudes are different, and are given by Eqs. (4-154) and (4-155).

If A_1 or A_2 is zero, only one frequency of oscillation appears. The resulting motion is called a *normal mode of vibration*. The normal mode of highest frequency is given by

$$x_1 = A_1 \cos(\omega_1 t + \theta_1), \tag{4-162}$$

$$x_2 = \frac{\Delta\omega^2}{2\kappa^2} \sqrt{\frac{m_1}{m_2}} A_1 \cos(\omega_1 t + \theta_1), \tag{4-163}$$

$$\omega_1^2 = \omega_{10}^2 + \tfrac{1}{2}\Delta\omega^2. \tag{4-164}$$

The frequency of oscillation is higher than ω_{10}. By referring to Fig. 4-10, we see that in this mode of oscillation the two masses m_1 and m_2 are oscillating out of phase, that is, their displacements are in opposite directions. The mode of oscillation of lower frequency is given by

$$x_1 = -\frac{\Delta\omega^2}{2\kappa^2} \sqrt{\frac{m_2}{m_1}} A_2 \cos(\omega_2 t + \theta_2), \tag{4-165}$$

$$x_2 = A_2 \cos(\omega_2 t + \theta_2), \tag{4-166}$$

$$\omega_2^2 = \omega_{20}^2 - \tfrac{1}{2}\Delta\omega^2. \tag{4-167}$$

In this mode, the two masses oscillate in phase at a frequency lower than ω_{20}. The most general motion of the system is given by Eqs. (4-160), (4-161), and is a superposition of the two normal modes of vibration.

The effect of coupling is thus to cause both masses to participate in the oscillation at each frequency, and to raise the highest frequency and lower the lowest frequency of oscillation. Even when both frequencies are initially equal, the coupling results in two frequencies of vibration, one higher and one lower than the frequency without coupling. When the coupling is very weak, i.e., when

$$\kappa^2 \ll \tfrac{1}{2}(\omega_{10}^2 - \omega_{20}^2), \tag{4-168}$$

then Eq. (4–150) becomes

$$\Delta\omega^2 \doteq \frac{2\kappa^4}{\omega_{10}^2 - \omega_{20}^2}.$$

(4–169)

For the highest frequency mode of vibration, the ratio of the amplitude of vibration of mass m_2 to that of mass m_1 is then

$$\frac{x_2}{x_1} = \frac{\Delta\omega^2}{2\kappa^2} \sqrt{\frac{m_1}{m_2}} \doteq \frac{\kappa^2}{\omega_{10}^2 - \omega_{20}^2} \sqrt{\frac{m_1}{m_2}}.$$

(4–170)

Thus, unless $m_2 \ll m_1$, the mass m_2 oscillates at much smaller amplitude than m_1. Similarly, it can be shown that for the low frequency mode of vibration, m_1 oscillates at much smaller amplitude than m_2. If two oscillators of different frequency are weakly coupled together, there are two normal modes of vibration of the system. In one mode, the oscillator of higher frequency oscillates at a frequency slightly higher than without coupling, and the other oscillates weakly out of phase at the same frequency. In the other mode, the oscillator of lowest frequency oscillates at a frequency slightly lower than without coupling, and the other oscillates weakly and in phase at the same frequency. At or near resonance, when the two natural frequencies ω_{10} and ω_{20} are equal, the condition for weak coupling [Eq. (4–168)] is not satisfied even when the coupling constant is very small. $\Delta\omega^2$ is then given by Eq. (4–152), and we find for the two normal modes of vibration:

$$\frac{x_2}{x_1} = \pm \sqrt{\frac{m_1}{m_2}},$$

(4–171)

$$\omega^2 = \omega_{10}^2 \pm \kappa^2.$$

(4–172)

The two oscillators oscillate in or out of phase with an amplitude ratio depending only on their mass ratio, and with a frequency higher or lower than the uncoupled frequency by an amount depending on the coupling constant.

An interesting special case is the case of two identical oscillators ($m_1 = m_2$, $k_1 = k_2$) coupled together. The general solution (4–160), (4–161) is, in this case,

$$x_1 = A_1 \cos(\omega_1 t + \theta_1) - A_2 \cos(\omega_2 t + \theta_2),$$

(4–173)

$$x_2 = A_1 \cos(\omega_1 t + \theta_1) + A_2 \cos(\omega_2 t + \theta_2),$$

(4–174)

where ω_1 and ω_2 are given by Eq. (4–172). If $A_2 = 0$, we have the high frequency normal mode of vibration, and if $A_1 = 0$, we have the low frequency normal mode. Let us suppose that initially m_2 is at rest in its equilibrium position, while m_1 is displaced a distance A from equilibrium and released at $t = 0$. The choice of constants which fits these initial conditions is

$$\theta_1 = \theta_2 = 0,$$
$$A_1 = -A_2 = \tfrac{1}{2}A,$$

(4–175)

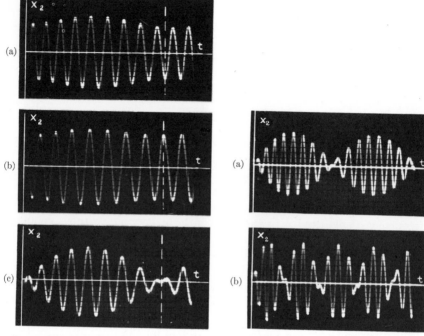

FIG. 4–11. Motion of coupled harmonic oscillators. (a) High frequency normal mode. (b) Low frequency normal mode. (c) m_1 initially displaced.

FIG. 4–14. Motion of two coupled oscillators. (a) Weak coupling. (b) Strong coupling.

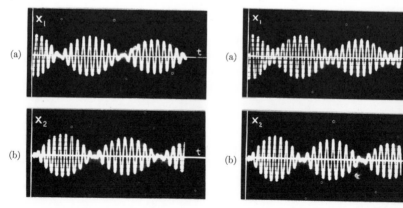

FIG. 4–12. Motion of two identical coupled oscillators.

FIG. 4–13. Motion of two non-identical coupled oscillators.

so that Eqs. (4–173), (4–174) become

$$x_1 = \tfrac{1}{2}A(\cos \omega_1 t + \cos \omega_2 t), \qquad (4\text{–}176)$$
$$x_2 = \tfrac{1}{2}A(\cos \omega_1 t - \cos \omega_2 t), \qquad (4\text{–}177)$$

which can be rewritten in the form

$$x_1 = A \cos \left(\frac{\omega_1 - \omega_2}{2} t\right) \cos \left(\frac{\omega_1 + \omega_2}{2} t\right), \qquad (4\text{–}178)$$

$$x_2 = -A \sin \left(\frac{\omega_1 - \omega_2}{2} t\right) \sin \left(\frac{\omega_1 + \omega_2}{2} t\right). \qquad (4\text{–}179)$$

If the coupling is small, ω_1 and ω_2 are nearly equal, and x_1 and x_2 oscillate rapidly at the angular frequency $(\omega_1 + \omega_2)/2 \doteq \omega_1 \doteq \omega_2$, with an amplitude which varies sinusoidally at angular frequency $(\omega_1 - \omega_2)/2$. The motion of each oscillator is a superposition of its two normal mode motions, which leads to beats, the beat frequency being the difference between the two normal mode frequencies. This is illustrated in Fig. 4–11, where oscillograms of the motion of x_2 are shown: (a) when the high frequency normal mode alone is excited, (b) when the low frequency normal mode is excited, and (c) when oscillator m_1 alone is initially displaced. In Fig. 4–12, oscillograms of x_1 and x_2 as given by Eqs. (4–178), (4–179) are shown. It can be seen that the oscillators periodically exchange their energy, due to the coupling between them. Figure 4–13 shows the same motion when the springs k_1 and k_2 are not exactly equal. In this case, oscillator m_1 does not give up all its energy to m_2 during the beats. Figure 4–14 shows that the effect of increasing the coupling is to increase the beat frequency $\omega_1 - \omega_2$ [Eq. (4–172)].

If a frictional force acts on each oscillator, the equations of motion (4–135) and (4–136) become

$$m_1\ddot{x}_1 + b_1\dot{x}_1 + k_1'x_1 + k_3x_2 = 0, \qquad (4\text{–}180)$$
$$m_2\ddot{x}_2 + b_2\dot{x}_2 + k_2'x_2 + k_3x_1 = 0, \qquad (4\text{–}181)$$

where b_1 and b_2 are the respective friction coefficients. The substitution (4–141), (4–142) leads to a fourth degree secular equation for p:

$$m_1m_2p^4 + (m_2b_1 + m_1b_2)p^3 + (m_2k_1' + m_1k_2' + b_1b_2)p^2$$
$$+ (b_1k_2' + b_2k_1')p + (k_1'k_2' - k_3^2) = 0. \qquad (4\text{–}182)$$

This equation cannot be solved so easily as Eq. (4–147). The four roots for p are, in general, complex, and have the form (if b_1 and b_2 are not too large)

$$p = -\gamma_1 \pm i\omega_1, \quad p = -\gamma_2 \pm i\omega_2. \qquad (4\text{–}183)$$

That the roots have this form with γ_1 and γ_2 positive can be shown (though not easily) algebraically from a study of the coefficients in Eq. (4–182). Physically, it is evident that the roots have the form (4–183), since this will lead to damped vibrations, the expected result of friction. If b_1 and b_2 are large enough, one or both of the pairs of complex roots may become a pair of real negative roots, the corresponding normal mode or modes being overdamped. A practical solution of Eq. (4–182) can, in general, be obtained only by numerical methods when numerical values for the constants are given, although an approximate algebraic solution can be found when the damping is very small.

The problem of the motion of a system of two coupled harmonic oscillators subject to a harmonically oscillating force applied to either mass can be solved by methods similar to those which apply to a single harmonic oscillator. A steady state solution can be found in which both oscillators oscillate at the frequency of the applied force with definite amplitudes and phases, depending on their masses, the spring constants, the damping, and the amplitude and phase of the applied force. The system is in resonance with the applied force when its frequency corresponds to either of the two normal modes of vibration, and the masses then vibrate at large amplitudes limited only by the damping. The general solution consists of the steady state solution plus the general solution of the unforced problem. A superposition principle can be proved according to which, if a number of forces act on either or both masses, the solution is the sum of the solutions with each force acting separately. This theorem can be used to treat the problem of arbitrary forces acting on the two masses.

Other types of coupling between the oscillators are possible in addition to coupling by means of a spring as in the example above. The oscillators may be coupled by frictional forces. A simple example would be the case where one mass slides over the other, as in Fig. 4–15. We assume that the force of friction is proportional to the relative velocity of the two masses. The equations of motion of m_1 and m_2 are then

$$m_1\ddot{x}_1 = -k_1 x_1 - b(\dot{x}_1 + \dot{x}_2), \qquad (4\text{–}184)$$
$$m_2\ddot{x}_2 = -k_2 x_2 - b(\dot{x}_2 + \dot{x}_1), \qquad (4\text{–}185)$$

or

$$m_1\ddot{x}_1 + b\dot{x}_1 + k_1 x_1 + b\dot{x}_2 = 0, \qquad (4\text{–}186)$$
$$m_2\ddot{x}_2 + b\dot{x}_2 + k_2 x_2 + b\dot{x}_1 = 0. \qquad (4\text{–}187)$$

The coupling is expressed in Eqs. (4–186), (4–187) by a term in the equation of motion of each oscillator depending on the velocity of the other. The

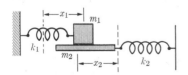

FIG. 4–15. Frictional coupling.

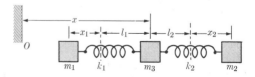

FIG. 4–16. Coupling through a mass.

oscillators may also be coupled by a mass, as in Fig. 4–16.   It is left to the reader to set up the equations of motion.   (See problem 22 at the end of this chapter.)

Two oscillators may be coupled in such a way that the force acting on one depends on the position, velocity, or acceleration of the other, or on any combination of these.   In general, all three types of coupling occur to some extent; a spring, for example, has always some mass, and is subject to some internal friction.   Thus the most general pair of equations for two coupled harmonic oscillators is of the form

$$m_1\ddot{x}_1 + b_1\dot{x}_1 + k_1x_1 + m_c\ddot{x}_2 + b_c\dot{x}_2 + k_cx_2 = 0, \qquad (4\text{–}188)$$
$$m_2\ddot{x}_2 + b_2\dot{x}_2 + k_2x_2 + m_c\ddot{x}_1 + b_c\dot{x}_1 + k_cx_1 = 0. \qquad (4\text{–}189)$$

These equations can be solved by the method described above, with similar results.   Two normal modes of vibration appear, if the frictional forces are not too great.

Equations of the form (4–188), (4–189), or the simpler special cases considered in the preceding discussions, arise not only in the theory of coupled mechanical oscillators, but also in the theory of coupled electrical circuits. Applying Kirchhoff's second law to the two meshes of the circuit shown in Fig. 4–17, with mesh currents i_1, i_2 around the two meshes as shown, we obtain

$$(L + L_1)\ddot{q}_1 + (R + R_1)\dot{q}_1 + \left(\frac{1}{C} + \frac{1}{C_1}\right)q_1 + L\ddot{q}_2 + R\dot{q}_2 + \frac{1}{C}q_2 = 0, \quad (4\text{–}190)$$

$$(L + L_2)\ddot{q}_2 + (R + R_2)\dot{q}_2 + \left(\frac{1}{C} + \frac{1}{C_2}\right)q_2 + L\ddot{q}_1 + R\dot{q}_1 + \frac{1}{C}q_1 = 0, \quad (4\text{–}191)$$

where q_1 and q_2 are the charges built up on C_1 and C_2 by the mesh currents i_1 and i_2.   These equations have the same form as Eqs. (4–188), (4–189), and can be solved by similar methods.   In electrical circuits, the damping is often fairly large, and finding the solution becomes a formidable task.

The discussion of this section can be extended to the case of any number of coupled mechanical or electrical harmonic oscillators.   The algebraic details become almost prohibitive, however, unless we make use of more advanced mathematical techniques. The form of the equations of motion is the same, with the equation of motion of each oscillator containing coupling terms depending on the position, velocity, and acceleration of one or more other oscillators. If the damping is not too great, we again find normal modes of vibration in which all oscillators oscillate at the same frequency with varying amplitudes and phases. There are as

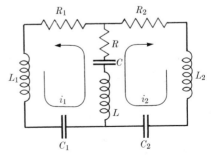

Fig. 4–17.   Coupled oscillating circuits.

many normal modes as there are oscillators.   The general solution of the problem is a superposition of these normal modes of vibration with arbitrary amplitudes and phases.

All mechanical and electrical vibration problems reduce in the limiting case of small amplitudes of vibration to problems involving one or several coupled harmonic oscillators.   Problems involving vibrations of strings, membranes, elastic solids, and electrical and acoustical vibrations in transmission lines, pipes, or cavities, can be reduced to problems of coupled oscillators, and exhibit similar normal modes of vibration.   The treatment of the behavior of an atom or molecule according to quantum mechanics results in a mathematical problem identical with the problem of coupled harmonic oscillators, in which the energy levels play the role of oscillators, and external perturbing influences play the role of the coupling mechanism.

PROBLEMS

1. Formulate and prove a conservation law for the angular momentum about the origin of a system of particles confined to a plane.

2. Water is poured into a barrel at the rate of 120 lb per minute from a height of 16 ft.   The barrel weighs 25 lb, and rests on a scale.   Find the scale reading after the water has been pouring into the barrel for one minute.

3. A scoop of mass m_1 is attached to an arm of length l and negligible weight. The arm is pivoted so that the scoop is free to swing in a vertical arc of radius l. At a distance l directly below the pivot is a pile of sand.   The scoop is lifted until the arm is at a 45° angle with the vertical, and released.   It swings down and scoops up a mass m_2 of sand.   To what angle with the vertical does the arm of the scoop rise after picking up the sand?   This problem is to be solved by considering carefully which conservation laws are applicable to each part of the swing of the scoop.   Friction is to be neglected, except that required to keep the sand in the scoop.

4. A rocket is to be fired vertically upward.   The initial mass is M_0, the exhaust velocity $-u$ is constant, and the rate of exhaust $-(dM/dt) = A$ is constant.   After a total mass ΔM is exhausted, the rocket engine runs out of fuel.   Neglecting air resistance and assuming that the acceleration g of gravity is constant, set up and solve the equation of motion, and show that if M_0, u, and ΔM are fixed, then the larger the rate of exhaust A, that is, the faster it uses up its fuel, the greater the maximum altitude reached by the rocket.

5. A particle of mass m_1, energy T_{1I} collides elastically with a particle of mass m_2, at rest.   If the mass m_2 leaves the collision at an angle ϑ_2 with the original direction of motion of m_1, find the energy T_{2F} delivered to particle m_2.   Show that T_{2F} is a maximum for a head-on collision, and that in this case the energy lost by the incident particle in the collision is

$$T_{1I} - T_{1F} = \frac{4m_1m_2}{(m_1 + m_2)^2} T_{1I}.$$

6. A cloud chamber picture shows the track of an incident particle which makes a collision and is scattered through an angle ϑ_1.   The track of the target particle makes an angle ϑ_2 with the direction of the incident particle.   Assuming that the collision was elastic and that the target particle was initially at rest, find the ratio m_1/m_2 of the two masses.   (Assume small velocities so that the classical expressions for energy and momentum may be used.)

7. Show that an elastic collision corresponds to a coefficient of restitution $e = 1$, that is, show that for a head-on elastic collision between two particles, Eq. (4-85) holds with $e = 1$.

8. Calculate the energy loss Q for a head-on collision between a particle of mass m_1, velocity v_1 with a particle of mass m_2 at rest, if the coefficient of restitution is e.

9. A particle of mass m_1, momentum p_{1I} collides elastically with a particle of mass m_2, momentum p_{2I} going in the opposite direction. If m_1 leaves the collision at an angle ϑ_1 with its original course, find its final momentum.

10. Find the relativistic corrections to Eq. (4-81) when the incident particle m_1 and the emitted particle m_3 move with speeds near the speed of light. Assume that the recoil particle m_4 is moving slowly enough so that the classical relation between energy and momentum can be used for it.

11. A particle of mass m_1, momentum p_1 collides with a particle of mass m_2 at rest. A reaction occurs from which two particles of masses m_3 and m_4 result, which leave the collision at angles ϑ_3 and ϑ_4 with the original path of m_1. Find the energy Q absorbed in the reaction in terms of the masses, the angles, and p_1.

12. A nuclear reaction whose Q is known occurs in a photographic plate in which the tracks of the incident particle m_1 and the two product particles m_3 and m_4 can be seen. Find the energy of the incident particle in terms of m_1, m_3, m_4, Q, and the measured angles ϑ_3 and ϑ_4 between the incident track and the two final tracks. What happens if $Q = 0$?

13. The Compton scattering of x-rays can be interpreted as the result of elastic collisions between x-ray photons and free electrons. According to quantum theory, a photon of wavelength λ has a kinetic energy hc/λ, and a linear momentum of magnitude h/λ, where h is Planck's constant and c is the speed of light. In the Compton effect, an incident beam of x-rays of known wavelength λ_I in a known direction is scattered in passing through matter, and the scattered radiation at an angle ϑ_1 to the incident beam is found to have a longer wavelength λ_F, which is a function of the angle ϑ_1. Assuming an elastic collision between an incident photon and an electron of mass m at rest, set up the equations expressing conservation of energy and momentum. Use the relativistic expressions for the energy and momentum of the electron. Show that the change in x-ray wavelength is

$$\lambda_F - \lambda_I = \frac{h}{mc}(1 - \cos \vartheta_1),$$

and that the ejected electron appears at an angle given by

$$\tan \vartheta_2 = \frac{\sin \vartheta_1}{\left(1 + \dfrac{h}{\lambda_I mc}\right)(1 - \cos \vartheta_1)}.$$

14. Work out a correction to Eq. (3-267) which takes into account the motion of the central mass M under the influence of the revolving mass m. A pair of stars revolve about each other, so close together that they appear in the telescope as a single star. It is determined from spectroscopic observations that the two stars are of equal mass and that each revolves in a circle with speed v and period τ under the gravitational attraction of the other. Find the mass m of each star by using your formula.

15. Show that if the incident particle is much heavier than the target particle

$(m_1 \gg m_2)$, the Rutherford scattering cross section $d\sigma$ [Eq. (3–276)] in laboratory coordinates is approximately

$$d\sigma \doteq \left(\frac{q_1 q_2}{2m_2 v_0^2}\right)^2 \frac{4\gamma^2}{[1 - (1 - \gamma^2\vartheta_1^2)^{\frac{1}{2}}]^2 (1 - \gamma^2\vartheta_1^2)^{\frac{1}{2}}} 2\pi \sin \vartheta_1 d\vartheta_1$$

if $\gamma\vartheta_1 < 1$, where $\gamma = m_1/m_2$. Otherwise, $d\sigma = 0$.

16. Find an expression analogous to Eq. (4–116) for the angle of recoil of the target particle (ϑ_2 in Fig. 4–7) in terms of the scattering angle Θ in the equivalent one-body problem. Show that, for an elastic collision,

$$\vartheta_2 = \tfrac{1}{2} (\pi - \Theta).$$

17. Assume that $m_2 \gg m_1$, and that $\Theta = \vartheta_1 + \delta$, in Eq. (4–117). Find a formula for δ in terms of ϑ_1. Show that the first order correction to the Rutherford scattering cross section [Eq. (3–276)], due to the finite mass of m_2, vanishes.

18. Set up the equations of motion for Fig. 4–10, assuming that the relaxed length of each spring is l, and that the distance between the walls is $3(l + a)$, so that the springs are stretched, even in the equilibrium position. Show that the equations can be put in the same form as Eqs. (4–135) and (4–136).

19. For the normal mode of vibration given by Eqs. (4–162), (4–163), find the force exerted on m_1 through the coupling spring, and show that the motion of x_1 satisfies the equation for a simple harmonic oscillator subject to this driving force.

20. The system of coupled oscillators shown in Fig. 4–10 is subject to an applied force

$$F = F_0 \cos \omega t,$$

applied to mass m_1. Set up the equations of motion and find the steady state solution. Sketch the amplitude and phase of the oscillations of each oscillator as functions of ω.

21. Find the two normal modes of vibration for a pair of identical damped coupled harmonic oscillators [Eqs. (4–180), (4–181)]. That is, $m_1 = m_2$, $b_1 = b_2$, $k_1 = k_2$. (*Hint:* If $k_3 = 0$, you can certainly find the solution. You will find this point helpful in factoring the secular equation.)

22. Set up the equations of motion for the system shown in Fig. 4–16. The relaxed lengths of the two springs are l_1, l_2. Separate the problem into two problems, one involving the motion of the center of mass, and the other involving the "internal motion" described by the two coordinates x_1, x_2. Find the normal modes of vibration.

CHAPTER 5

RIGID BODIES. STATICS

5–1 The dynamical problem of the motion of a rigid body. In order to apply the theorems of the preceding chapter to the motion of a rigid body, we regard a rigid body as a system of many particles whose positions relative to one another remain fixed. We may define a rigid body as a system of particles whose mutual distances are all constant. The forces which hold the particles at fixed distances from one another are internal forces, and may be imagined as exerted by rigid weightless rods connected between all pairs of particles. Forces like this which maintain certain fixed relations between the particles of a system are called *forces of constraint*. Such forces of constraint can always be regarded as satisfying Newton's third law (strong form), since the constraints *could* be maintained by rigid rods fastened to the particles by frictionless universal joints. We may therefore apply the theorems of conservation of linear and angular momentum to the motion of a rigid body. For a perfectly rigid body, the theorem of conservation of mechanical energy holds also, since we can show by Newton's third law that the forces of constraint do no work in a rigid motion of the system of particles. The work done by the force exerted by a moving rod on a particle at one end is equal and opposite to the work done by the force exerted by the rod on a particle at the other end, since both particles have the same component of velocity in the direction of the rod (Fig. 5–1):

$$\mathbf{F}_{2\to1} \cdot \mathbf{v}_1 + \mathbf{F}_{1\to2} \cdot \mathbf{v}_2 = \mathbf{F}_{2\to1} \cdot \mathbf{v}_1 - \mathbf{F}_{2\to1} \cdot \mathbf{v}_2 \qquad (5\text{–}1)$$
$$= \mathbf{F}_{2\to1} \cdot (\mathbf{v}_1 - \mathbf{v}_2)$$
$$= 0.$$

We shall base our derivation of the equations of motion of a rigid body on these conservation laws. No actual solid body is ever perfectly rigid, so that our theory of the motion of rigid bodies will be an idealized approximation to the motion of actual bodies. However, in most applications the deviation of actual solid bodies from true rigidity is not significant. In a like spirit is our assumption that the ideal rigid body can be imagined as made up of ideal point particles held at fixed distances from one another.

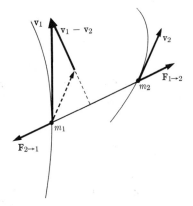

Fig. 5–1. Forces exerted by two particles connected by a rigid rod.

177

A solid body of ordinary size is composed of such a large number of atoms and molecules that for most purposes it is more convenient to represent its structure by specifying the average density ρ of mass per unit volume at each point in the body. The density is defined by:

$$\rho = \frac{dM}{dV},\tag{5-2}$$

where dM is the total mass in a volume dV which is to be chosen large enough to contain a large number of atoms, yet small enough so that the properties of the material are practically uniform within the volume dV. Only when a dV satisfying these two requirements can be chosen in the neighborhood of a point in the body can the density ρ be properly defined at that point.   Sums over all the particles, such as occur in the expressions for total mass, total momentum, etc., can be replaced by integrals over the volume of the body. For example, the total mass is

$$M = \sum_i m_i = \iiint_{(body)} \rho \, dV.\tag{5-3}$$

Further examples will appear in the following sections.

In order to describe the position of a rigid body in space, six coordinates are needed.   We may, for example, specify the coordinates (x_1, y_1, z_1) of some point P_1 in the body.   Any other point P_2 of the body a distance r from P_1 will then lie somewhere on a sphere of radius r with center at (x_1, y_1, z_1).   We can locate P_2 on this sphere with two coordinates, for example, the spherical coordinate angles θ_2, φ_2 with respect to a set of axes through the point (x_1, y_1, z_1).   Any third point P_3 a distance $a \neq 0$ from the line through P_1 and P_2 must now lie on a circle of radius a about this line.   We can locate P_3 on this circle with one coordinate.   We thus require a total of six coordinates to locate the three points P_1, P_2, P_3 of the body, and when three noncollinear points are fixed, the locations of all points of a rigid body are fixed.   There are many possible ways of choosing six coordinates by which the position of a body in space can be specified.   Usually three of the six coordinates are used as above to locate some point in the body.   The remaining three coordinates determine the orientation of the body about this point.

If a body is not connected to any supports, so that it is free to move in any manner, it is convenient to choose the center of mass as the point to be located by three coordinates (X, Y, Z), or by the vector $\mathbf{R}$.   The motion of the center of mass $\mathbf{R}$ is then determined by the linear momentum theorem, which can be expressed in the form (4–18):

$$M\ddot{\mathbf{R}} = \mathbf{F},\tag{5-4}$$

where M is the total mass and $\mathbf{F}$ is the total external force.   The discussion of this part of the motion of the body is then reduced to the problem

of Chapter 3. It remains to discuss the rotational motion of the body
about the point **R**. If a body is connected to supports or pivots in such a
way that it can only rotate about some fixed point or some fixed axis, then
there is no problem of translational motion; the only problem is to discuss
the rotational motions about the fixed point or fixed axis.

The treatment of rotational motions about either the center of mass **R**
or about a fixed point P is based on the angular momentum theorem
[Eq. (4–28)]:

$$\frac{d\mathbf{L}}{dt} = \mathbf{N}, \qquad (5\text{--}5)$$

where **L** is the angular momentum and **N** is the torque about the point **R**
or P. The difficulty in applying Eq. (5–5) lies in the choice of three
coordinates to describe the orientation of the body in space. The first
thought that comes to mind is to choose a zero position for the body, and
to specify any other orientation by specifying the angles of rotation $\varphi_x, \varphi_y, \varphi_z$,
about three perpendicular axes, required to bring the body to this orienta-
tion. However, a little experimenting with a solid body will convince any-
one that no suitable coordinates of this sort exist. Consider, for example,
the position specified by $\varphi_x = 90°$, $\varphi_y = 90°$, $\varphi_z = 0$. If a body is first
rotated 90° about the x-axis, and then 90° about the y-axis, the final position will be found to be different from that resulting from a 90° rotation
about the y-axis followed by a 90° rotation about the x-axis. It turns out
that no simple symmetric set of coordinates can be found to describe the
orientation of a body, analogous to the coordinates x,y,z which locate the
position of a point in space. We therefore omit the treatment of the rather
difficult problem of the rotational motion of a body around a point, which
is most simply and elegantly treated by advanced mathematical techniques
that are beyond the scope of this text.* We shall discuss only the simple
problem of rotational motions about a fixed axis.

5–2 Rotation about an axis. It requires only one coordinate to specify
the orientation of a body which is free to rotate only about a fixed axis.
Let the fixed axis be taken as the z-axis, and let a line $\overline{OA}$ in the body,
through the axis and lying in (or parallel to) the xy-plane, be chosen. We
fix the position of the body by specifying the angle θ between the line $\overline{OA}$
fixed in the body and the x-axis. Choosing cylindrical coordinates to
locate each particle in the body, we now compute the total angular momentum about the z-axis. (See Fig. 5–2.) We shall write r_i instead of ρ_i to
represent the distance of particle m_i from the z-axis, in order to avoid confusion with the density ρ:

$$L = \sum_i m_i r_i^2 \dot{\varphi}_i. \qquad (5\text{--}6)$$

---

* See, e.g., Goldstein, *Classical Mechanics.* Cambridge: Addison-Wesley Pub.
Co., Inc., 1950. (Chapters 4 and 5.)

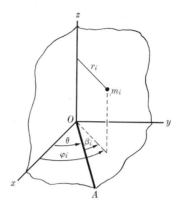

FIG. 5-2.   Coordinates of a particle in a rigid body.

Let β_i be the angle between the direction of the line $\overline{OA}$ in the body and the direction of the radius from the z-axis to the particle m_i.   Then, for a rigid body, β_i is constant, and

$$\varphi_i = \theta + \beta_i, \tag{5-7}$$
$$\dot{\varphi}_i = \dot{\theta}. \tag{5-8}$$

Substituting in Eq. (5-6), we have

$$L = \sum_i m_i r_i^2 \dot{\theta}$$
$$= \left(\sum_i m_i r_i^2\right) \dot{\theta}$$
$$= I_z \dot{\theta}, \tag{5-9}$$

where

$$I_z = \sum_i m_i r_i^2. \tag{5-10}$$

The quantity I_z is a constant for a given body rotating about a given axis, and is called the *moment of inertia* about that axis.   We may also express I_z as an integral over the body:

$$I_z = \iiint\limits_{(body)} \rho r^2 \, dV. \tag{5-11}$$

It is sometimes convenient to introduce the *radius of gyration* k_z defined by the equation

$$M k_z^2 = I_z; \tag{5-12}$$

that is, k_z is a radius such that if all the mass of the body were situated a distance k_z from the axis, its moment of inertia would be I_z.

Using Eq. (5-9), we may write the component of Eq. (5-5) along the axis of rotation in the form

$$\frac{dL}{dt} = I_z\ddot{\theta} = N_z, \tag{5-13}$$

where N_z is the total external torque about the axis. Equation (5–13) is the equation of motion for rotation of a rigid body about a fixed axis. It has the same form as Eq. (2–1) for the motion of a particle along a straight line. The problem of rotation of a body about a fixed axis is therefore equivalent to the problem treated in Chapter 2. All methods and results of Chapter 2 can be extended directly to the present problem according to the following scheme of analogy:

Rectilinear motion		Rotation about a fixed axis	
position:	x	angular position:	θ
velocity:	$v = \dot{x}$	angular velocity:	$\omega = \dot{\theta}$
acceleration:	$a = \ddot{x}$	angular acceleration:	$\alpha = \ddot{\theta}$
force:	F	torque:	N_z
mass:	m	moment of inertia:	I_z
potential energy:		potential energy:	

$$V(x) = -\int_{x_s}^{x} F(x)\,dx \qquad\qquad V(\theta) = -\int_{\theta_s}^{\theta} N_z(\theta)\,d\theta$$

$$F(x) = -\frac{dV}{dx} \qquad\qquad N_z(\theta) = -\frac{dV}{d\theta}$$

kinetic energy:	$T = \frac{1}{2}m\dot{x}^2$	kinetic energy:	$T = \frac{1}{2}I_z\dot{\theta}^2$
linear momentum:	$p = m\dot{x}$	angular momentum:	$L = I_z\dot{\theta}$

The only mathematical difference between the two problems is that the moment of inertia I_z depends upon the location of the axis in the body, while the mass of a body does not depend on its position or on its motion. This does not affect the treatment of rotation about a single fixed axis.

The rotational potential and kinetic energies defined by the equations

$$V(\theta) = -\int_{\theta_s}^{\theta} N_z(\theta)\,d\theta, \tag{5-14}$$

$$N_z = -\frac{dV}{d\theta}, \tag{5-15}$$

$$T = \frac{1}{2}I_z\dot{\theta}^2, \tag{5-16}$$

are not merely analogous to the corresponding quantities defined by Eqs. (2–41), (2–47), and (2–5) for linear motion. They are, in fact, equal to the potential and kinetic energies, defined in Chapters 3 and 4, of the system of particles making up the rigid body. The potential energy defined by Eq. (5–14), for example, is the work done against the forces whose torque is N_z, when the body is rotated through the angle $\theta - \theta_s$. The kinetic energy defined by Eq. (5–16) is just the sum of the ordinary kinetic energies of motion of the particles making up the body. The proof of these statements is left as an exercise.

5–3 The simple pendulum.   As an example of the treatment of rotational motion, we consider the motion of a simple pendulum, consisting of a mass m suspended from a fixed point O by a string or weightless rigid rod of length l.   If a string supports the mass m, we must suppose that it remains taut, so that the distance l from m to O remains constant; otherwise we cannot treat the system as a rigid one.   We consider only motions of the pendulum in one vertical plane, in order to be able to apply the simple theory of motion about a single fixed axis through O.   We then have (Fig. 5–3)

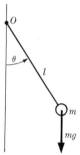

$$I_z = ml^2, \qquad (5\text{--}17)$$
$$N_z = -mgl \sin \theta, \qquad (5\text{--}18)$$

where the z-axis is an axis through O perpendicular to the plane in which the pendulum is swinging.   The torque is taken as negative, since it acts in such a direction as to decrease the angle θ.   Substituting in the equation of motion (5–13), we find

Fig. 5–3.   The simple pendulum.

$$\ddot{\theta} = -\frac{g}{l} \sin \theta. \qquad (5\text{--}19)$$

This equation is not easy to solve.   If, however, we consider only small oscillations of the pendulum (say $\theta \ll \pi/2$), then $\sin \theta \doteq \theta$, and we can write

$$\ddot{\theta} + \frac{g}{l}\, \theta \doteq 0. \qquad (5\text{--}20)$$

This is of the same form as Eq. (2–84) for the harmonic oscillator.   Its solution is

$$\theta = \kappa \cos(\omega t + \beta), \qquad (5\text{--}21)$$

where

$$\omega = \left(\frac{g}{l}\right)^{\frac{1}{2}}, \qquad (5\text{--}22)$$

and κ and β are arbitrary constants which determine the amplitude and phase of the oscillation.   Notice that the frequency of oscillation is independent of the amplitude, provided the amplitude is small enough so that Eq. (5–20) is a good approximation.   This is the basis for the use of a pendulum to regulate the speed of a clock.

We can treat the problem of motion at large amplitudes by means of the energy integral.   The potential energy associated with the torque given by Eq. (5–18) is

$$V(\theta) = -\int_{\theta_s}^{\theta} -mgl \sin \theta \; d\theta$$
$$= -mgl \cos \theta, \qquad (5\text{--}23)$$

where we have taken $\theta_s = \pi/2$ for convenience. We could have written down $V(\theta)$ right away as the gravitational potential energy of a mass m, referred to the horizontal plane through O as the level of zero potential energy. The energy integral is

$$\tfrac{1}{2}ml^2\dot{\theta}^2 - mgl\cos\theta = E. \tag{5-24}$$

We could prove that E is constant from the equation of motion (5–13), but we need not, since the analogy described in the preceding section guarantees that all theorems for one-dimensional linear motion will hold in their analogous forms for rotational motion about an axis. The potential energy $V(\theta)$ is plotted in Fig. 5–4. We see that for $-mgl < E < mgl$, the motion is an oscillating one, becoming simple harmonic motion for E slightly greater than $-mgl$. For $E > mgl$, the motion is nonoscillatory; θ steadily increases or steadily decreases, with $\dot{\theta}$ oscillating between a maximum and minimum value. Physically, when $E > mgl$, the pendulum has enough energy to swing around in a complete circle. (In this case, of course, the mass must be held by a rigid rod instead of a string, unless θ is very large.) This motion is still a periodic one, the pendulum making one complete revolution each time θ increases or decreases by 2π. In either case, the attempt to solve Eq. (5–24) for θ leads to the equation

$$\int_{\theta_0}^{\theta} \frac{d\theta}{\left(\dfrac{E}{mgl} + \cos\theta\right)^{\frac{1}{2}}} = \left(\frac{2g}{l}\right)^{\frac{1}{2}} t. \tag{5-25}$$

The integral on the left must be evaluated in terms of elliptic functions. The period of the motion can be obtained by integrating between appropriate limits. When the motion is oscillatory ($E < mgl$), the maximum value κ of θ is given, according to Eq. (5–24), by

$$E = -mgl\cos\kappa. \tag{5-26}$$

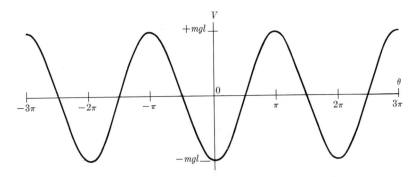

Fig. 5–4.　Potential energy for simple pendulum.

Equation (5–25) becomes, in this case,

$$\int_{\theta_0}^{\theta} \frac{d\theta}{(\cos\theta - \cos\kappa)^{\frac{1}{2}}} = \left(\frac{2g}{l}\right)^{\frac{1}{2}} t, \tag{5–27}$$

which can also be written

$$\int_{\theta_0}^{\theta} \frac{d\theta}{\left(\sin^2\frac{\kappa}{2} - \sin^2\frac{\theta}{2}\right)^{\frac{1}{2}}} = 2\left(\frac{g}{l}\right)^{\frac{1}{2}} t. \tag{5–28}$$

The angle θ oscillates between the limits $\pm\kappa$. We now introduce a new variable φ which runs from 0 to 2π for one cycle of oscillation of θ:

$$\sin\varphi = \frac{\sin\dfrac{\theta}{2}}{\sin\dfrac{\kappa}{2}} = \frac{1}{a}\sin\frac{\theta}{2}, \tag{5–29}$$

where

$$a = \sin\frac{\kappa}{2}. \tag{5–30}$$

With these substitutions, Eq. (5–28) can be written

$$\int_0^{\varphi} \frac{d\varphi}{(1 - a^2\sin^2\varphi)^{\frac{1}{2}}} = \left(\frac{g}{l}\right)^{\frac{1}{2}} t, \tag{5–31}$$

where we have taken $\theta_0 = 0$, for convenience. The integral is now in a standard form for elliptic integrals. When a is small, the integrand can be expanded in a power series in a^2:

$$\int_0^{\varphi} [1 + \tfrac{1}{2}a^2\sin^2\varphi + \cdots]\, d\varphi = \left(\frac{g}{l}\right)^{\frac{1}{2}} t. \tag{5–32}$$

This can be integrated term by term:

$$\varphi + \tfrac{1}{8}a^2(2\varphi - \sin 2\varphi) + \cdots = \left(\frac{g}{l}\right)^{\frac{1}{2}} t. \tag{5–33}$$

The period of the motion is obtained by setting $\varphi = 2\pi$:

$$\tau = 2\pi\left(\frac{l}{g}\right)^{\frac{1}{2}}\left(1 + \frac{a^2}{4} + \cdots\right). \tag{5–34}$$

Thus as the amplitude of oscillation becomes large, the period becomes slightly longer than for small oscillations, a prediction which is readily verified experimentally by setting up two pendulums of equal length and setting them to swinging at unequal amplitudes. Equation (5–33) can be solved approximately for φ by successive approximations, and the result substituted in Eq. (5–29), which can be solved for θ by successive approximations. The result, to a second approximation, is

$$\theta \doteq \left(\kappa + \frac{\kappa^3}{192}\right) \sin \omega't + \frac{\kappa^3}{192} \sin 3\omega't, \tag{5–35}$$

where

$$\omega' = \frac{2\pi}{\tau} = \left(\frac{g}{l}\right)^{\frac{1}{2}}\left(1 - \frac{\kappa^2}{16} + \cdots\right). \tag{5–36}$$

If we neglect terms in κ^2 and κ^3, this solution agrees with Eq. (5–21). At larger amplitudes in second approximation, the frequency is slightly lower than at small amplitudes, and the motion of θ contains a small third harmonic term.

5–4 The compound pendulum. A rigid body suspended and free to swing about an axis is called a *compound pendulum*. We assume that the axis does not pass through the center of mass, and we specify the position of the body by the angle θ between a vertical line and a perpendicular line drawn from a point O on the axis, through the center of mass G (Fig. 5–5). In order to compute the total torque exerted by gravity, we anticipate a theorem, to be proved later, that the total torque is the same as if the total gravitational force were applied at the center of mass G. We then have, using Eqs. (5–12) and (5–13),

$$Mk_O^2\ddot{\theta} = -Mgh \sin \theta, \tag{5–37}$$

where h is the distance $\overline{OG}$. This equation is the same as Eq. (5–19) for a simple pendulum of length l, if we take

$$l = \frac{k_O^2}{h}. \tag{5–38}$$

The point O' a distance l from O along the line through the center of mass G is called the *center of oscillation*. If all the mass M were at O', the motion of the pendulum would be the same as its actual motion, for any given initial conditions. If the distance $\overline{O'G}$ is h', we have

$$l = h + h', \tag{5–39}$$
$$hh' = k_O^2 - h^2. \tag{5–40}$$

It will be shown in the next section that the moment of inertia about any axis equals the moment of inertia about a parallel axis through

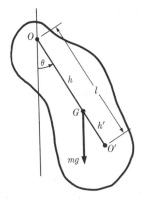

Fig. 5–5. The compound pendulum.

the center of mass G plus Mh^2, where h is the distance from the axis to G. Let k_G be the radius of gyration about G. We then have

$$k_O^2 = k_G^2 + h^2,\qquad(5\text{–}41)$$

so that Eq. (5–40) becomes

$$hh' = k_G^2.\qquad(5\text{–}42)$$

Since this equation is symmetrical in h and h', we conclude that if the body were suspended about a parallel axis through O', the center of oscillation would be at O. The acceleration g of gravity can be measured very accurately by measuring the period of small oscillations of a pendulum and using Eq. (5–22). If a compound pendulum is used, the radius of gyration must be known, or the period measured about two axes, preferably O,O', so that the radius of gyration can be eliminated from the equations.

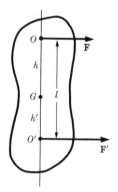

Consider a rigid body suspended from an axis about which it is free to move. Let it be struck a blow at a point O' a distance l from the axis, the direction of the blow being perpendicular to the line $\overline{OO'}$ from the axis to O'. Place O' so that the line $\overline{OO'}$ passes through the center of mass G, and let h,h' be the distances $\overline{OG},\overline{O'G}$ (Fig. 5–6). The impulse delivered at the point O' by the force F' during the blow is

FIG. 5–6. Rigid body pivoted at O and struck a blow at O'.

$$J' = \int F'\,dt.\qquad(5\text{–}43)$$

At the instant the blow is struck, a force F will, in general, have to be exerted on the body at the point O on the axis in order to keep O fixed. The impulse delivered to the body at O is

$$J = \int F\,dt.\qquad(5\text{–}44)$$

An equal and opposite impulse $-J$ is delivered by the body to the support at O. The momentum theorem for the component P of linear momentum of the body in the direction of F is:

$$\frac{dP}{dt} = \frac{d}{dt}(Mh\dot\theta) = F + F',\qquad(5\text{–}45)$$

where $\dot\theta$ is the angular velocity of the body about O. From this we have, for the momentum just after the blow,

$$Mh\dot\theta = J + J',\qquad(5\text{–}46)$$

assuming that the body is initially at rest. The conservation theorem of angular momentum about O is:

$$\frac{dL}{dt} = \frac{d}{dt}(Mk_O^2\dot\theta) = F'l. \tag{5-47}$$

Integrating, we have, for the angular momentum just after the blow,

$$Mk_O^2\dot\theta = J'l. \tag{5-48}$$

We eliminate $\dot\theta$ between Eqs. (5-46) and (5-48):

$$hl = k_O^2\left(1 + \frac{J}{J'}\right). \tag{5-49}$$

We now ask for the condition that no impulsive force be exerted on the axis at O at the instant of the blow, i.e., $J = 0$:

$$hl = k_O^2. \tag{5-50}$$

This equation is identical with Eq. (5-38) and may also be expressed in the symmetrical form [Eq. (5-42)]

$$hh' = k_G^2. \tag{5-51}$$

The point O' at which a blow must be struck in order that no impulse be felt at the point O is called the *center of percussion* relative to O. We see that the center of percussion is the same as the center of oscillation relative to O, and that O is the center of percussion relative to O'. If the body is unsupported, and is struck at O', its initial motion will be a rotation about O. For example, a batter tries to hit a baseball at the center of percussion relative to his hands. If the ball hits very far from the center of percussion, the blow is transmitted to his hands by the bat.

5-5 Computation of centers of mass and moments of inertia. We have given in Section 4-1 the following definition of center of mass for a system of particles:

$$\mathbf{R} = \frac{1}{M}\sum_i m_i \mathbf{r}_i. \tag{5-52}$$

For a solid body, the sum may be expressed as an integral:

$$\mathbf{R} = \frac{1}{M}\int\int\int \rho\mathbf{r}\, dV, \tag{5-53}$$

or, in component form,

$$X = \frac{1}{M}\int\int\int \rho x\, dV, \tag{5-54}$$

$$Y = \frac{1}{M}\int\int\int \rho y\, dV, \tag{5-55}$$

$$Z = \frac{1}{M}\int\int\int \rho z\, dV. \tag{5-56}$$

The integrals can be extended either over the volume of the body, or over all space, since $\rho = 0$ outside the body.   These equations define a point G of the body whose coordinates are (X,Y,Z).   We should first prove that the point G thus defined is independent of the choice of coordinate system. Since Eq. (5–52) or (5–53) is in vector form, and makes no reference to any particular set of axes, the definition of G certainly does not depend on any particular choice of directions for the axes.   We should prove, how-ever, that G is independent also of the choice of origin.   Consider a system of particles, and let any particle m_i be located by vectors $\mathbf{r}_i$ and $\mathbf{r}'_i$ with respect to any two origins O and O'.   If $\mathbf{a}$ is the vector from O to O', the relation between $\mathbf{r}_i$ and $\mathbf{r}'_i$ is (Fig. 5–7)

$$\mathbf{r}_i = \mathbf{r}'_i + \mathbf{a}. \qquad (5\text{–}57)$$

The centers of mass G,G' with re-spect to O,O' are located by the vectors $\mathbf{R}$ and $\mathbf{R}'$, where $\mathbf{R}'$ is defined by

$$\mathbf{R}' = \frac{1}{M} \sum_i m_i \mathbf{r}'_i. \qquad (5\text{–}58)$$

Using Eq. (5–57), we can rewrite Eq. (5–58):

$$\mathbf{R}' = \frac{1}{M} \sum_i m_i(\mathbf{r}_i - \mathbf{a})$$

$$= \frac{1}{M} \sum_i m_i \mathbf{r}_i - \frac{1}{M} \mathbf{a} \sum_i m_i$$

$$= \mathbf{R} - \mathbf{a}. \qquad (5\text{–}59)$$

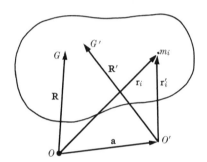

Fig. 5–7.   Location of center of mass relative to two different origins.

Thus $\mathbf{R}$ and $\mathbf{R}'$ are vectors locating the same point with respect to O and O' so that G and G' are the same point.

    General theorems like the one above can be proved either for a system of particles or for a body described by a density ρ.   Whichever point of view is adopted in any proof, a parallel proof can always be given from the other point of view.

    Much of the labor involved in the calculation of the position of the center of mass from Eqs. (5–54), (5–55), (5–56) can often be avoided by the use of certain laborsaving theorems, including the theorem proved above which allows us a free choice of coordinate axes and origin.   We have first the following theorem regarding symmetrical bodies:

    THEOREM.   *If a body is symmetrical with respect to a plane, its center of mass lies in that plane.* (5–60)

When we say a body is symmetrical with respect to a plane, we mean that for every particle on one side of the plane there is a particle of equal mass located at its mirror image in the plane.   For a continuously distributed mass, we mean that the density at any point equals the density at its mirror image in the plane.   Choose the origin in the plane of symmetry, and let the plane of symmetry be the xy-plane. Then in computing Z from Eq. (5–56) [or (5–52)], for each volume element (or particle) at a point (x,y,z) above the xy-plane, there is, by symmetry, a volume element of equal mass at the point $(x,y,-z)$ below the xy-plane, and the contributions of these two elements to the integral in Eq. (5–56) will cancel. Hence $Z = 0$, and the center of mass lies in the xy-plane. This proves Theorem (5–60). The theorem has a number of obvious corollaries:

> *If a body is symmetrical in two planes, its center of mass lies on their line of intersection.* (5–61)

> *If a body is symmetrical about an axis, its center of mass lies on that axis.* (5–62)

> *If a body is symmetrical in three planes with one common point, that point is its center of mass.* (5–63)

> *If a body has spherical symmetry about a point (i.e., if the density depends only on the distance from that point), that point is its center of mass.* (5–64)

These theorems enable us to locate the center of mass immediately in some cases, and to reduce the problem to a computation of only one or two coordinates of the center of mass in other cases. One should be on the lookout for symmetries, and use them to simplify the problem. Other cases not included in these theorems will occur (e.g., the parallelepiped), where it will be evident that certain integrals will be equal or will cancel, and the center of mass can be located without computing them.

Another theorem which often simplifies the location of the center of mass is that if a body is composed of two or more parts whose centers of mass are known, then the center of mass of the composite body can be computed by regarding its component parts as single particles located at their respective centers of mass. Let a body, or system of particles, be composed of n parts of masses $M_1, \ldots, M_n$. Let any part M_k be composed of N_k particles of masses $m_{k1}, \ldots, m_{kN_k}$, located at the points $\mathbf{r}_{k1}, \ldots, \mathbf{r}_{kN_k}$. Then the center of mass of the part M_k is located at the point

$$\mathbf{R}_k = \frac{1}{M_k} \sum_{l=1}^{N_k} m_{kl} \mathbf{r}_{kl}, \tag{5–65}$$

and

$$M_k = \sum_{l=1}^{N_k} m_{kl}. \tag{5–66}$$

The center of mass of the entire body is located at the point

$$\mathbf{R} = \frac{1}{M} \sum_{k=1}^{n} \sum_{l=1}^{N_k} m_{kl} \mathbf{r}_{kl}, \tag{5–67}$$

where

$$M = \sum_{k=1}^{n} \sum_{l=1}^{N_k} m_{kl}. \qquad (5\text{--}68)$$

By Eq. (5–65), Eq. (5–67) becomes

$$\mathbf{R} = \frac{1}{M} \sum_{k=1}^{n} M_k \mathbf{R}_k, \qquad (5\text{--}69)$$

and by Eq. (5–66), Eq. (5–68) becomes

$$M = \sum_{k=1}^{n} M_k. \qquad (5\text{--}70)$$

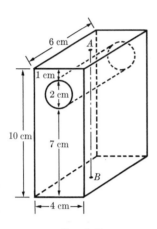

FIG. 5–8.

Equations (5–69) and (5–70) are the mathematical statement of the theorem to be proved.

As an example, let us consider a uniform rectangular block with a cylindrical hole drilled out, as shown in Fig. 5–8. By the symmetry about the two vertical planes bisecting the block parallel to its sides, we conclude that the center of mass lies along the vertical line $\overline{AB}$ through the centers of the top and bottom faces. Let the center of mass of the block lie a distance Z below A, and let the density of the block be ρ. If the hole were not cut out, the mass of the block would be 6 cm $\times$ 4 cm $\times$ 10 cm $\times$ ρ, and its center of mass would be at the midpoint of $\overline{AB}$, 5 cm from A. The mass of the material drilled out is π cm^2 $\times$ 6 cm $\times$ ρ, and its center of mass, before it was removed, was on $\overline{AB}$, 2 cm below A. Hence the theorem (5–69) above allows us to write

(6 cm $\times$ 4 cm $\times$ 10 cm $\times$ ρ) $\times$ 5 cm $=$ (π cm^2 $\times$ 6 cm $\times$ ρ) $\times$ 2 cm
    $+$ 6 cm $\times$ (4 cm $\times$ 10 cm $-$ π cm^2) $\times$ ρ $\times$ Z.

The solution for Z is

$$Z = \frac{6 \times 4 \times 10 \times 5 - \pi \times 6 \times 2}{6 \times (4 \times 10 - \pi)} \text{ cm.}$$

As a second example, we locate the center of mass of a hemisphere of radius a. By symmetry, if the density is uniform, the center of mass lies on the axis of symmetry, which we take as the z-axis. We have then to compute only the integral in Eq. (5–56). The integral can be set up in rectangular, cylindrical, or spherical coordinates (Fig. 5–9):

Rectangular: $Z = \dfrac{1}{M} \displaystyle\int_{z=0}^{a} \int_{y=-(a^2-z^2)^{\frac{1}{2}}}^{(a^2-z^2)^{\frac{1}{2}}} \int_{x=-(a^2-z^2-y^2)^{\frac{1}{2}}}^{(a^2-z^2-y^2)^{\frac{1}{2}}} \rho z \, dx \, dy \, dz.$

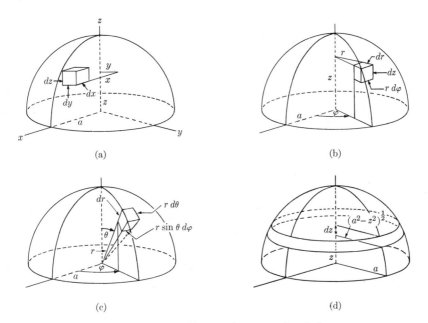

FIG. 5-9. Methods of integrating over a hemisphere.

Cylindrical: $\quad Z = \dfrac{1}{M} \displaystyle\int_{z=0}^{a} \int_{\varphi=0}^{2\pi} \int_{r=0}^{(a^2-z^2)^{\frac{1}{2}}} \rho z r \, dr \, d\varphi \, dz.$

Spherical: $\quad Z = \dfrac{1}{M} \displaystyle\int_{r=0}^{a} \int_{\theta=0}^{\pi/2} \int_{\varphi=0}^{2\pi} (\rho r \cos\theta) r^2 \sin\theta \, dr \, d\theta \, d\varphi.$

Any one of these expressions can be used to evaluate Z for any density distribution. If ρ is uniform, we can also build up the hemisphere out of rings or disks and save one or two integrations. For example, building up the hemisphere out of disks perpendicular to the z-axis (this is equivalent to carrying out the integration over r and φ in cylindrical coordinates), we can write

$$Z = \frac{1}{M} \int_{z=0}^{a} z\rho\pi(a^2 - z^2) \, dz$$

$$= \left(\frac{1}{\frac{2}{3}\pi a^3 \rho}\right)\!\left(\frac{\pi a^4 \rho}{4}\right) = \tfrac{3}{8}a, \qquad (5\text{-}71)$$

where the integrand is $z\rho$ times the volume of a disk of thickness dz, radius $(a^2 - z^2)^{\frac{1}{2}}$.

When the density ρ is uniform, the center of mass of a body depends only on its geometrical shape, and is given by

$$\mathbf{R} = \frac{1}{V} \int\!\!\int\!\!\int_V \mathbf{r} \, dV. \qquad (5\text{-}72)$$

The point G whose coordinate $\mathbf{R}$ is given by Eq. (5–72) is called the *centroid* of the volume V. If we replace the volume V by an area A or curve C in space, we obtain formulas for the centroid of an area or of a curve:

$$\mathbf{R} = \frac{1}{A} \int\!\!\int_A \mathbf{r} \, dA, \tag{5–73}$$

$$\mathbf{R} = \frac{1}{s} \int_C \mathbf{r} \, ds, \tag{5–74}$$

where s is the length of the curve C. The following two theorems, due to Pappus, relate the centroid of an area or curve to the volume or area swept out by it when it is rotated about an axis:

THEOREM 1.   *If a plane curve rotates about an axis in its own plane which does not intersect it, the area of the surface of revolution which it generates is equal to the length of the curve multiplied by the length of the path of its centroid.* (5–75)

THEOREM 2.   *If a plane area rotates about an axis in its own plane which does not intersect it, the volume generated is equal to the area times the length of the path of its centroid.* (5–76)

The proof of Theorem 1 is very simple, with the notation indicated in Fig. 5–10:

$$A = \int_C 2\pi y \, ds$$

$$= 2\pi \int_C y \, ds$$

$$= 2\pi Y s, \tag{5–77}$$

where Y is the y-coordinate of the centroid of the curve C, and s is its length. The proof of Theorem 2 is similar and is left to the reader. These theorems may be used to determine areas and volumes of figures sym-

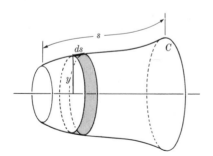

FIG. 5–10.   Pappus' first theorem.

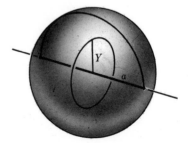

FIG. 5–11.   Sphere formed by rotating a semicircle.

metrical about an axis when the centroids of the generating curves or areas are known, and conversely. We locate, for example, the position of the center of mass of a uniform semicircular disk of radius a, using Pappus' second theorem. If the disk is rotated about its diameter, the volume of the sphere generated, by Pappus' theorem (Fig. 5–11), is

$$\tfrac{4}{3}\pi a^3 = \left(\frac{\pi a^2}{2}\right)(2\pi Y),$$

from which we obtain

$$Y = \frac{4a}{3\pi}. \tag{5–78}$$

The moment of inertia I of a body about an axis is defined by Eq. (5–10):

$$I = \sum_i m_i r_i^2, \tag{5–79}$$

or

$$I = \int \int \int \rho r^2 \, dV, \tag{5–80}$$

where r is the distance from each point or particle of the body to the given axis. We first prove several laborsaving theorems regarding moments of inertia:

PARALLEL AXIS THEOREM. *The moment of inertia of a body about any given axis is the moment of inertia about a parallel axis through the center of mass, plus the moment of inertia about the given axis if all the mass of the body were located at the center of mass.* (5–81)

To prove this theorem, let I_O be the moment of inertia about a z-axis through the point O, and let I_G be the moment of inertia about a parallel axis through the center of mass G. Let $\mathbf{r}$ and $\mathbf{r}'$ be the vectors to any point P in the body, from O and G, respectively, and let $\mathbf{R}$ be the vector from O to G. The components of these vectors will be designated by (x,y,z), (x',y',z'), and (X,Y,Z). Then, since (Fig. 5–12)

$$\mathbf{r} = \mathbf{r}' + \mathbf{R},$$

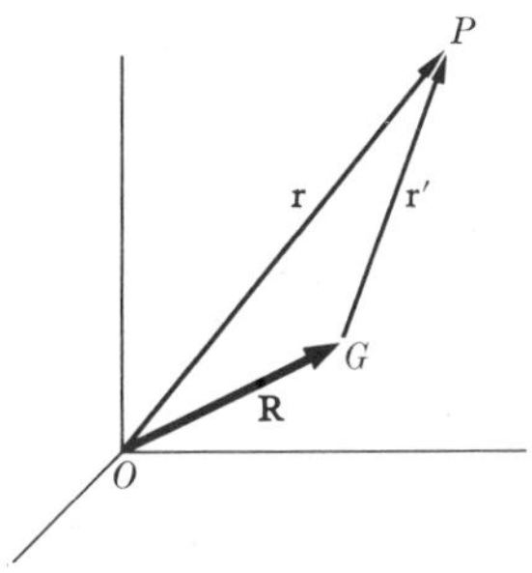

we see that

FIG. 5–12. Location of point P with respect to points O and G.

$$x^2 + y^2 = (x' + X)^2 + (y' + Y)^2$$
$$= x'^2 + y'^2 + X^2 + Y^2 + 2Xx' + 2Yy',$$

so that the moment of inertia I_O is

$$I_O = \int\int\int (x^2 + y^2)\rho\, dV$$

$$= \int\int\int (x'^2 + y'^2)\rho\, dV + (X^2 + Y^2)\int\int\int \rho\, dV + 2X\int\int\int x'\rho\, dV$$

$$+ 2Y\int\int\int y'\rho\, dV. \quad (5\text{-}82)$$

The first integral is I_G, and the integral in the second term is the total mass M of the body.   The integrals in the last two terms are the same as the integrals occurring in Eqs. (5–54) and (5–55), and define the x- and y-coordinates of the center of mass relative to G.   Since G is the center of mass, these integrals are zero, and we have

$$I_O = I_G + M(X^2 + Y^2). \quad (5\text{-}83)$$

This is the mathematical statement of the Parallel Axis Theorem.   If we know the moment of inertia about any axis, and can locate the center of mass, we can use this theorem to determine the moment of inertia about any other parallel axis.

The moment of inertia of a composite body about any axis may be found by adding the moments of inertia of its parts about the same axis, a statement which is obvious from the definition of moment of inertia.   This fact can be put to use in the same way as the analogous result for the center of mass of a composite body.

A body whose mass is concentrated in a single plane is called a *plane lamina*.   We have the following theorem for a plane lamina:

PERPENDICULAR AXIS THEOREM.   *The sum of the moments of inertia of a plane lamina about any two perpendicular axes in the plane of the lamina is equal to the moment of inertia about an axis through their point of intersection perpendicular to the lamina.* (5–84)

The proof of this theorem is very simple.   Consider any particle of mass m in the xy-plane.   Its moments of inertia about the x- and y-axes are

$$I_x = my^2, \quad I_y = mx^2. \quad (5\text{-}85)$$

Adding these, we have the moment of inertia of m about the z-axis:

$$I_x + I_y = m(x^2 + y^2) = I_z. \quad (5\text{-}86)$$

Since the moment of inertia of any lamina in the xy-plane is the sum of the moments of inertia of the particles of which it is composed, we have Theorem (5–84).

We illustrate these theorems by finding the moments of inertia of a uniform circular ring of radius a, mass M, lying in the xy-plane (Fig. 5–13).

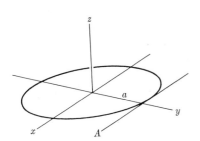

FIG. 5–13. A ring of radius a.

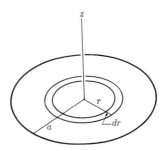

FIG. 5–14.   Finding the moment of inertia of a disk.

The moment of inertia about a z-axis perpendicular to the plane of the ring through its center is easily computed:

$$I_z = Ma^2. \tag{5–87}$$

The moments I_x and I_y are evidently equal, and we have, therefore, by Theorem (5–84),

$$I_x = \tfrac{1}{2}I_z = \tfrac{1}{2}Ma^2. \tag{5–88}$$

The moment of inertia about an axis A tangent to the ring is, by the Parallel Axis Theorem,

$$I_A = I_x + Ma^2 = \tfrac{3}{2}Ma^2. \tag{5–89}$$

The moment of inertia of a solid body can be set up in whatever coordinate system may be convenient for the problem at hand. If the body is uniform and of simple shape, its moment of inertia can be computed by considering it as built up out of rods, rings, disks, etc. For example, the moment of inertia of a circular disk about an axis perpendicular to it through its center can be found by regarding the disk as made up of rings (Fig. 5–14) and using Eq. (5–87):

$$I_z = \int_0^a r^2 \rho 2\pi r \, dr = \frac{\pi a^4 \rho}{2}$$
$$= \tfrac{1}{2}Ma^2. \tag{5–90}$$

The moment of inertia of a solid sphere can be calculated from Eq. (5–90) by regarding the sphere as made up of disks (Fig. 5–15):

$$I = \int_\pi^0 \frac{a^2 \sin^2 \theta}{2} \left(\rho \pi a^2 \sin^2 \theta\right) d(a \cos \theta)$$
$$= \frac{8\pi \rho a^5}{15}$$
$$= \tfrac{2}{5}Ma^2. \tag{5–91}$$

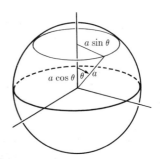

FIG. 5–15.   Finding the moment of inertia of a solid sphere.

A body with a piece cut out can be treated by setting its moment of inertia equal to the moment of inertia of the original body minus the moment of inertia of the piece cut out, all moments being taken, of course, about the same axis.

5–6 Statics of rigid bodies. The equations of motion of a rigid body are Eqs. (5–4) and (5–5):

$$M\ddot{\mathbf{R}} = \sum_i \mathbf{F}_i^e, \tag{5-92}$$

$$\frac{d\mathbf{L}_O}{dt} = \sum_i \mathbf{N}_{iO}^e. \tag{5-93}$$

Equation (5–92) determines the motion of the center of mass, located by the vector $\mathbf{R}$, in terms of the sum of all external forces acting on the body. Equation (5–93) determines the rotational motion about a point O, which may be the center of mass or a point fixed in space, in terms of the total external torque about the point O. Thus if the total external force acting on a rigid body and the total external torque about a suitable point are given, its motion is determined. This would not be true if the body were not rigid, since then it would be deformed by the external forces in a manner depending on the particular points at which they are applied. Since we are concerned only with external forces throughout this section, we may omit the superscript e. It is only necessary to give the total torque about any one point O, since the torque about any other point O' can then be found from the following formula:

$$\sum_i \mathbf{N}_{iO'} = \sum_i \mathbf{N}_{iO} + (\mathbf{r}_O - \mathbf{r}_{O'}) \times \sum_i \mathbf{F}_i, \tag{5-94}$$

where $\mathbf{r}_O, \mathbf{r}_{O'}$ are vectors drawn to the points O, O' from any convenient origin. That is, the total torque about O' is the total torque about O plus the torque about O' if the total force were acting at O. The proof of Eq. (5–94) is very simple. Let $\mathbf{r}_i$ be the vector from the origin to the point at which $\mathbf{F}_i$ acts. Then

$$\sum_i \mathbf{N}_{iO'} = \sum_i (\mathbf{r}_i - \mathbf{r}_{O'}) \times \mathbf{F}_i$$

$$= \sum_i (\mathbf{r}_i - \mathbf{r}_O + \mathbf{r}_O - \mathbf{r}_{O'}) \times \mathbf{F}_i$$

$$= \sum_i (\mathbf{r}_i - \mathbf{r}_O) \times \mathbf{F}_i + \sum_i (\mathbf{r}_O - \mathbf{r}_{O'}) \times \mathbf{F}_i$$

$$= \sum_i \mathbf{N}_{iO} + (\mathbf{r}_O - \mathbf{r}_{O'}) \times \sum_i \mathbf{F}_i.$$

If, in particular, a rigid body is at rest, the left members of Eqs. (5–92) and (5–93) are zero, and we have

$$\sum_i \mathbf{F}_i = \mathbf{0}, \tag{5-95}$$

$$\sum_i \mathbf{N}_i = 0. \tag{5–96}$$

These are the conditions to be satisfied by the external forces and torques in order for a rigid body to be in equilibrium. They are not sufficient to guarantee that the body is at rest, for it might still be in uniform translational and rotational motion, but if the body is initially at rest, it will remain at rest when these conditions are satisfied. It is sufficient for the total torque in Eq. (5–96) to be zero about any point, since then, by Eq. (5–94), it will be zero also about every other point if Eq. (5–95) holds.

In computing the torque due to a force $\mathbf{F}$, it is necessary to know not only the vector $\mathbf{F}$ (magnitude and direction), but also the point P of the body at which the force acts. But if we draw a line through P in the direction of $\mathbf{F}$, then if $\mathbf{F}$ acts at any other point P' of this line, its torque will be the same, since, from the definition of the cross product, it can be seen (Fig. 5–16) that

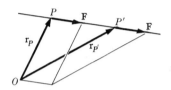

Fig. 5–16. The torque is independent of where along its line of action a force acts.

$$\mathbf{r}_P \times \mathbf{F} = \mathbf{r}_{P'} \times \mathbf{F}. \tag{5–97}$$

(The areas of the parallelograms involved are equal.) The line through P in the direction of $\mathbf{F}$ is called the *line of action* of the force. It is often convenient in computing torques to remember that the force may be considered to act anywhere along its line of action. A distinction is sometimes made in this connection between "free" and "sliding" vectors, the force being a "sliding" vector. The terminology is likely to prove confusing, however, since as far as the motion of the center of mass is concerned [Eq. (5–92)], the force is a "free" vector, i.e., may act anywhere, whereas in computing torques, the force is a "sliding" vector, and for a nonrigid body, each force must be localized at the point where it acts. It is better to define vector, as we defined it in Section 3–1, as a quantity having magnitude and direction, without reference to any particular location in space. Then, in the case of force, we need for some purposes to specify not only the force vector $\mathbf{F}$ itself, but in addition the point or line on which it acts.

A theorem due to Varignon states that if $\mathbf{C} = \mathbf{A} + \mathbf{B}$, then the moment of $\mathbf{C}$ about any point equals the sum of the moments of $\mathbf{A}$ and $\mathbf{B}$, provided $\mathbf{A}$, $\mathbf{B}$, and $\mathbf{C}$ act at the same point. The theorem is an immediate consequence of the vector identity given by Eq. (3–27):

$$\mathbf{r} \times \mathbf{C} = \mathbf{r} \times \mathbf{A} + \mathbf{r} \times \mathbf{B}, \quad \text{if} \quad \mathbf{C} = \mathbf{A} + \mathbf{B}. \tag{5–98}$$

This theorem allows us to compute the torque due to a force by adding the torques due to its components. Combining Varignon's theorem with

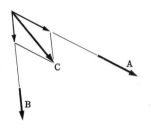

FIG. 5–17. A single force **C** whose torque is the sum of the torques of **A** and **B**.

the result of the preceding paragraph, we may reduce the torque due to two forces **A,B** acting in a plane, as shown in Fig. 5–17, to the torque due to the single force **C**, since both **A** and **B** may be considered to act at the intersection of their lines of action, and Eq. (5–98) then allows us to add them. We could now add **C** similarly to any third force acting in the plane. This process can be continued as long as the lines of action of the forces being added are not parallel, and is related to a more general theorem regarding forces in a plane to be proved below.

Since, for a rigid body, the motion is determined by the total force and total torque, we shall call two systems of forces acting on a rigid body *equivalent* if they give the same total force, and the same total torque about every point. In view of Eq. (5–94), two systems of forces are then equivalent if they give the same total force, and the same total torque about any single point. It is of interest to know, for any system of forces, what is the simplest system of forces equivalent to it.

If a system of forces $\mathbf{F}_i$ acting at points $\mathbf{r}_i$ is equivalent to a single force $\mathbf{F}$ acting at a point $\mathbf{r}$, then the force $\mathbf{F}$ acting at $\mathbf{r}$ is said to be the *resultant* of the system of forces $\mathbf{F}_i$. If $\mathbf{F}$ is the resultant of the system of forces $\mathbf{F}_i$, then we must have

$$\mathbf{F} = \sum_i \mathbf{F}_i, \qquad (5\text{–}99)$$

$$(\mathbf{r} - \mathbf{r}_0) \times \mathbf{F} = \sum_i (\mathbf{r}_i - \mathbf{r}_0) \times \mathbf{F}_i, \qquad (5\text{–}100)$$

where $\mathbf{r}_0$ is any point about which moments are taken. By Eq. (5–94), if Eq. (5–99) holds, and Eq. (5–100) holds for any point $\mathbf{r}_0$, it holds for every point $\mathbf{r}_0$. The force $-\mathbf{F}$ acting at $\mathbf{r}$ is called the *equilibrant* of the system; if the equilibrant is added to the system of forces, the conditions for equilibrium are satisfied.

An example of a system of forces having a resultant is the system of gravitational forces acting on a body near the surface of the earth. We shall show that the resultant in this case acts at the center of mass. Let the acceleration of gravity be $\mathbf{g}$. Then the force acting on a particle m_i is

$$\mathbf{F}_i = m_i\mathbf{g}. \qquad (5\text{–}101)$$

The total force is

$$\mathbf{F} = \sum_i m_i\mathbf{g} = M\mathbf{g}, \qquad (5\text{–}102)$$

where M is the total mass.   The total torque about any point O is, with O as origin,

$$\sum_i \mathbf{N}_{iO} = \sum_i (\mathbf{r}_i \times m_i \mathbf{g})$$
$$= \sum_i (m_i \mathbf{r}_i \times \mathbf{g})$$
$$= \left(\sum_i m_i \mathbf{r}_i \right) \times \mathbf{g}$$
$$= M\mathbf{R} \times \mathbf{g}$$
$$= \mathbf{R} \times M\mathbf{g}, \qquad (5\text{-}103)$$

where $\mathbf{R}$ is the vector from O to the center of mass.   Thus the total torque is given by the force $M\mathbf{g}$ acting at the center of mass.   Because of this result, the center of mass is also called the *center of gravity*.   We shall see in the next chapter that, in general, this result holds only in a uniform gravitational field, i.e., when $\mathbf{g}$ is the same at all points of the body.   If the system of forces acting on a rigid body has a resultant, the forces may be replaced by this resultant in determining the motion of the body.

A system of forces whose sum is zero is called a *couple:*

$$\sum_i \mathbf{F}_i = 0. \qquad (5\text{-}104)$$

A couple evidently has no resultant, except in the trivial case where the total torque is zero also, in which case the resultant force is zero.   By Eqs. (5–94) and (5–104), a couple exerts the same total torque about every point:

$$\sum_i \mathbf{N}_{iO'} = \sum_i \mathbf{N}_{iO}. \qquad (5\text{-}105)$$

Thus a couple is characterized by a single vector, the total torque, and all couples with the same total torque are equivalent.   The simplest system equivalent to any given couple, if we exclude the trivial case where the total torque is zero, is a pair of equal and opposite forces $\mathbf{F}, -\mathbf{F}$, acting at points P, P' separated by a vector $\mathbf{r}$ (Fig. 5–18) such that

$$\sum_i \mathbf{N}_{iO} = \mathbf{r} \times \mathbf{F}. \qquad (5\text{-}106)$$

Equation (5–106) states that the moment of the given couple about O equals the moment of the couple $(\mathbf{F}, -\mathbf{F})$ about P'; the two systems are therefore equivalent, since the point about which the moment of a couple is computed is immaterial. The force $\mathbf{F}$ and the points P and P'

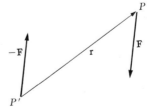

Fig. 5–18.   A simple couple.

are by no means uniquely determined.   Since only the cross product $\mathbf{r} \times \mathbf{F}$
is determined by Eq. (5–106), we can choose P arbitrarily; we can choose
the vector $\mathbf{F}$ arbitrarily except that it must lie in the plane perpendicular to
the total torque; and we can then choose $\mathbf{r}$ as any vector lying in the same
plane and determining with $\mathbf{F}$ a parallelogram whose area is the magnitude
of the total torque.

The problem of finding the simplest system equivalent to any given system of forces is solved by the following theorems:

THEOREM I.   *Every system of forces is equivalent to a single force
through an arbitrary point, plus a couple (either or both of which
may be zero).*   (5–107)

To prove this, we show how to find the equivalent single force and couple.
Let the arbitrary point P be chosen, let the sum of all the forces in the system be $\mathbf{F}$, and let their total torque about the point P be $\mathbf{N}$.   Then, if we
let the single force $\mathbf{F}$ act at P, and add a couple whose torque is $\mathbf{N}$, we have
a system equivalent to the original system.   Since the couple can be com-
posed of two forces, one of which may be allowed to act at an arbitrary
point, we may let one force of the couple act at the point P, and add it to
$\mathbf{F}$ to get a single force acting at P plus the other force of the couple.   This
proves

THEOREM II.   *Any system of forces can be reduced to an equivalent system which contains at most two forces.*   (5–108)

The following theorem can be proved in two ways:

THEOREM III.   *A single nonzero force and a couple in the same
plane (i.e., such that the torque vector of the couple is perpendicular
to the single force) have a resultant and, conversely, a single force
is equivalent to an equal force through any arbitrary point, plus a
couple.*   (5–109)

Since a couple with torque $\mathbf{N}$ is equivalent to a pair of equal and opposite
forces, $\mathbf{F}, -\mathbf{F}$, where $\mathbf{F}$ may be chosen arbitrarily in the plane perpendicular
to $\mathbf{N}$, we may always choose $\mathbf{F}$ equal to the single force mentioned in the
theorem.   Furthermore, we may choose the point of action of $\mathbf{F}$ arbitrarily.
Given a single nonzero force $\mathbf{F}$ acting at P, and a couple, we form a couple
$(\mathbf{F}, -\mathbf{F})$ equivalent to the given couple, and let $-\mathbf{F}$ act at P; $\mathbf{F}$ and $-\mathbf{F}$
then cancel at P, and the remaining force $\mathbf{F}$ of the couple is the single re-
sultant.   The converse can be proved by a similar argument.

The other method of proof is as follows.   Let the given force $\mathbf{F}$ act at a
point P, and let the total torque of the couple be $\mathbf{N}$.   Then the torque of
the system about the point P is $\mathbf{N}$.   We take any vector $\mathbf{r}$, in the plane
perpendicular to $\mathbf{N}$, which forms with $\mathbf{F}$ a parallelogram of area N, and
let P' be the point displaced from P by the vector $\mathbf{r}$.   If the single force $\mathbf{F}$

acts at P', the torque about P will then be **N**, and hence this single force is equivalent to the original force **F** acting at P plus the couple. We can combine Theorems I and III to obtain

THEOREM IV. *Every system of forces is equivalent to a single force plus a couple whose torque is parallel to the single force. (Or, alternatively, every system of forces is equivalent to a couple plus a single force perpendicular to the plane of the couple.)*   (5–110)

To prove this, we use Theorem I to reduce any system to a single force plus a couple, and use Theorem III to eliminate any component of the couple perpendicular to the single force. The point of application of the single force mentioned in Theorem IV is no longer arbitrary, as its line of action will be fixed when we apply Theorem III. Either the single force or the couple may vanish in special cases. For a system of forces in a plane, all torques about any point in the plane are perpendicular to the plane. Hence Theorem IV reduces to

THEOREM V. *Any system of forces in a plane has a resultant, unless it is a couple.*   (5–111)

In practice, the reduction of a complicated system of forces to a simpler system is a problem whose simplest solution is usually obtained by an ingenious application of the various theorems and techniques mentioned in this section. One method which always works, and which is often the simplest if the system of forces is very complicated, is to follow the procedure suggested by the proofs of the above theorems. Find the total force **F** by vector addition, and the total torque **N** about some conveniently chosen point P. Then **F** acting at P, plus a couple of torque **N**, together form a system equivalent to the original system. If **F** is zero, the original system reduces to a couple. If **N** is perpendicular to **F**, the system has a resultant, which can be found by either of the methods indicated in the proof of Theorem III. If **N** is not perpendicular to **F**, and neither is zero, then the system has no resultant, and can be reduced to a system of two forces, as in the derivation of Theorem II, or to a single force and a couple whose torque is parallel to it, as in Theorem IV. It is a matter of taste, or of convenience for the purpose at hand, which of these latter reductions is regarded as the simplest. In fact, for determining the motion of a body, the most convenient reduction is certainly just the reduction given by Theorem I, with the arbitrary point taken as the center of mass.

5–7 Statics of structures. The determination of the forces acting at various points in a solid structure is a problem of utmost importance in all phases of mechanical engineering. There are two principal reasons for wanting to know these forces. First, the engineer must be sure that the materials and construction are such as will withstand the forces which will be acting, without breaking or crushing, and usually without suffering permanent deformation.   Second, since no construction materials are really rigid, but deform elastically and sometimes plastically when subject to forces, it is necessary to calculate the amount of this deformation, and to take it into account, if it is significant, in designing the structure.   When deformation or breaking of a structure is under consideration, the structure obviously cannot be regarded as a rigid body, and we are interested in the actual system of forces acting on and in the structure.   Theorems regarding equivalent systems of forces are not of direct interest in such problems, but are often useful as tools in analyzing parts of the structure which may, to a sufficient approximation, be regarded as rigid, or in suggesting possible equivalent redistributions of forces which would subject the structure to less objectionable stresses while maintaining it in equilibrium.

If a structure is at rest, Eqs. (5–95) and (5–96) are applicable either to the structure as a whole, or to any part of it.   It must be kept in mind that the forces and torques which are to be included in the sums are those which are external to and acting on whichever part of the structure is under consideration.   If the structure is moving, the more general equations (5–92) and (5–93) are applicable.   Either pair of vector equations represents, in general, six component equations, or three if all forces lie in a single plane.   (Why three?)   It may be that the structure is so constructed that when certain of the external forces and their points of application are given, all the internal forces and torques acting on each part of the structure can be determined by appropriate applications of Eqs. (5–95) and (5–96) (in the case of a structure at rest).   Such a structure is said to be *statically determinate*.   An elementary example is shown in Fig. 5–19, which shows a horizontal flagpole AB hinged at point A to a wall and supported by a cable BC.   A force W acts on the pole as shown.   When the force W and the dimensions of the structure are given, it is a simple matter to apply Eqs. (5–95) and (5–96) to the pole and to calculate the force F_1 exerted by the cable and the force F_2 acting through the hinge.   Many examples of statically determinate structures are given in any elementary physics textbook.

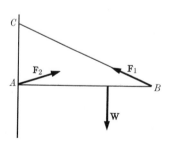

FIG. 5–19.   The flagpole problem.

Suppose now that the hinge at A in Fig. 5–19 were replaced by a welded joint, so that the flagpole would support the load even without the cable BC, provided the joint at A does not break.   Then, given only the weight W, it is evidently impossible to determine the force F_1 exerted by the cable; F_1 may have any value from zero to a rather large value, depending on how tightly the cable is drawn up and on how much stress is applied to the joint at A. Such a structure is said to be *statically indeterminate*. A statically indeterminate structure is one in which the forces acting on its parts are not completely determined by the external forces, but depend also on the distribution of stresses within the structure. To find the internal forces in an indeterminate structure, we would need to know the elastic characteristics of its parts and the precise way in which these parts are distorted. Such problems are usually far more difficult than problems involving determinate structures. Many methods of calculating internal forces in mechanical structures have been developed for application to engineering problems, and some of these are useful in a wide variety of physical problems.

5–8 Stress and strain. If an imaginary surface cuts through any part of a solid structure (a rod, string, cable, or beam), then, in general, the material on one side of this surface will be exerting a force on the material on the other side, and conversely, according to Newton's third law. These internal forces which act across any surface within the solid are called *stresses*. The *stress* is defined as the force per unit area acting across any given surface in the material. If the material on each side of any surface pushes on the material on the other side with a force perpendicular to the surface, the stress is called a *compression*. If the stress is a pull perpendicular to the surface, it is called a *tension*. If the force exerted across the surface is parallel to the surface, it is called a *shearing stress*. Figure 5–20 illustrates these stresses in the case of a beam. The vector labeled $\mathbf{F}_{l \to r}$ represents the force exerted by the left half of the beam on the right half, and the equal and opposite force $\mathbf{F}_{r \to l}$ is exerted on the material on the left by the material on the right. A stress at an angle to a surface can be resolved into a shear component and a tension or compression component. In the most general case, the stress may act in any direction relative to the surface, and may depend on the orientation of the surface. The description of the state of stress of a solid material in the most general case is rather complicated, and is best accomplished by using the mathematical techniques of tensor algebra. Since these methods lie outside the scope of this text, we shall consider only cases in which either the stress is a pure compression, independent

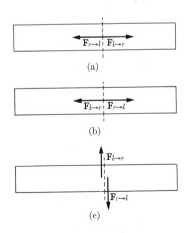

Fig. 5–20. Stresses in a beam. (a) Compression. (b) Tension. (c) Shear.

of the orientation of the surface, or in which only one surface is of interest at any point, so that only a single stress vector is needed to specify the force per unit area across that surface.

If we consider a small volume ΔV of any shape in a stressed material, the material within this volume will be acted on by stress forces exerted across the surface by the material surrounding it. If the material is not perfectly rigid, it will be deformed so that the material in the volume ΔV may have a different shape and size from that which it would have if there were no stress. This deformation of a stressed material is called *strain*. The nature and amount of strain depend on the nature and magnitude of the stresses and on the nature of the material. A suitable definition of *strain*, stating how it is to be measured, will have to be made for each kind of strain. A tension, for example, produces an extension of the material, and the strain would be defined as the fractional increase in length.

If a wire of length l and cross-sectional area A is stretched to length $l + \Delta l$ by a force F, the definitions of stress and strain are

$$\text{stress} = F/A, \qquad (5\text{-}112)$$
$$\text{strain} = \Delta l/l. \qquad (5\text{-}113)$$

It is found experimentally that when the strain is not too large, the stress is proportional to the strain for solid materials. This is Hooke's law, and it is true for all kinds of stress and the corresponding strains. It is also plausible on theoretical grounds for the reasons suggested in the preliminary discussion in Section 2–7. The ratio of stress to strain is therefore constant for any given material if the strain is not too large. In the case of extension of a material in one direction due to tension, this ratio is called *Young's modulus*, and is

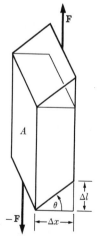

$$Y = \frac{\text{stress}}{\text{strain}} = \frac{Fl}{A \, \Delta l}. \quad (5\text{-}114)$$

If a substance is subjected to a pressure increment Δp, the resulting deformation will be a change in volume, and the strain will be defined by

$$\text{strain} = \frac{\Delta V}{V}. \quad (5\text{-}115)$$

The ratio of stress to strain in this case is called the *bulk modulus B:*

$$B = \frac{\text{stress}}{\text{strain}} = -\frac{\Delta p \, V}{\Delta V}, \quad (5\text{-}116)$$

where the negative sign is introduced in order to make B positive.

Fig. 5–21. Shearing strain.

In the case of a shearing stress, the stress is again defined by Eq. (5–112), where F is the force acting across and parallel to the area A. The resulting shearing strain consists in a motion of A parallel to itself through a distance Δl, relative to a plane parallel to A at a distance Δx from A (Fig. 5–21). The shearing strain is then defined by:

$$\text{strain} = \frac{\Delta l}{\Delta x} = \tan \theta, \qquad (5\text{–}117)$$

where θ is the angle through which a line perpendicular to A is turned as a result of the shearing strain. The ratio of stress to strain in this case is called the *shear modulus n*:

$$n = \frac{\text{stress}}{\text{strain}} = \frac{F}{A \tan \theta}. \qquad (5\text{–}118)$$

An extensive study of methods of solving problems in statics is outside the scope of this text. We shall restrict ourselves in the next three sections to the study of three special types of problems which illustrate the analysis of a physical system, to determine the forces which act upon its parts and to determine the effect of these forces in deforming the system.

5–9 Equilibrium of flexible strings and cables. An ideal flexible string is one which will support no compression or shearing stress, nor any bending moment, so that the force exerted across any point in the string can only be a tension directed along the tangent to the string at that point. Chains and cables used in many structures can be regarded for most purposes as ideal flexible strings.

Let us first take a very simple problem in which a string of negligible weight is suspended between two points P_0 and P_2, and a force $\mathbf{F}_1$ acts at a point P_1 on the string (Fig. 5–22). Let T_0 be the tension in the segment $\overline{P_0 P_1}$, and T_1 the tension in the segment $\overline{P_1 P_2}$. Let l_0 and l_1 be the lengths of these segments of the string, and let l_{02} be the distance between P_0 and P_2. The angles α, β between the two segments of string and the line $\overline{P_0 P_2}$ are determined by the cosine law:

$$\cos \alpha = \frac{l_{02}^2 + l_0^2 - l_1^2}{2 l_0 l_{02}}, \quad \cos \beta = \frac{l_{02}^2 + l_1^2 - l_0^2}{2 l_1 l_{02}}, \qquad (5\text{–}119)$$

so that the position of the point P_1 is independent of the force $\mathbf{F}_1$, provided the string does not stretch. Since the bit of string at the point P_1 is in equilibrium, the vector sum of the three forces $\mathbf{F}_1$, T_0, and T_1 acting on the string at P_1 must vanish, so that these forces form a closed triangle, as indicated in Fig. 5–22. The tensions are then determined in terms of the angle between the force $\mathbf{F}_1$ and the direction of the line $\overline{P_0 P_2}$, by the sine law:

$$T_0 = F_1 \frac{\sin (\beta + \gamma)}{\sin (\alpha + \beta)}, \quad T_1 = F_1 \frac{\sin (\gamma - \alpha)}{\sin (\alpha + \beta)}. \qquad (5\text{–}120)$$

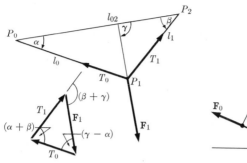

FIG. 5–22.　A flexible string held at three points.

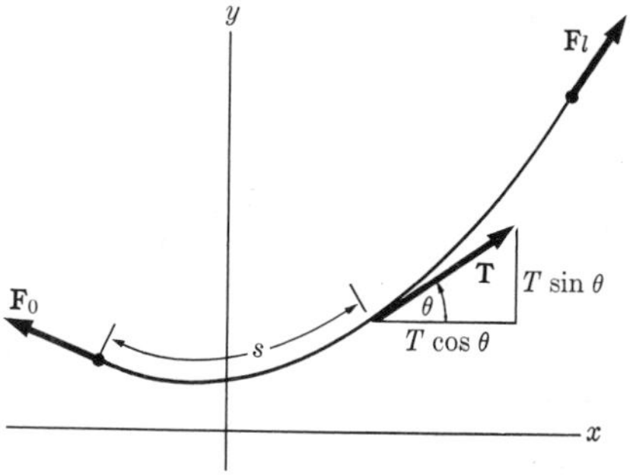

FIG. 5–23.　A flexible string hanging under its own weight.

Now suppose that the string stretches according to Hooke's law, so that

$$l_0 = l_0'(1 + kT_0), \quad l_1 = l_1'(1 + kT_1), \tag{5–121}$$

where l_0', l_1' are the unstretched lengths, and k is a constant [$1/k$ would be Young's modulus, Eq. (5–114), multiplied by the cross-sectional area of the string]. The unknown quantities T_0, T_1, l_0, and l_1 can be eliminated from Eqs. (5–119) by substitution from Eqs. (5–120) and (5–121). We then have two rather complicated equations to be solved for the angles α and β. The solution must be carried out by numerical methods when numerical values of l_0', l_1', k, l_{02}, F_1, and γ are given. When α and β are found, T_0, T_1, l_0, and l_1 can be found from Eqs. (5–120) and (5–121). One way of solving these equations by successive approximations is to assume first that the string does not stretch, so that $l_0 = l_0'$, $l_1 = l_1'$, and to calculate α and β from Eqs. (5–119), and T_0, T_1 from Eqs. (5–120). Using these values of T_0, T_1, we then calculate l_0, l_1 from Eqs. (5–121). The new values of l_0, l_1 can be used in Eqs. (5–119) to get better values for α, β from which better values of T_0, T_1 can be calculated. These can be used to get still better values for l_0, l_1 from Eqs. (5–121), and so on. As this process is repeated, the successive calculated values of $\alpha, \beta, T_0, T_1, l_0, l_1$ will converge toward the true values. If the string stretches only very little, the first few repetitions will be sufficient to give very close values. The method suggested here is an example of a very general class of methods of solution of physical problems by successive approximations. It is an example of what are called *relaxation methods* of solving statics problems.

We next consider a string acted on by forces distributed continuously along the length of the string. A point on the string will be specified by its distance s from one end, measured along the string. Let $\mathbf{f}(s)$ be the force per unit length at the point s, that is, the force on a small segment of length ds is $\mathbf{f}\, ds$. Then the total force acting on the length of string between the end $s = 0$ and the point s is zero if the string is in equilibrium:

$$\mathbf{F}_0 + \int_0^s \mathbf{f}\, ds + \mathbf{T}(s) = \mathbf{0}, \tag{5-122}$$

where $\mathbf{F}_0$ is the supporting force at the end $s = 0$, and $\mathbf{T}(s)$ is a vector whose magnitude is the tension at the point s, oriented in the direction of increasing s. By differentiating Eq. (5-122) with respect to s, we obtain a differential equation for $\mathbf{T}(s)$:

$$\frac{d\mathbf{T}}{ds} = -\mathbf{f}. \tag{5-123}$$

The simplest and most important application of Eq. (5-123) is to the case of a string having a weight w per unit length. If the string is acted on by no other forces except at the ends, it will hang in a vertical plane, which we take to be the xy-plane, with the x-axis horizontal and the y-axis vertical. Let θ be the angle between the string and the x-axis (Fig. 5-23). Then the horizontal and vertical components of Eq. (5-123) become:

$$\frac{d}{ds}(T \sin \theta) = w, \tag{5-124}$$

$$\frac{d}{ds}(T \cos \theta) = 0. \tag{5-125}$$

Equation (5-125) implies that

$$T \cos \theta = C. \tag{5-126}$$

The horizontal component of tension is constant, as it should be since the external forces on the string are all vertical, except at the ends. By dividing Eq. (5-124) by C, and using Eq. (5-126), we eliminate the tension:

$$\frac{d \tan \theta}{ds} = \frac{w}{C}. \tag{5-127}$$

If we represent the string by specifying the function $y(x)$, we have the relations

$$\tan \theta = \frac{dy}{dx} = y', \tag{5-128}$$

$$ds = [(dx)^2 + (dy)^2]^{\frac{1}{2}} = dx(1 + y'^2)^{\frac{1}{2}}, \tag{5-129}$$

so that Eq. (5-127) becomes

$$\frac{dy'}{dx} = \frac{w}{C}(1 + y'^2)^{\frac{1}{2}}. \tag{5-130}$$

This can be integrated, if w is constant:

$$\int \frac{dy'}{(1 + y'^2)^{\frac{1}{2}}} = \int \frac{w}{C}\, dx, \tag{5-131}$$

$$\sinh^{-1} y' = \frac{wx}{C} + \alpha, \tag{5-132}$$

where α is a constant. We solve for y':

$$y' = \frac{dy}{dx} = \sinh\left(\frac{wx}{C} + \alpha\right). \tag{5-133}$$

This can be integrated again, and we obtain

$$y = \beta + \frac{C}{w}\cosh\left(\frac{wx}{C} + \alpha\right). \tag{5-134}$$

The curve represented by Eq. (5–134) is called a *catenary*, and is the form in which a uniform string will hang if acted on by no force other than its own weight, except at the ends. The constants C, β, and α are to be chosen so that y has the proper value at the end points, and so that the total length of the string has the proper value. The total length is

$$l = \int ds = \int_{x_0}^{x_l} (1 + y'^2)^{\frac{1}{2}}\, dx$$

$$= \int_{x_0}^{x_l} \cosh\left(\frac{wx}{C} + \alpha\right) dx$$

$$= \frac{C}{w}\left[\sinh\left(\frac{wx_l}{C} + \alpha\right) - \sinh\left(\frac{wx_0}{C} + \alpha\right)\right]. \tag{5-135}$$

5–10 Equilibrium of solid beams. A horizontal beam subject to vertical forces is one of the simplest examples of a structure subject to shearing forces and bending moments. To simplify the problem, we shall consider only the case when the beam is under no compression or tension, and we shall assume that the beam is so cいnstructed and the forces so applied that the beam bends in only one vertical plane, without any torsion (twisting) about the axis of the beam. We find first the stresses within the beam from a knowledge of the external forces, and then determine the distortion of the beam due to these stresses.

Points along the beam will be located by a coordinate x measured horizontally from the left end of the beam (Fig. 5–24). Let vertical forces $F_1, \ldots, F_n$ act at the distances $x_1, \ldots, x_n$ from the left end. A force will be taken as positive if it is directed upward. Let AA' be a plane perpendicular to the beam at any distance x from the end. According to Theorem I (5–107), of Section 5–6, the system of forces exerted across the plane AA' by the material on the right against that on

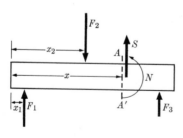

Fig. 5–24. Forces acting on a beam.

the left is equivalent to a single force $\mathbf{S}$ through any point in the plane, and a couple of torque $\mathbf{N}$. (Note that in applying Theorem I, we are treating the plane AA' as a rigid body, that is, we are assuming that the cross-sectional plane AA' is not distorted by the forces acting on it.) In the case we are considering there is no compression or tension and all forces are vertical, so that $\mathbf{S}$ is directed vertically. We shall define the *shearing force S* as the vertical force acting across AA' from right to left; S will be taken as positive when this force is directed upward, negative when it is downward.* By Newton's third law, the force acting across AA' from left to right is $-S$. Since we are assuming no torsion about the axis of the beam (x-axis), and since all the forces are vertical, the torque $\mathbf{N}$ will be directed horizontally and perpendicular to the beam. We shall define the *bending moment N* as the torque exerted from right to left across AA' about a horizontal axis in the plane AA'; N will be taken as positive when it tends to rotate the plane AA' in a counterclockwise direction. Since S is vertical, the torque will be the same about any horizontal axis in the plane AA'.

The shearing force S and bending moment N can be determined by applying the conditions of equilibrium [Eqs. (5–95) and (5–96)] to the part of the beam to the left of the plane AA'. The total force and total torque about a horizontal axis in the plane AA' are, if we neglect the weight of the beam,

$$\sum_{x_i < x} F_i + S = 0, \tag{5–136}$$

$$-N_0 - \sum_{x_i < x} (x - x_i)F_i + N = 0, \tag{5–137}$$

where the sums are taken over all forces acting to the left of AA' and N_0 is the bending moment, if any, exerted by the left end of the beam against its support. The torque N_0 will appear only if the beam is clamped or otherwise fastened at its left end. The force exerted by any clamp or other support at the end is to be included among the forces F_i. If the beam has a weight w per unit length, this should be included in the equilibrium equations:

$$\sum_{x_i < x} F_i - \int_0^x w \, dx + S = 0, \tag{5–138}$$

$$-N_0 - \sum_{x_i < x} (x - x_i)F_i + \int_0^x (x - x')w \, dx' + N = 0. \tag{5–139}$$

---

* This sign convention for S is in agreement with sign conventions throughout this book, where the upward direction is taken as positive. Sign conventions for shearing force and bending moment are not uniform in physics and engineering texts, and one must be careful in reading the literature to note what sign convention is adopted by each author.

The shearing force and bending moment at a distance x from the end are therefore

$$S = -\sum_{x_i < x} F_i + \int_0^x w \, dx, \qquad (5\text{-}140)$$

$$N = N_0 + \sum_{x_i < x} (x - x_i)F_i - \int_0^x (x - x')w \, dx'. \qquad (5\text{-}141)$$

If there is any additional force distributed continuously along the beam, this can be included in w as an additional weight per unit length. If the beam is free at its ends, the shearing force and bending moment must be zero at the ends. If we set $S = N = 0$ at the right end of the beam, equations (5-140) and (5-141) may be solved for two of the forces acting on the beam when the others are known. If the beam is fastened or clamped at either end, S and N may have any values there. Equations (5-140) and (5-141) determine S and N everywhere along the beam when all the forces are known, including the force and torque exerted through the clamp, if any, on the left end. The shearing force and bending moment may be plotted as functions of x whose slopes at any point are obtained by differentiating Eqs. (5-140) and (5-141):

$$\frac{dS}{dx} = w, \qquad (5\text{-}142)$$

$$\frac{dN}{dx} = \sum_{x_i < x} F_i - \int_0^x w \, dx' = -S. \qquad (5\text{-}143)$$

The shearing force increases by $-F_i$ from left to right across a point x_i where a force F_i acts.

Let us now consider the distortion produced by the shearing forces and bending moments in a beam of uniform cross section throughout its length. In Fig. 5-25(a) is shown an undistorted horizontal beam through which are drawn a horizontal line OO' and a vertical plane AA'. In Fig. 5-25(b) the beam is under a shearing strain, the effect of which is to slide the various vertical planes relative to one another so that the line OO' makes an angle θ

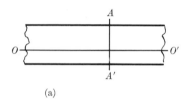

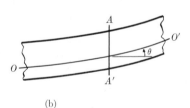

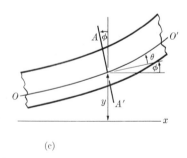

FIG. 5-25. Distortion of a beam by shearing and bending. (a) Undistorted beam. (b) Beam in shear. (c) Beam bent and in shear.

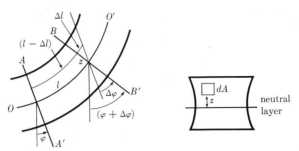

FIG. 5–26.   Strains in a bent beam.

with the normal to the plane AA'.   According to Eq. (5–118), the angle θ is given in terms of the shearing force S and the shear modulus n by:

$$\theta = \frac{S}{nA},\qquad (5\text{–}144)$$

where A is the cross-sectional area, and we have made the approximation $\tan\theta \doteq \theta$, since θ will be very small.   In Fig. 5–25(c), we show the further effect of bending the beam.   The plane AA' now makes an angle φ with the vertical.   It is assumed that the cross-sectional surface AA' remains plane and retains its shape when the beam is under stress, although this may not be strictly true near the points where forces are applied.   In order to determine φ, we consider two planes AA' and BB' initially vertical and a small distance l apart.   When the beam is bent, AA' and BB' will make angles φ and $\varphi + \Delta\varphi$ with the vertical (Fig. 5–26).   Due to the bending, the fibers on the outside of the curved beam will be stretched and those on the inside will be compressed.   Somewhere within the beam will be a neutral layer of unstretched fibers, and we shall agree to draw the line OO' so that it lies in this neutral layer.   A line between AA' and BB' parallel to OO' and a distance z above OO' will be compressed to a length $l - \Delta l$, where (see Fig. 5–26)

$$\Delta l = z\,\Delta\varphi.\qquad (5\text{–}145)$$

The compressive force dF exerted across an element of area dA a distance z above the neutral layer OO' will be given by Eq. (5–114) in terms of Young's modulus:

$$\frac{dF}{dA} = Y\frac{\Delta l}{l} = Yz\frac{\Delta\varphi}{l},\qquad (5\text{–}146)$$

or, if we let $l = ds$, an infinitesimal element of length along the line OO',

$$\frac{dF}{dA} = Yz\frac{d\varphi}{ds}.\qquad (5\text{–}147)$$

This equation is important in the design of beams, as it determines the stress of compression or tension at any distance z from the neutral layer.

The total compressive force through the cross-sectional area A of the beam will be

$$F = \int\!\!\int_A dF = Y\frac{d\varphi}{ds}\int\!\!\int_A z\,dA. \tag{5-148}$$

Since we are assuming no net tension or compression of the beam, $F = 0$, and

$$\int\!\!\int_A z\,dA = 0. \tag{5-149}$$

This implies that the neutral layer contains the centroid of the area A of the beam, and we may require that OO' be drawn through the centroid of the cross-sectional area of the beam. The bending moment exerted by the forces dF is

$$N = \int\!\!\int_A z\,dF = Y\frac{d\varphi}{ds}\int\!\!\int_A z^2\,dA$$

$$= Yk^2A\,\frac{d\varphi}{ds}, \tag{5-150}$$

where

$$k^2 = \frac{1}{A}\int\!\!\int_A z^2\,dA, \tag{5-151}$$

and k is the radius of gyration of the cross-sectional area of the beam about a horizontal axis through its centroid. The differential equation for φ is therefore

$$\frac{d\varphi}{ds} = \frac{N}{Yk^2A}. \tag{5-152}$$

Let the upward deflection of the beam from a horizontal x-axis be $y(x)$, measured to the line OO' (Fig. 5-25). Then $y(x)$ is to be determined by solving the equation

$$\frac{dy}{dx} = \tan(\theta + \varphi), \tag{5-153}$$

when θ and φ have been determined from Eqs. (5-144) and (5-152). If we assume that both θ and φ are very small angles, Eqs. (5-152) and (5-153) become

$$\frac{d\varphi}{dx} = \frac{N}{Yk^2A}, \tag{5-154}$$

$$\frac{dy}{dx} = \theta + \varphi. \tag{5-155}$$

When there are no concentrated forces F_i along the beam, we may differentiate Eq. (5-155) and make use of Eqs. (5-154), (5-144), (5-142), and (5-143) to obtain

$$\frac{d^2y}{dx^2} = \frac{w}{nA} + \frac{N}{Yk^2A}, \tag{5-156}$$

$$\frac{d^4y}{dx^4} = \frac{1}{nA}\frac{d^2w}{dx^2} - \frac{w}{Yk^2A}. \tag{5-157}$$

If bending can be neglected, as in a short, thick beam, Eq. (5–156) with $N = 0$ becomes a second order differential equation to be solved for $y(x)$. For a longer beam, Eq. (5–157) must be used. These equations can also be used when concentrated loads F_i are present, by solving them for each segment of the beam between the points where the forces F_i are applied, and fitting the solutions together properly at these points. The solutions on either side of a point x_i where a force F_i is applied must be chosen so that y, φ, N are continuous across x_i, while S, dN/dx, dy/dx, d^3y/dx^3 increase across the point x_i by an amount determined by Eqs. (5–140), (5–143), (5–155), and (5–156). The solution of Eq. (5–156) will contain two arbitrary constants, and that of Eq. (5–157), four, which are to be determined by the conditions at the ends of the beam or segment of beam.

As an example, we consider a uniform beam of weight W, length L, clamped in a horizontal position (i.e., so that $\varphi = 0$)* at its left end ($x = 0$), and with a force $F_1 = -W'$ exerted on its right end ($x = L$). In this case, Eq. (5–157) becomes

$$\frac{d^4y}{dx^4} = -\frac{W}{Yk^2AL}. \tag{5-158}$$

The solution is

$$y = -\frac{Wx^4}{24\,Yk^2AL} + \tfrac{1}{6}C_3x^3 + \tfrac{1}{2}C_2x^2 + C_1x + C_0. \tag{5-159}$$

To determine the constants C_0, C_1, C_2, C_3, we have at the left end of the beam:

$$y = C_0 = 0, \tag{5-160}$$

$$\frac{dy}{dx} = C_1 = \theta = \frac{S}{nA} = -\frac{W + W'}{nA}, \tag{5-161}$$

where we have used Eqs. (5–155) and (5–144). We need two more conditions, which may be determined in a variety of ways. The easiest way in this case is to apply Eq. (5–156) and its derivative at the left end of the beam:

$$\frac{d^2y}{dx^2} = C_2 = \frac{W}{nAL} - \frac{W'L + \tfrac{1}{2}WL}{Yk^2A}, \tag{5-162}$$

$$\frac{d^3y}{dx^3} = C_3 = \frac{1}{Yk^2A}\frac{dN}{dx} = -\frac{S}{Yk^2A} = \frac{W' + W}{Yk^2A}, \tag{5-163}$$

---

* The condition $\varphi = 0$ means that the plane AA' is vertical, that is, the beam would be horizontal if there were no shearing strain.

where we have used Eq. (5–143). The deflection of the beam at any point x is then

$$y = -\frac{L^3}{Yk^2A}\left[\frac{Wx^2}{4L^2}\left(1 - \frac{2}{3}\frac{x}{L} + \frac{1}{6}\frac{x^2}{L^2}\right) + \frac{W'x^2}{2L^2}\left(1 - \frac{1}{3}\frac{x}{L}\right)\right]$$
$$- \frac{L}{nA}\left[\frac{Wx}{L}\left(1 - \frac{1}{2}\frac{x}{L}\right) + \frac{W'x}{L}\right]. \quad (5\text{–}164)$$

The deflection at $x = L$ is

$$y = -\frac{L^3}{Yk^2A}\left[\tfrac{1}{8}W + \tfrac{1}{3}W\right] - \frac{L}{nA}\left[\tfrac{1}{2}W + W'\right]. \quad (5\text{–}165)$$

The first term in each equation is the deflection due to bending, and the second is that due to shear. The first term is proportional to L^3, and inversely proportional to k^2. The second term is proportional to L and independent of k. Hence bending is more important for long, thin beams, and shear is more important for short, thick beams. Our analysis here is probably not very accurate for short, thick beams, since, as pointed out above, some of our assumptions are not valid near points of support or points where loads are applied (where "near" means relative to the cross-sectional dimensions of the beam).

5–11 Equilibrium of fluids. A *fluid* is defined as a substance which will support no shearing stress when in equilibrium. Liquids and gases fit this definition, and even very viscous substances like pitch, or tar, or the material in the interior of the earth, will eventually come to an equilibrium in which shearing stresses are absent, if they are left undisturbed for a sufficiently long time. The stress F/A across any small area A in a fluid in equilibrium must be normal to A, and in practically all cases it will be a compression rather than a tension.

We first prove that the stress F/A near any point in the fluid is independent of the orientation of the surface A. Let any two directions be given, and construct a small triangular prism with two equal faces $A_1 = A_2$ perpendicular to the two given directions. The third face A_3 is to form with A_1 and A_2 a cross section having the shape of an isosceles triangle (Fig. 5–27). Let $\mathbf{F_1}, \mathbf{F_2}, \mathbf{F_3}$ be the stress forces perpendicular to the faces A_1, A_2, A_3. If the fluid in the prism is in equilibrium,

$$\mathbf{F_1} + \mathbf{F_2} + \mathbf{F_3} = 0. \quad (5\text{–}166)$$

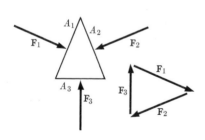

Fig. 5–27. Forces on a triangular prism in a fluid.

The forces on the end faces of the prism need not be included here, since they are perpendicular to $\mathbf{F_1}$,

$\mathbf{F}_2$, and $\mathbf{F}_3$, and must therefore separately add to zero. It follows from Eq. (5–166), and from the way the prism has been constructed, that $\mathbf{F}_1$, $\mathbf{F}_2$, and $\mathbf{F}_3$ must form an isosceles triangle (Fig. 5–27), and therefore that

$$F_1 = F_2. \tag{5–167}$$

Since the directions of $\mathbf{F}_1$ and $\mathbf{F}_2$ are any two directions in the fluid, and since $A_1 = A_2$, the stress F/A is the same in all directions. The stress in a fluid is called the *pressure p:*

$$p = \frac{F_1}{A_1} = \frac{F_2}{A_2}. \tag{5–168}$$

Now suppose that in addition to the pressure the fluid is subject to an external force $\mathbf{f}$ per unit volume of fluid, that is, any small volume dV in the fluid is acted on by a force $\mathbf{f}\,dV$. Such a force is called a *body force;* $\mathbf{f}$ is the body force density. The most common example is the gravitational force, for which

$$\mathbf{f} = \rho\mathbf{g}, \tag{5–169}$$

where $\mathbf{g}$ is the acceleration of gravity, and ρ is the density. In general, the body force density may differ in magnitude and direction at different points in the fluid. In the usual case, when the body force is given by Eq. (5–169), $\mathbf{g}$ will be constant and $\mathbf{f}$ will be constant in direction; if ρ is constant, $\mathbf{f}$ will also be constant in magnitude. Let us consider two nearby points P_1,P_2 in the fluid, separated by a vector $d\mathbf{r}$. We construct a cylinder of length $d\mathbf{r}$ and cross-sectional area dA, whose end faces contain the points P_1 and P_2. Then the total component of force in the direction of $d\mathbf{r}$ acting on the fluid in the cylinder, since the fluid is in equilibrium, will be

$$\mathbf{f} \cdot d\mathbf{r}\, dA + p_1\, dA - p_2\, dA = 0,$$

where p_1 and p_2 are the pressures at P_1 and P_2. The difference in pressure between two points a distance $d\mathbf{r}$ apart is therefore

$$dp = p_2 - p_1 = \mathbf{f} \cdot d\mathbf{r}. \tag{5–170}$$

The total difference in pressure between two points in the fluid located by vectors $\mathbf{r}_1$ and $\mathbf{r}_2$ will be

$$p_2 - p_1 = \int_{\mathbf{r}_1}^{\mathbf{r}_2} \mathbf{f} \cdot d\mathbf{r}, \tag{5–171}$$

where the line integral on the right is to be taken along some path lying entirely within the fluid from $\mathbf{r}_1$ to $\mathbf{r}_2$. Given the pressure p_1 at $\mathbf{r}_1$, Eq. (5–171) allows us to compute the pressure at any other point $\mathbf{r}_2$ which can be joined to $\mathbf{r}_1$ by a path lying within the fluid. The difference in pressure between any two points depends only on the body force. Hence any change in pressure at any point in a fluid in equilibrium must be accompanied by an equal change at all other points if the body force does not change. This is Pascal's law.

According to the geometrical definition (3–107) of the gradient, Eq. (5–170) implies that

$$\mathbf{f} = \nabla p. \qquad (5\text{–}172)$$

The pressure gradient in a fluid in equilibrium must be equal to the body force density. This result shows that the net force per unit volume due to pressure is $-\nabla p$. The pressure p is a sort of potential energy per unit volume in the sense that its negative gradient represents a force per unit volume due to pressure. However, the integral of $p\,dV$ over a volume does not represent a potential energy except in very special cases. Equation (5–172) implies that the surfaces of constant pressure in the fluid are everywhere perpendicular to the body force. According to Eqs. (3–187) and (5–172), the force density $\mathbf{f}$ must satisfy the equation

$$\nabla \times \mathbf{f} = 0. \qquad (5\text{–}173)$$

This is therefore a necessary condition on the body force in order for equilibrium to be possible. It is also a sufficient condition for the possibility of equilibrium. This follows from the discussion in Section 3–12, for if Eq. (5–173) holds, then it is permissible to define a function $p(\mathbf{r})$ by the equation

$$p(\mathbf{r}) = p_1 + \int_{\mathbf{r}_1}^{\mathbf{r}} \mathbf{f} \cdot d\mathbf{r}, \qquad (5\text{–}174)$$

where p_1 is the pressure at some fixed point $\mathbf{r}_1$, and the integral may be evaluated along any path from $\mathbf{r}_1$ to $\mathbf{r}$ within the fluid. If the pressure in the fluid at every point $\mathbf{r}$ has the value $p(\mathbf{r})$ given by (5–174), then Eq. (5–172) will hold, and the body force $\mathbf{f}$ per unit volume will everywhere be balanced by the pressure force $-\nabla p$ per unit volume. Equation (5–174) therefore defines an equilibrium pressure distribution for any body force satisfying Eq. (5–173).

The problem of finding the pressure within a fluid in equilibrium, if the body force density $\mathbf{f}(\mathbf{r})$ is given, is evidently mathematically identical with the problem discussed in Section 3–12 of finding the potential energy for a given force function $\mathbf{F}(\mathbf{r})$. We first check that $\nabla \times \mathbf{f}$ is zero everywhere within the fluid, in order to be sure that an equilibrium is possible. We then take a point $\mathbf{r}_1$ at which the pressure is known, and use Eq. (5–174) to find the pressure at any other point, taking the integral along any convenient path.

The total body force acting on a volume V of the fluid is

$$\mathbf{F}_b = \int\!\!\int_V\!\!\int \mathbf{f}\,dV. \qquad (5\text{–}175)$$

The total force due to the pressure on the surface A of V is

$$\mathbf{F}_p = -\int\int_A \mathbf{n}p\, dA, \tag{5-176}$$

where $\mathbf{n}$ is the outward normal unit vector at any point on the surface. These two must be equal and opposite, since the fluid is in equilibrium:

$$\mathbf{F}_p = -\mathbf{F}_b. \tag{5-177}$$

Equation (5–176) gives the total force due to pressure on the surface of the volume V, whether or not V is occupied by fluid. Hence we conclude from Eq. (5–177) that a body immersed in a fluid in equilibrium is acted on by a force $\mathbf{F}_p$ due to pressure, equal and opposite to the body force $\mathbf{F}_b$ which would be exerted on the volume V if it were occupied by fluid in equilibrium. This is Archimedes' principle. Combining Eqs. (5–172), (5–175), (5–176), and (5–177), we have

$$\int\int_A \mathbf{n}p\, dA = \int\int\int_V \nabla p\, dV. \tag{5-178}$$

This equation resembles Gauss' divergence theorem [Eq. (3–115)], except that the integrands are $\mathbf{n}p$ and ∇p instead of $\mathbf{n}\cdot\mathbf{A}$ and $\nabla\cdot\mathbf{A}$. Gauss' theorem can, in fact, be proved in a very useful general form which allows us to replace the factor $\mathbf{n}$ in a surface integral by ∇ in the corresponding volume integral without any restrictions on the form of the integrand except that it must be so written that the differentiation symbol ∇ operates on the entire integrand.* Given this result, we could start with Eqs. (5–175), (5–176), and (5–177), and deduce Eq. (5–172):

$$\mathbf{F}_b + \mathbf{F}_p = \int\int\int_V \mathbf{f}\, dV - \int\int_A \mathbf{n}p\, dA$$

$$= \int\int\int_V (\mathbf{f} - \nabla p)\, dV = 0. \tag{5-179}$$

Since this must hold for any volume V, Eq. (5–172) follows.

So far we have been considering only the pressure, i.e., the stress, in a fluid. The strain produced by the pressure within a fluid is a change in volume per unit mass of the fluid or, equivalently, a change in density. If Hooke's law is satisfied, the change dV in a volume V produced by a small change dp in pressure can be calculated from Eq. (5–116), if the bulk modulus B is known:

$$\frac{dV}{V} = -\frac{dp}{B}. \tag{5-180}$$

---

* For the proof of this theorem, see Phillips, *Vector Analysis*. New York: John Wiley and Sons, 1933. (Chapter III, Section 34.)

If the mass of fluid in the volume V is M, then the density is

$$\rho = \frac{M}{V}, \tag{5-181}$$

and the change $d\rho$ in density corresponding to an infinitesimal change dV in volume is given by

$$\frac{d\rho}{\rho} = -\frac{dV}{V}, \tag{5-182}$$

so that the change in density produced by a small pressure change dp is

$$\frac{d\rho}{\rho} = \frac{dp}{B}. \tag{5-183}$$

After a finite change in pressure from p_0 to p, the density will be

$$\rho = \rho_0 \exp\left(\int_{p_0}^{p} \frac{dp}{B}\right). \tag{5-184}$$

In any case, the density of a fluid is determined by its equation of state in terms of the pressure and temperature. The equation of state for a perfect gas is

$$pV = RT, \tag{5-185}$$

where T is the absolute temperature, V is the volume per mole, and R is the universal gas constant:

$$R = 8.314 \times 10^7 \text{ erg-deg}^{-1} \text{ C-mole}^{-1}. \tag{5-186}$$

By substitution from Eq. (5-181), we obtain the density in terms of pressure and temperature:

$$\rho = \frac{Mp}{RT}, \tag{5-187}$$

where M is the molecular weight.

Let us apply these results to the most common case, in which the body force is the gravitational force on a fluid in a uniform vertical gravitational field [Eq. (5-169)]. If we apply Eq. (5-173) to this case, we have

$$\nabla \times \mathbf{f} = \nabla \times (\rho\mathbf{g}) = 0. \tag{5-188}$$

Since $\mathbf{g}$ is constant, the differentiation implied by the ∇ symbol operates only on ρ, and we can move the scalar ρ from one factor of the cross product to the other to obtain:

$$(\nabla\rho) \times \mathbf{g} = 0, \tag{5-189}$$

that is, the density gradient must be parallel to the gravitational field. The density must be constant on any horizontal plane *within* the fluid. Equation (5-189) may also be derived from Eq. (5-188) by writing out explicitly the components of the vectors $\nabla \times (\rho\mathbf{g})$ and $(\nabla\rho) \times \mathbf{g}$, and verifying that they are the same.* According to Eq. (5–172), the pressure is also constant in any horizontal plane *within* the fluid. Pressure and density are therefore functions only of the vertical height z within the fluid. From Eqs. (5–172) and (5–169) we obtain a differential equation for pressure as a function of z:

$$\frac{dp}{dz} = -\rho g. \qquad (5\text{–}190)$$

If the fluid is incompressible, and ρ is **uniform, the solution is**

$$p = p_0 - \rho g z, \qquad (5\text{–}191)$$

where p_0 is the pressure at $z = 0$. If the fluid is a perfect gas, either p or ρ may be eliminated from Eq. (5–190) by means of Eq. (5–187). If we eliminate the density, we have

$$\frac{dp}{dz} = -\frac{Mg}{RT} p. \qquad (5\text{–}192)$$

As an example, if we assume that the atmosphere is uniform in temperature and composition, we can solve Eq. (5–192) for the atmospheric pressure as a function of altitude:

$$p = p_0 \exp\left(-\frac{Mg}{RT} z\right). \qquad (5\text{–}193)$$

PROBLEMS

1. (a) Prove that the total kinetic energy of the system of particles making up a rigid body, as defined by Eq. (4–37), is correctly given by Eq. (5–16) when the body rotates about a fixed axis. (b) Prove that the potential energy given by Eq. (5–14) is the total work done against the external forces when the body is rotated from θ_s to θ, if N_z is the sum of the torques about the axis of rotation due to the external forces.

2. Prove, starting with the equation of motion (5–13) for rotation, that if N_z is a function of θ alone, then $T + V$ is constant.

3. The balance wheel of a watch consists of a ring of mass M, radius a, with spokes of negligible mass. The hairspring exerts a restoring torque $N_z = -k\theta$. Find the motion if the balance wheel is rotated through an angle θ_0 and released.

4. A wheel of mass M, radius of gyration k, spins smoothly on a fixed horizontal axle of radius a which passes through a hole of slightly larger radius at the hub of the wheel. The coefficient of friction between the bearing surfaces is μ. If the wheel is initially spinning with angular velocity ω_0, find the time and the number of turns that it takes to stop.

---

*Equation (5–189) holds also in a nonuniform gravitational field, since $\nabla \times \mathbf{g} = \mathbf{0}$, by Eq. (6–21).

5. An airplane propeller of moment of inertia I is subject to a driving torque

$$N = N_0(1 + \alpha \cos \omega_0 t),$$

and to a frictional torque due to air resistance

$$N_f = -b\dot{\theta}.$$

Find its steady state motion.

6. Derive Eqs. (5–35) and (5–36).

7. A compound pendulum is arranged to swing about either of two parallel axes through two points O, O' located on a line through the center of mass. The distances h, h' from O, O' to the center of mass, and the periods τ, τ' of small amplitude vibrations about the axes through O and O' are measured. O and O' are arranged so that each is approximately the center of oscillation relative to the other. If $\tau = \tau'$, find a formula for g in terms of measured quantities. If $\tau' = \tau(1 + \delta)$, where $\delta \ll 1$, find a correction to be added to your previous formula so that it will be correct to terms of order δ.

8. A baseball bat held horizontally at rest is struck at a point O' by a ball which delivers a horizontal impulse J' perpendicular to the bat. Let the bat be initially parallel to the x-axis, and let the baseball be traveling in the negative direction parallel to the y-axis.   The center of mass G of the bat is initially at the origin, and the point O' is at a distance h' from G.   Assuming that the bat is let go just as the ball strikes it, and neglecting the effect of gravity, calculate and sketch the motion $x(t), y(t)$ of the center of mass, and also of the center of percussion, during the first few moments after the blow, say until the bat has rotated a quarter turn. Comment on the difference between the initial motion of the center of mass and that of the center of percussion.

9. A circular disk of radius a lies in the xy-plane with its center at the origin. The half of the disk above the x-axis has a density σ per unit area, and the half below the x-axis has a density 2σ.   Find the center of mass G, and the moments of inertia about the x-, y-, and z-axes, and about parallel axes through G.   Make as much use of laborsaving theorems as possible.

10. (a) Work out a formula for the moments of inertia of a cone of mass m, height h, and generating angle α, about its axis of symmetry, and about an axis through the apex perpendicular to the axis of symmetry.   Find the center of mass

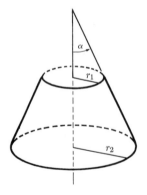

Fig. 5–28. Frustum of a cone.

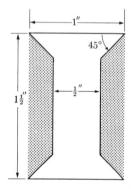

Fig. 5–29. How much thread can be wound on this spool?

of the cone.   (b) Use these results to determine the center of mass of the frustum
of a cone, shown in Fig. 5–28, and to calculate the moments of inertia about horizontal axes through each base and through the center of mass. The mass of the
frustum is M.

11. How many yards of thread 0.03 inch in diameter can be wound on the
spool shown in Fig. 5–29?

12. Given that the volume of a cone is one-third the area of the base times the
height, locate by Pappus' theorem the centroid of a right triangle whose legs are
of lengths a and b.

13. Prove that Pappus' second theorem holds even if the axis of revolution inter-
sects the surface, provided that we take as volume the difference in the volumes
generated by the two parts into which the surface is divided by the axis.   What
is the corresponding generalization of the first theorem?

14. (a) Find a formula for the radius
of gyration of a uniform rod of length l
about an axis through one end making
an angle α with the rod.   (b) Using
this result, find the moment of inertia of
an equilateral triangular pyramid, constructed out of six uniform rods, about
an axis through its centroid and one of
its vertices.

15. (a) Reduce the system of ·forces
acting on the cube shown in Fig. 5–30 to
an equivalent single force acting at the
center of the cube, plus a couple composed of two forces acting at two adjacent corners. (b) Reduce this system to
a system of two forces, and state where
these forces act.   (c) Reduce this system to a single force plus a torque
parallel to it.

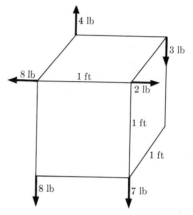

FIG. 5–30.   A system of forces acting on
a cube.

16. A cable 20 ft long is suspended between two points A and B, 15 ft apart.
The line AB makes an angle of 30° with the horizontal (B higher).   A weight of
500 lb is hung from a point C 8 ft from the end of the cable at A.   (a) Find the position of point C, and the tensions in the cable, if the cable does not stretch.   (b) If
the cable is $\frac{1}{2}$ inch in diameter and has a Young's modulus of 32,000 lb-in^{-2}, find the
position of point C and the tensions, taking cable stretch into account.   Carry
out two successive approximations, and estimate the accuracy of your result.

17. (a) A cable of length l, weight w per unit length, is suspended from the
points $x = \pm a$ on the x-axis.   The y-axis is vertical.   By requiring that $y = 0$ at
$x = \pm a$, and that the total length of cable be l, show that $\alpha = 0$ in Eq. (5–134),
and set up equations to be solved for β and C.   (b) Show that the same results
can be obtained for α and C by requiring that the cable be symmetrical about the
y-axis, and that the forces at its ends balance the weight of the cable.   (c) Set up
the equations from which β, α, and C are to be determined if a weight W is hung
at the mid-point of the cable.

18. A bridge of weight w per unit length is to be hung from cables of negligible
weight, as shown in Fig. 5–31.   It is desired to determine the shape of the suspension cables so that the vertical cables, which are equally spaced, will support equal
weights.   Assume that the vertical cables are so closely spaced that we can regard
the weight w per unit length as continuously distributed along the suspension cable.

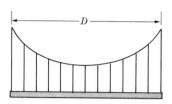

FIG. 5-31.   A suspension bridge.

The problem then differs from that treated in the text, where the string had a weight w per unit length s along the string, in that here there is a weight w per unit horizontal distance x. Set up a differential equation for the shape $y(x)$ of the suspension cable, and solve for $y(x)$ if the ends are at the points $y = 0$, $x = \pm \frac{1}{2}D$, and if the maximum tension in the cable is to be T_0.

19. A cable is to be especially designed to hang vertically and to support a load W at a distance l below the point of support. The cable is to be made of a material having a Young's modulus Y and a weight w per unit volume. Inasmuch as the length l of the cable is to be fairly great, it is desired to keep the weight of the cable to a minimum by making the cross-sectional area $A(z)$ of the cable, at a height z above the lower end, just great enough to support the load beneath it. The cable material can safely support a load just great enough to stretch it 1%. Determine the function $A(z)$ when the cable is supporting the given load.

20. An I-beam has upper and lower flanges of width a, connected by a center web of height b. The web and flanges are of the same thickness c, assumed negligible with respect to a and b, and are made of a material with Young's modulus Y, shear modulus n. The beam has a weight W, length L, and rests on supports at each end. A load W' rests on the mid-point of the beam. Find the deflection of the beam at its mid-point. Separate the deflection into terms due to shear and to bending, and into terms due to the beam weight W and the load W'.

21. An empty pipe of inner radius a, outer radius b, is made of material with Young's modulus Y, shear modulus n, density ρ. A horizontal section of length L is clamped at both ends. Find the deflection at the center. Find the increase in deflection when the pipe is filled with a fluid of density ρ_0.

22. Find the atmospheric pressure as a function of altitude on the assumption that the temperature decreases with altitude, the decrease being proportional to the altitude.

23. If the bulk modulus of water is B, and the atmospheric pressure at the surface of the ocean is p_0, find the pressure as a function of depth in the ocean, taking into account the compressibility of the water. Assume that B is constant. Look up B for water, and estimate the error that would be made at a depth of 5 miles if the compressibility were neglected.

CHAPTER 6

GRAVITATION

6–1 Centers of gravity for extended bodies. You will recall that we formulated the law of gravitation in Section 1–5. Any two particles of masses m_1 and m_2, a distance r apart, attract each other with a force whose magnitude is given by Eq. (1–11):

$$F = \frac{Gm_1m_2}{r^2}, \tag{6-1}$$

where

$$G = 6.658 \times 10^{-8} \text{ dyne-cm}^2\text{-gm}^{-2}, \tag{6-2}$$

as determined by measurements of the forces between large lead spheres, carried out by means of a delicate torsion balance. Equation (6–1) can be written in a vector form which gives both the direction and magnitude of the attractive forces. Let r_1 and r_2 be the position vectors of the two particles. Then the gravitational force on m_2 due to m_1 is

$$\mathbf{F}_{1\to2} = \frac{Gm_1m_2}{|\mathbf{r}_1 - \mathbf{r}_2|^3} (\mathbf{r}_1 - \mathbf{r}_2). \tag{6-3}$$

The vector $(\mathbf{r}_1 - \mathbf{r}_2)$ gives the force the correct direction, and its magnitude is divided out by the extra factor $|\mathbf{r}_1 - \mathbf{r}_2|$ in the denominator.

The law of gravitation as formulated in Eq. (6–3) is applicable only to particles or to bodies whose dimensions are negligible compared with the distance between them; otherwise the distance $|\mathbf{r}_1 - \mathbf{r}_2|$ is not precisely defined, nor is it immediately clear at what points and in what directions the forces act. For extended bodies, we must imagine each body divided into pieces or elements, small compared with the distances between the bodies, and compute the forces on each of the elements of one body due to each of the elements of the other bodies.

Consider now an extended body of mass M and a particle of mass m at a point P (Fig. 6–1). If the body of mass M is divided into small pieces of masses m_i, each piece is attracted toward m by a force which we shall call $\mathbf{F}_i$. Now the system of forces $\mathbf{F}_i$ can be resolved accord-

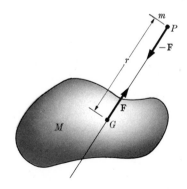

Fig. 6–1. Gravitational attraction between a particle and an extended body.

223

ing to Theorem I of Section 5–6 (5–107) into a single force through an arbitrary point, plus a couple.   Let this single force be **F**:

$$\mathbf{F} = \sum_i \mathbf{F}_i, \qquad (6\text{--}4)$$

and let the arbitrary point be taken as the point P.   Since none of the forces $\mathbf{F}_i$ exerts any torque about P, the total torque about P is zero, and the couple vanishes.   The system of forces therefore has a resultant **F** acting along a line through the mass m.   The force acting on m is $-\mathbf{F}$, since Newton's third law applies to each of the forces $\mathbf{F}_i$ in Eq. (6–4). We locate on this line of action of **F** a point G a distance r from P such that

$$|\mathbf{F}| = \frac{GmM}{r^2}. \qquad (6\text{--}5)$$

Then the system of gravitational forces between the body M and the particle m is equivalent to the single resultant forces **F** on M and $-\mathbf{F}$ on m which would act if all the mass of the body M were concentrated at G. The point G is called the *center of gravity* of the body M *relative to the point P; G* is not, in general, at the center of mass of body M, nor even on the line joining P with the center of mass.   The parts of the body close to P are attracted more strongly than those farther away, whereas in finding the center of mass, all parts of the body are treated alike.   Furthermore, the position of the point G will depend on the position of P.   When P is far away compared with the dimensions of the body, the acceleration of gravity due to m will be nearly constant over the body and, in this case, we showed in Section 5–6 that G will coincide with the center of mass. Also, in the case of a uniform sphere or a spherically symmetrical distribution of mass, we shall show in the next section that the center of gravity always lies at the center of the sphere.   The relative character of the concept of center of gravity makes it of little use except in the case of a sphere or of a body in a uniform gravitational field.

For two extended bodies, no unique centers of gravity can in general be defined, even relative to each other, except in special cases, as when the bodies are far apart, or when one of them is a sphere.   The system of gravitational forces on either body due to the other may or may not have a resultant; if it does, the two resultants are equal and opposite and act along the same line.   However, even in this case, we cannot define definite centers of gravity G_1, G_2 for the two bodies relative to each other, since equation (6–5) specifies only the distance $\overline{G_1 G_2}$.

The general problem of determining the gravitational forces between bodies is usually best treated by means of the concepts of the field theory of gravitation discussed in the next section.

6-2 Gravitational field and gravitational potential. The gravitational force $\mathbf{F}_m$ acting on a particle of mass m at a point $\mathbf{r}$, due to other particles m_i at points $\mathbf{r}_i$, is the vector sum of the forces due to each of the other particles acting separately:

$$\mathbf{F}_m = \sum_i \frac{m m_i G(\mathbf{r}_i - \mathbf{r})}{|\mathbf{r}_i - \mathbf{r}|^3}. \tag{6-6}$$

If, instead of point masses m_i, we have mass continuously distributed in space with a density $\rho(\mathbf{r})$, the force on a point mass m at $\mathbf{r}$ is

$$\mathbf{F}_m = \int \int \int \frac{m G(\mathbf{r}' - \mathbf{r}) \rho(\mathbf{r}')}{|\mathbf{r}' - \mathbf{r}|^3} \, dV'. \tag{6-7}$$

The integral may be taken over the region containing the mass whose attraction we are computing, or over all space if we let $\rho = 0$ outside this region. Now the force $\mathbf{F}_m$ is proportional to the mass m, and we define the *gravitational field intensity* (or simply *gravitational field*) $\mathbf{g}(\mathbf{r})$, at any point $\mathbf{r}$ in space, due to any distribution of mass, as the force per unit mass which would be exerted on any small mass m at that point:

$$\mathbf{g}(\mathbf{r}) = \frac{\mathbf{F}_m}{m}, \tag{6-8}$$

where $\mathbf{F}_m$ is the force that would be exerted on a point mass m at the point $\mathbf{r}$. We can write formulas for $\mathbf{g}(\mathbf{r})$ for point masses or continuously distributed mass:

$$\mathbf{g}(\mathbf{r}) = \sum_i \frac{m_i G(\mathbf{r}_i - \mathbf{r})}{|\mathbf{r}_i - \mathbf{r}|^3}, \tag{6-9}$$

$$\mathbf{g}(\mathbf{r}) = \int \int \int \frac{G(\mathbf{r}' - \mathbf{r}) \rho(\mathbf{r}')}{|\mathbf{r}' - \mathbf{r}|^3} \, dV'. \tag{6-10}$$

The field $\mathbf{g}(\mathbf{r})$ has the dimensions of acceleration, and is in fact the acceleration experienced by a particle at the point $\mathbf{r}$, on which no forces act other than the gravitational force.

The calculation of the gravitational field $\mathbf{g}(\mathbf{r})$ from Eq. (6-9) or (6-10) is difficult except in a few simple cases, partly because the sum and integral call for the addition of a number of vectors. Since the gravitational forces between pairs of particles are central forces, they are conservative, as we showed in Section 3-12, and a potential energy can be defined for a particle of mass m subject to gravitational forces. For two particles m and m_i, the potential energy is given by Eqs. (3-229) and (3-230):

$$V_{m m_i} = \frac{-G m m_i}{|\mathbf{r} - \mathbf{r}_i|}. \tag{6-11}$$

The potential energy of a particle of mass m at point r due to a system of particles m_i is then

$$V_m(\mathbf{r}) = \sum_i \frac{-Gmm_i}{|\mathbf{r} - \mathbf{r}_i|}. \tag{6-12}$$

We define the *gravitational potential* $\mathcal{G}(\mathbf{r})$ at point $\mathbf{r}$ as the negative of the potential energy per unit mass of a particle at point $\mathbf{r}$. [This choice of sign in $\mathcal{G}(\mathbf{r})$ is conventional in gravitational theory.]

$$\mathcal{G}(\mathbf{r}) = -\frac{V_m(\mathbf{r})}{m}. \tag{6-13}$$

For a system of particles,

$$\mathcal{G}(\mathbf{r}) = \sum_i \frac{m_i G}{|\mathbf{r} - \mathbf{r}_i|}. \tag{6-14}$$

If $\rho(\mathbf{r})$ represents a continuous distribution of mass, its gravitational potential is

$$\mathcal{G}(\mathbf{r}) = \int \int \int \frac{G\rho(\mathbf{r}')}{|\mathbf{r} - \mathbf{r}'|} \, dV'. \tag{6-15}$$

Because it is a scalar point function, the potential $\mathcal{G}(\mathbf{r})$ is easier to work with for many purposes than is the field $\mathbf{g}(\mathbf{r})$. In view of the relation (3–185) between force and potential energy, $\mathbf{g}$ may easily be calculated, when $\mathcal{G}$ is known, from the relation

$$\mathbf{g} = \nabla \mathcal{G}. \tag{6-16}$$

The inverse relation is

$$\mathcal{G}(\mathbf{r}) = \int_{\mathbf{r}_s}^{\mathbf{r}} \mathbf{g} \cdot d\mathbf{r}. \tag{6-17}$$

The definition of $\mathcal{G}(\mathbf{r})$, like that of potential energy $V(\mathbf{r})$, involves an arbitrary additive constant or, equivalently, an arbitrary point $\mathbf{r}_s$ at which $\mathcal{G} = 0$. Usually $\mathbf{r}_s$ is taken at an infinite distance from all masses, as in Eqs. (6–14) and (6–15).

The concepts of gravitational field and gravitational potential are mathematically identical to those of electric field intensity and electrostatic potential in electrostatics, except that the negative sign in Eq. (6–13) is conventional in gravitational theory, and except that all masses are positive and all gravitational forces are attractive, so that the force law has the opposite sign from that in electrostatics. The subject of potential theory is an extensive one, and we can give here only a very brief introductory treatment.

As an example of the use of the concept of potential, we calculate the potential due to a thin homogeneous spherical shell of matter of mass M, density σ per unit area, and radius a:

$$M = 4\pi a^2 \sigma. \tag{6-18}$$

The potential at a point P is computed by integrating over a set of ring elements as in Fig. 6-2. The potential of a ring of radius $a \sin \theta$, width $a \, d\theta$, all of whose mass is at the same distance r from P, will be

$$d\mathcal{G} = \frac{G\sigma(2\pi a \sin \theta)a \, d\theta}{r},$$

and the total potential at P of the spherical shell is

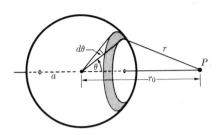

Fig. 6-2. Method of computing potential of a spherical shell.

$$\mathcal{G}(P) = \int_0^\pi \frac{G\sigma(2\pi a \sin \theta)a \, d\theta}{r}$$

$$= \frac{MG}{2} \int_0^\pi \frac{\sin \theta \, d\theta}{(r_0^2 + a^2 - 2ar_0 \cos \theta)^{\frac{1}{2}}}$$

$$= \frac{MG}{2ar_0} [(r_0 + a) - |r_0 - a|]. \tag{6-19}$$

We have two cases, according to whether P is outside or inside the shell:

$$\mathcal{G}(P) = \frac{MG}{r_0}, \quad r_0 \geq a, \qquad \mathcal{G}(P) = \frac{MG}{a}, \quad r_0 \leq a. \tag{6-20}$$

Thus outside the shell, the potential is the same as for a point mass M at the center of the shell. The gravitational field outside a spherical shell is then the same as if all the mass of the shell were at its center. The same statement then holds for the gravitational field outside any spherically symmetrical distribution of mass, since the total field is the sum of the fields due to the shells of which it is composed. This proves the statement made in the previous section; a spherically symmetrical distribution of mass attracts (and therefore is attracted by) any other mass outside it as if all its mass were at its center. Inside a spherical shell, the potential is constant, and it follows from Eq. (6-16) that the gravitational field is there zero. Hence a point inside a spherically symmetric distribution of mass at a distance r from the center is attracted as if the mass inside the sphere of radius r were at the center; the mass outside this sphere exerts no net force. These results would be somewhat more difficult to prove by computing the gravitational forces directly, as the reader can readily verify. Indeed, it took Newton twenty years! The calculation of the force of attraction of the moon by the earth described in the last section of Chapter 1 was made by Newton twenty years before he published his law of gravitation. It is likely that he waited until he could prove an assumption implicit in that calculation, namely, that the earth attracts any body outside it as if all the mass of the earth were concentrated at its center.

6–3 Gravitational field equations. It is of interest to find differential equations satisfied by the functions $\mathbf{g(r)}$ and $\mathcal{G(r)}$. From Eq. (6–16) it follows that

$$\nabla \times \mathbf{g} = 0. \tag{6–21}$$

When written out in any coordinate system, this vector equation becomes a set of three partial differential equations connecting the components of the gravitational field. In rectangular coordinates,

$$\frac{\partial g_z}{\partial y} - \frac{\partial g_y}{\partial z} = 0, \quad \frac{\partial g_x}{\partial z} - \frac{\partial g_z}{\partial x} = 0, \quad \frac{\partial g_y}{\partial x} - \frac{\partial g_x}{\partial y} = 0. \tag{6–22}$$

These equations alone do not determine the gravitational field, for they are satisfied by every gravitational field. To determine the gravitational field, we need an equation connecting $\mathbf{g}$ with the distribution of matter.

Let us study the gravitational field $\mathbf{g}$ due to a point mass m. Consider any volume V containing the mass m, and let $\mathbf{n}$ be the unit vector normal at each point to the surface S that bounds V (Fig. 6–3). Let us compute the surface integral

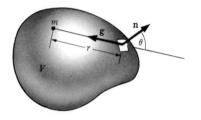

$$I = \int \int_S \mathbf{n} \cdot \mathbf{g} \, dS. \tag{6–23}$$

The physical or geometric meaning of this integral can be seen if we introduce the concept of lines of force, drawn everywhere in the direction of $\mathbf{g}$, and in such a manner that the number of lines per square centi-

FIG. 6–3. A mass m enclosed in a volume V.

meter at any point is equal to the gravitational field intensity. Then I is the number of lines passing out through the surface S, and is called the *flux* of $\mathbf{g}$ through S. The element of solid angle $d\Omega$ subtended at the position of m by an element of surface dS is defined as the area swept out on a sphere of unit radius by a radius from m which sweeps over the surface element dS. This area is

$$d\Omega = \frac{dS \cos \theta}{r^2}. \tag{6–24}$$

From Fig. 6–3, we have the relation

$$\mathbf{n} \cdot \mathbf{g} = - \frac{mG \cos \theta}{r^2}. \tag{6–25}$$

When use is made of these two relations, the integral I [Eq. (6–23)] becomes

$$I = \int \int_S -mG \, d\Omega = -4\pi mG. \tag{6–26}$$

The integral I is independent of the position of m within the surface S. This result is analogous to the corresponding result in electrostatics that there are 4π lines of force coming from every unit charge. Since the gravitational field of a number of masses is the sum of their individual fields, we have, for a surface S surrounding a set of masses m_i:

$$I = \int\!\!\int_S \mathbf{n} \cdot \mathbf{g} \, dS = -\sum_i 4\pi m_i G. \tag{6-27}$$

For a continuous distribution of mass within S, this equation becomes

$$\int\!\!\int_S \mathbf{n} \cdot \mathbf{g} \, dS = -\int\!\!\int\!\!\int_V 4\pi G\rho \, dV. \tag{6-28}$$

We now apply Gauss' divergence theorem [Eq. (3-115)] to the left side of this equation:

$$\int\!\!\int_S \mathbf{n} \cdot \mathbf{g} \, dS = \int\!\!\int\!\!\int_V \boldsymbol{\nabla} \cdot \mathbf{g} \, dV. \tag{6-29}$$

Subtracting Eq. (6-28) from Eq. (6-29), we arrive at the result

$$\int\!\!\int\!\!\int_V (\boldsymbol{\nabla} \cdot \mathbf{g} + 4\pi G\rho) \, dV = 0. \tag{6-30}$$

Now Eq. (6-30) must hold for any volume V, and this can only be true if the integrand vanishes:

$$\boldsymbol{\nabla} \cdot \mathbf{g} = -4\pi G\rho. \tag{6-31}$$

This equation in cartesian coordinates has the form

$$\frac{\partial g_x}{\partial x} + \frac{\partial g_y}{\partial y} + \frac{\partial g_z}{\partial z} = -4\pi G\rho(x,y,z). \tag{6-32}$$

When $\rho(x,y,z)$ is given, the set of equations (6-22) and (6-32) can be shown to determine the gravitational field (g_x, g_y, g_z) uniquely, if we add the boundary condition that $\mathbf{g} \to 0$ as $|\mathbf{r}| \to \infty$. Substituting from Eq. (6-16), we get an equation satisfied by the potential:

$$\nabla^2 \mathcal{G} = -4\pi G\rho, \tag{6-33}$$

or

$$\frac{\partial^2 \mathcal{G}}{\partial x^2} + \frac{\partial^2 \mathcal{G}}{\partial y^2} + \frac{\partial^2 \mathcal{G}}{\partial z^2} = -4\pi G\rho. \tag{6-34}$$

·This single equation determines $\mathcal{G}(x,y,z)$ uniquely if we add the condition that $\mathcal{G} \to 0$ as $|\mathbf{r}| \to \infty$. This result we quote from potential theory without proof. The solution of Eq. (6-33) is, in fact, Eq. (6-15). It is often easier to solve the partial differential equation (6-34) directly than to compute the integral in Eq. (6–15). Equations (6–33), (6–16), and (6–8) together constitute a complete summary of Newton's theory of gravitation, as likewise do Eqs. (6–31), (6–21), and (6–8); that is, all the results of the theory can be derived from either of these sets of equations.

Equation (6–33) is called *Poisson's equation*. Equations of this form turn up frequently in physical theories. For example, the electrostatic potential satisfies an equation of the same form, where ρ is the electric charge density. If $\rho = 0$, Eq. (6–33) takes the form

$$\nabla^2 \mathcal{G} = 0. \tag{6–35}$$

This is called *Laplace's equation*. An extensive mathematical theory of Eqs. (6–33) and (6–35) has been developed.* A discussion of potential theory is, however, outside the scope of this text.

PROBLEMS

1. Assuming that the earth is a sphere of uniform density, with radius a, mass M, calculate the gravitational field intensity and the gravitational potential at all points inside and outside the earth, taking $\mathcal{G} = 0$ at an infinite distance.

2. Assuming that the interior of the earth can be treated as an incompressible fluid in equilibrium, (a) calculate the pressure within the earth as a function of distance from the center. (b) Using appropriate values for the earth's mass and radius, calculate the pressure in tons per square inch at the center.

3. Show that if the sun were surrounded by a spherical cloud of dust of uniform density ρ, the gravitational field within the dust cloud would be

$$\mathbf{g} = -\left(\frac{MG}{r^2} + \frac{4\pi}{3}\rho Gr\right)\frac{\mathbf{r}}{r},$$

where M is the mass of the sun, and $\mathbf{r}$ is a vector from the sun to any point in the dust cloud.

4. Assume that the density of a star is a function only of the radius r measured from the center of the star, and is given by †

$$\rho = \frac{Ma^2}{2\pi r(r^2 + a^2)^2},$$

where M is the mass of the star, and a is a constant which determines the size of the star. Find the gravitational field intensity and the gravitational potential as functions of r.

5. (a) Set up the equations to be solved for the pressure as a function of radius in a spherically symmetric mass M of gas, assuming that the gas obeys the perfect gas laws and that the temperature is known as a function of radius. (b) Find the pressure and temperature as functions of radius for the star of problem 4, if the star is composed of a perfect gas of atomic weight A.

---

* O. D. Kellogg, *Foundations of Potential Theory*. Berlin: J. Springer, 1929.

† The expression for ρ is chosen to make the problem easy to solve; not because it has more than a remote resemblance to the density variations within any actual star.

6. (a) Assume that ordinary cold matter collapses, under a pressure greater than a certain critical pressure p_0, to a state of very high density ρ_1. A planet of mass M is constructed of matter of mean density ρ_0 in its normal state. Assuming uniform density and conditions of fluid equilibrium, at what mass M_0 and radius r_0 will the pressure at the center reach the critical value p_0? (b) If $M > M_0$, the planet will have a very dense core of density ρ_1 surrounded by a crust of density ρ_0. Calculate the resulting pressure distribution within the planet in terms of the radius r_1 of the core and the radius r_2 of the planet. Show that if M is somewhat larger than M_0, then the radius r_2 of the planet is less than r_0. (The planet Jupiter is said to have a mass very nearly equal to the critical mass M_0, so that if it were heavier it might be smaller.)

7. (a) Calculate the gravitational potential of a uniform circular ring of matter of radius a, mass M, at a distance r from the center of the ring in a direction making an angle θ with the axis of the ring. Assume that $r \gg a$, and calculate the potential only to second order in a/r. (b) Calculate to the same approximation the components of the gravitational field of the ring at the specified point.

8. (a) Find the gravitational potential and the field intensity due to a thin rod of length l and mass M at a point a distance r from the center of the rod in a direction making an angle θ with the rod. Assume that $r \gg l$, and carry the calculations only to second order in l/r. (b) Locate the center of gravity of the rod relative to the specified point.

9. Consider a spherical mountain of radius a, mass M, floating in equilibrium in the earth, and whose density is half that of the earth. Assume that a is much less than the earth's radius, so that the earth's surface can be regarded as flat in the neighborhood of the mountain. If the mountain were not present, the gravitational field intensity near the earth's surface would be g_0. (a) Find the difference between g_0 and the actual value of g at the top of the mountain. (b) If the top of the mountain is eroded flat, level with the surrounding surface of the earth, and if this occurs in a short time compared with the time required for the mountain to float in equilibrium again, find the difference between g_0 and the actual value of g at the earth's surface at the center of the eroded mountain.

10. Show that the gravitational field equations (6–21), (6–31), and (6–33) are satisfied by the field intensity and potential which you calculated in problem 1.

CHAPTER 7

MOVING COORDINATE SYSTEMS

7–1 Moving origin of coordinates. Let a point in space be located by vectors $\mathbf{r},\mathbf{r}^*$ with respect to two origins of coordinates O,O^*, and let O^* be located by a vector $\mathbf{h}$ with respect to O (Fig. 7–1). Then the relation between the coordinates $\mathbf{r}$ and $\mathbf{r}^*$ is given by

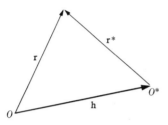

$$\mathbf{r} = \mathbf{r}^* + \mathbf{h}, \qquad (7\text{–}1)$$
$$\mathbf{r}^* = \mathbf{r} - \mathbf{h}. \qquad (7\text{–}2)$$

In terms of rectangular coordinates, with axes x^*,y^*,z^*, parallel to axes x,y,z, respectively, these equations can be written:

Fig. 7–1. Change of origin of coordinates.

$$x = x^* + h_x, \quad y = y^* + h_y, \quad z = z^* + h_z; \qquad (7\text{–}3)$$
$$x^* = x - h_x, \quad y^* = y - h_y, \quad z^* = z - h_z. \qquad (7\text{–}4)$$

Now if the origin O^* is moving with respect to the origin O, which we regard as fixed, the relation between the velocities relative to the two systems is obtained by differentiating Eq. (7–1):

$$\mathbf{v} = \frac{d\mathbf{r}}{dt} = \frac{d\mathbf{r}^*}{dt} + \frac{d\mathbf{h}}{dt}$$
$$= \mathbf{v}^* + \mathbf{v}_h, \qquad (7\text{–}5)$$

where $\mathbf{v}$ and $\mathbf{v}^*$ are the velocities of the moving point relative to O and O^*, and $\mathbf{v}_h$ is the velocity of O^* relative to O. We are supposing that the axes x^*,y^*,z^* remain parallel to x,y,z. This is called a *translation* of the starred coordinate system with respect to the unstarred system. Written out in cartesian components, Eq. (7–5) becomes the time derivative of Eq. (7–3). The relation between relative accelerations is

$$\mathbf{a} = \frac{d^2\mathbf{r}}{dt^2} = \frac{d^2\mathbf{r}^*}{dt^2} + \frac{d^2\mathbf{h}}{dt^2}$$
$$= \mathbf{a}^* + \mathbf{a}_h. \qquad (7\text{–}6)$$

Again these equations can easily be written out in terms of their rectangular components.

Newton's equations of motion hold in the fixed coordinate system, so that we have, for a particle of mass m subject to a force $\mathbf{F}$:

$$m \frac{d^2\mathbf{r}}{dt^2} = \mathbf{F}. \qquad (7\text{–}7)$$

232

Using Eq. (7–6), we can write this equation in the starred coordinate system:

$$m \frac{d^2\mathbf{r}^*}{dt^2} + m\mathbf{a}_h = \mathbf{F}. \qquad (7\text{–}8)$$

If O^* is moving at constant velocity relative to O, then $\mathbf{a}_h = \mathbf{0}$, and we have

$$m \frac{d^2\mathbf{r}^*}{dt^2} = \mathbf{F}. \qquad (7\text{–}9)$$

Thus Newton's equations of motion, if they hold in any coordinate system, hold also in any other coordinate system moving with uniform velocity relative to the first. This is the Newtonian principle of relativity. It implies that, so far as mechanics is concerned, we cannot specify any unique fixed coordinate system or *frame of reference* to which Newton's laws are supposed to refer; if we specify one such system, any other system moving with constant velocity relative to it will do as well. This property of Eq. (7–7) is sometimes expressed by saying that Newton's equations of motion remain *invariant,* or that they are *covariant,* with respect to uniform translations of the coordinates. The concept of frame of reference is not quite the same as that of a coordinate system, in that if we make a change of coordinates that does not involve the time, we do not regard this as a change of frame of reference. A frame of reference includes all coordinate systems at rest with respect to any particular one. The principle of relativity proposed by Einstein asserts that the relativity principle is not restricted to mechanics, but holds for all physical phenomena. The special theory of relativity is the result of the application of this principle to all types of phenomena, particularly electromagnetic phenomena. It turns out that this can only be done by modifying Newton's equations of motion slightly and, in fact, even Eqs. (7–5) and (7–6) require modification.*

For any motion of O^*, we can write Eq. (7–8) in the form

$$m \frac{d^2\mathbf{r}^*}{dt^2} = \mathbf{F} - m\mathbf{a}_h. \qquad (7\text{–}10)$$

This equation has the same form as the equation of motion (7–7) in a fixed coordinate system, except that in place of the force $\mathbf{F}$, we have $\mathbf{F} - m\mathbf{a}_h$. The term $-m\mathbf{a}_h$ we may call a fictitious force. We can treat the motion of a mass m relative to a moving coordinate system using Newton's equations of motion if we add this fictitious force to the actual force which acts. From the point of view of classical mechanics, it is not a force at all, but part of the mass-times-acceleration transposed to the other side of the equation. The essential distinction is that the real forces $\mathbf{F}$ acting on m depend on the positions and motions of other bodies, whereas the fictitious

---

* P. G. Bergmann, *Introduction to the Theory of Relativity.* New York: Prentice-Hall, 1946. (Part 1.)

force depends on the acceleration of the starred coordinate system with respect to the fixed coordinate system. In the general theory of relativity, terms like $-m\mathbf{a}_h$ are regarded as legitimate forces in the starred coordinate system, on the same footing with the force $\mathbf{F}$, so that in all coordinate systems the same law of motion holds. This, of course, can only be done if it can be shown how to deduce the force $-m\mathbf{a}_h$ from the positions and motions of other bodies. The program is not so simple as it may seem from this brief outline, and modifications in the laws of motion are required to carry it through.*

7–2 Rotating coordinate systems. We now consider coordinate systems x,y,z and x^*,y^*,z^* whose axes are rotated relative to one another as in Fig. 7–2, where, for the present, the origins of the two sets of axes coincide. Introducing unit vectors $\mathbf{i},\mathbf{j},\mathbf{k}$ associated with axes x,y,z, and unit vectors $\mathbf{i}^*,\mathbf{j}^*,\mathbf{k}^*$ associated with axes x^*,y^*,z^*, we can express the position vector $\mathbf{r}$ in terms of its components along either set of axes:

$$\mathbf{r} = x\mathbf{i} + y\mathbf{j} + z\mathbf{k}, \qquad (7\text{–}11)$$
$$\mathbf{r} = x^*\mathbf{i}^* + y^*\mathbf{j}^* + z^*\mathbf{k}^*. \qquad (7\text{–}12)$$

Note that since the origins now coincide, a point is represented by the same vector $\mathbf{r}$ in both systems; only the components of $\mathbf{r}$ are different along the different axes. The relations between the coordinate systems can be obtained by taking the dot product of either the starred or the unstarred unit vectors with Eqs. (7–11) and (7–12). For example, if we compute $\mathbf{i} \cdot \mathbf{r}, \mathbf{j} \cdot \mathbf{r}, \mathbf{k} \cdot \mathbf{r}$, from Eqs. (7–11) and (7–12) and equate the results, we obtain

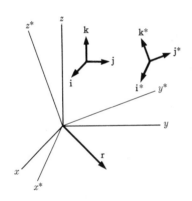

Fig. 7–2. Rotation of coordinate axes.

$$\begin{aligned}
x &= x^*(\mathbf{i}^* \cdot \mathbf{i}) + y^*(\mathbf{j}^* \cdot \mathbf{i}) + z^*(\mathbf{k}^* \cdot \mathbf{i}), \\
y &= x^*(\mathbf{i}^* \cdot \mathbf{j}) + y^*(\mathbf{j}^* \cdot \mathbf{j}) + z^*(\mathbf{k}^* \cdot \mathbf{j}), \qquad (7\text{–}13)\\
z &= x^*(\mathbf{i}^* \cdot \mathbf{k}) + y^*(\mathbf{j}^* \cdot \mathbf{k}) + z^*(\mathbf{k}^* \cdot \mathbf{k}).
\end{aligned}$$

The dot products $(\mathbf{i}^* \cdot \mathbf{i})$, etc., are the cosines of the angles between the corresponding axes. Similar formulas for x^*,y^*,z^* in terms of x,y,z can easily be obtained by the same process. These formulas are rather complicated and unwieldy, and we shall fortunately be able to avoid using them in most cases. Equations (7–11), (7–12), and (7–13) do not depend on the fact that the vector $\mathbf{r}$ is drawn from the origin. Analogous formulas apply in terms of the components of any vector $\mathbf{A}$ along the two sets of axes.

---

* Bergmann, *loc. cit.* (Part 2.)

The time derivative of any vector **A** was defined by Eq. (3–52):

$$\frac{d\mathbf{A}}{dt} = \lim_{\Delta t \to 0} \frac{\mathbf{A}(t + \Delta t) - \mathbf{A}(t)}{\Delta t}. \tag{7-14}$$

In attempting to apply this definition in the present case, we encounter a difficulty if the coordinate systems are rotating with respect to each other. A vector which is constant in one coordinate system is not constant in the other, but rotates. The definition requires us to subtract $\mathbf{A}(t)$ from $\mathbf{A}(t + \Delta t)$. During the time Δt, coordinate system x^*,y^*,z^* has rotated relative to x,y,z, so that at time $t + \Delta t$, the two systems will not agree as to which vector is (or was) $\mathbf{A}(t)$, i.e., which vector is in the same position that **A** was in at time t. The result is that the time derivative of a given vector will be different in the two coordinate systems. Let us use d/dt to denote the time derivative with respect to the unstarred coordinate system, which we regard as fixed, and d^*/dt to denote the time derivative with respect to the rotating starred coordinate system. We make this distinction with regard to vectors only; there is no ambiguity with regard to numerical quantities, and we denote their time derivatives by d/dt, or by a dot, which will have the same meaning in all coordinate systems. Let the vector **A** be given by

$$\mathbf{A} = A_x\mathbf{i} + A_y\mathbf{j} + A_z\mathbf{k}, \tag{7-15}$$
$$\mathbf{A} = A_x^*\mathbf{i}^* + A_y^*\mathbf{j}^* + A_z^*\mathbf{k}^*. \tag{7-16}$$

The unstarred time derivative of **A** may be obtained by differentiating Eq. (7–15), regarding **i,j,k** as constant vectors in the fixed system:

$$\frac{d\mathbf{A}}{dt} = \dot{A}_x\mathbf{i} + \dot{A}_y\mathbf{j} + \dot{A}_z\mathbf{k}. \tag{7-17}$$

Similarly, the starred derivative of **A** is given in terms of its starred components by

$$\frac{d^*\mathbf{A}}{dt} = \dot{A}_x^*\mathbf{i}^* + \dot{A}_y^*\mathbf{j}^* + \dot{A}_z^*\mathbf{k}^*. \tag{7-18}$$

We may regard Eqs. (7–17) and (7–18) as the definitions of unstarred and starred time derivatives of a vector. We can also obtain a formula for d/dt in starred components by taking the unstarred derivative of Eq. (7–16), remembering that the unit vectors $\mathbf{i}^*,\mathbf{j}^*,\mathbf{k}^*$ are moving relative to the unstarred system, and have time derivatives:

$$\frac{d\mathbf{A}}{dt} = \dot{A}_x^*\mathbf{i}^* + \dot{A}_y^*\mathbf{j}^* + \dot{A}_z^*\mathbf{k}^* + A_x^*\frac{d\mathbf{i}^*}{dt} + A_y^*\frac{d\mathbf{j}^*}{dt} + A_z^*\frac{d\mathbf{k}^*}{dt}. \tag{7-19}$$

A similar formula could be obtained for $d^*\mathbf{A}/dt$ in terms of its unstarred components.

Let us now suppose that the starred coordinate system is rotating about some axis OQ through the origin, with an angular velocity ω (Fig. 7–3).

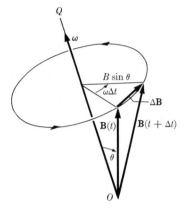

FIG. 7-3. Time derivative of a rotating vector.

We define the *vector angular velocity* $\boldsymbol{\omega}$ as a vector of magnitude ω directed along the axis OQ in the direction of advance of a right-hand screw rotating with the starred system. Consider a vector $\mathbf{B}$ at rest in the starred system. Its starred derivative is zero, and we now show that its unstarred derivative is

$$\frac{d\mathbf{B}}{dt} = \boldsymbol{\omega} \times \mathbf{B}. \qquad (7\text{--}20)$$

In order to subtract $\mathbf{B}(t)$ from $\mathbf{B}(t + \Delta t)$, we draw these vectors with their tails together, and it will be convenient to place them with their tails on the axis of rotation. (The time derivative depends only on the components of $\mathbf{B}$ along the axes, and not on the position of $\mathbf{B}$ in space.) We first verify from Fig. 7–3 that the direction of $d\mathbf{B}/dt$ is given correctly by Eq. (7–20), recalling the definition [Eq. (3–24) and Fig. 3–11] of the cross product. The magnitude of $d\mathbf{B}/dt$ as given by Eq. (7–20) is

$$\left|\frac{d\mathbf{B}}{dt}\right| = |\boldsymbol{\omega} \times \mathbf{B}| = \omega B \sin \theta. \qquad (7\text{--}21)$$

This is the correct formula, since it can be seen from Fig. 7–3 that, when Δt is small,

$$|\Delta \mathbf{B}| = (B \sin \theta)(\omega\, \Delta t).$$

When Eq. (7–20) is applied to the unit vectors $\mathbf{i}^*, \mathbf{j}^*, \mathbf{k}^*$, Eq. (7–19) becomes, if we make use of Eqs. (7–18) and (7–16):

$$\frac{d\mathbf{A}}{dt} = \frac{d^*\mathbf{A}}{dt} + A_x^*(\boldsymbol{\omega} \times \mathbf{i}^*) + A_y^*(\boldsymbol{\omega} \times \mathbf{j}^*) + A_z^*(\boldsymbol{\omega} \times \mathbf{k}^*)$$

$$= \frac{d^*\mathbf{A}}{dt} + \boldsymbol{\omega} \times \mathbf{A}. \qquad (7\text{--}22)$$

This is the fundamental relationship between time derivatives for rotating coordinate systems. It may be remembered by noting that the time derivative of any vector in the unstarred coordinate system is its derivative in the starred system plus the unstarred derivative it would have if it were at rest in the starred system. Equation (7–22) applies even when the angular velocity vector $\boldsymbol{\omega}$ is changing in magnitude and direction with time. Taking the derivative of right and left sides of Eq. (7–22), and applying Eq. (7–22) again to $\mathbf{A}$ and $d^*\mathbf{A}/dt$, we have for the second time derivative of any vector $\mathbf{A}$:

$$\frac{d^2\mathbf{A}}{dt^2} = \frac{d}{dt}\left(\frac{d^*\mathbf{A}}{dt}\right) + \boldsymbol{\omega} \times \frac{d\mathbf{A}}{dt} + \frac{d\boldsymbol{\omega}}{dt} \times \mathbf{A}$$

$$= \frac{d^{*2}\mathbf{A}}{dt^2} + \boldsymbol{\omega} \times \frac{d^*\mathbf{A}}{dt} + \boldsymbol{\omega} \times \left(\frac{d^*\mathbf{A}}{dt} + \boldsymbol{\omega} \times \mathbf{A}\right) + \frac{d\boldsymbol{\omega}}{dt} \times \mathbf{A}$$

$$= \frac{d^{*2}\mathbf{A}}{dt^2} + 2\boldsymbol{\omega} \times \frac{d^*\mathbf{A}}{dt} + \boldsymbol{\omega} \times (\boldsymbol{\omega} \times \mathbf{A}) + \frac{d\boldsymbol{\omega}}{dt} \times \mathbf{A}. \qquad (7\text{--}23)$$

In view of Eq. (3–29), the starred and unstarred derivatives of any vector parallel to the axis of rotation are the same, according to Eq. (7–22). In particular,

$$\frac{d\boldsymbol{\omega}}{dt} = \frac{d^*\boldsymbol{\omega}}{dt}.$$

It is to be noted that the vector $\boldsymbol{\omega}$ on both sides of this equation is the angular velocity of the starred system relative to the unstarred system, although its time derivative is calculated with respect to the unstarred system on the left side, and with respect to the starred system on the right. The angular velocity of the unstarred system relative to the starred system will be $-\boldsymbol{\omega}$.

We now show that the relations derived above for a rotating coordinate system are perfectly general, in that they apply to any motion of the starred axes relative to the unstarred axes. Let the unstarred rates of change of the starred unit vectors be given in terms of components along the starred axes by

$$\frac{d\mathbf{i}^*}{dt} = a_{11}\mathbf{i}^* + a_{12}\mathbf{j}^* + a_{13}\mathbf{k}^*,$$

$$\frac{d\mathbf{j}^*}{dt} = a_{21}\mathbf{i}^* + a_{22}\mathbf{j}^* + a_{23}\mathbf{k}^*, \qquad (7\text{--}24)$$

$$\frac{d\mathbf{k}^*}{dt} = a_{31}\mathbf{i}^* + a_{32}\mathbf{j}^* + a_{33}\mathbf{k}^*.$$

By differentiating the equation

$$\mathbf{i}^* \cdot \mathbf{i}^* = 1, \qquad (7\text{--}25)$$

we obtain

$$\frac{d\mathbf{i}^*}{dt} \cdot \mathbf{i}^* = 0. \qquad (7\text{--}26)$$

From this and the corresponding equations for $\mathbf{j}^*$ and $\mathbf{k}^*$, we have

$$a_{11} = a_{22} = a_{33} = 0. \qquad (7\text{--}27)$$

By differentiating the equation

$$\mathbf{i}^* \cdot \mathbf{k}^* = 0, \qquad (7\text{--}28)$$

we obtain

$$\frac{d\mathbf{i}^*}{dt} \cdot \mathbf{k}^* = -\mathbf{i}^* \cdot \frac{d\mathbf{k}^*}{dt}. \qquad (7\text{--}29)$$

From this and the other two analogous equations, we have

$$a_{31} = -a_{13}, \quad a_{12} = -a_{21}, \quad a_{23} = -a_{32}. \tag{7-30}$$

Let a vector $\boldsymbol{\omega}$ be defined in terms of its starred components by:

$$\omega_x^* = a_{23}, \quad \omega_y^* = a_{31}, \quad \omega_z^* = a_{12}. \tag{7-31}$$

Equations (7–24) can now be rewritten, with the help of Eqs. (7–27), (7–30), and (7–31), in the form

$$\frac{d\mathbf{i}^*}{dt} = \boldsymbol{\omega} \times \mathbf{i}^*,$$

$$\frac{d\mathbf{j}^*}{dt} = \boldsymbol{\omega} \times \mathbf{j}^*, \tag{7-32}$$

$$\frac{d\mathbf{k}^*}{dt} = \boldsymbol{\omega} \times \mathbf{k}^*.$$

According to Eq. (7–20), these time derivatives of $\mathbf{i}^*, \mathbf{j}^*, \mathbf{k}^*$ are just those to be expected if the starred unit vectors are rotating with an angular velocity $\boldsymbol{\omega}$. Thus no matter how the starred coordinate axes may be moving, we can define at any instant an angular velocity vector $\boldsymbol{\omega}$, given by Eq. (7–31), such that the time derivatives of any vector relative to the starred and unstarred coordinate systems are related by Eqs. (7–22) and (7–23).

Let us now suppose that the starred coordinate system is moving so that its origin O^* remains fixed at the origin O of the fixed coordinate system. Then any point in space is located by the same position vector $\mathbf{r}$ in both coordinate systems [Eqs. (7–11) and (7–12)]. By applying equations (7–22) and (7–23) to the position vector $\mathbf{r}$, we obtain formulas for the relation between velocities and accelerations in the two coordinate systems:

$$\frac{d\mathbf{r}}{dt} = \frac{d^*\mathbf{r}}{dt} + \boldsymbol{\omega} \times \mathbf{r}, \tag{7-33}$$

$$\frac{d^2\mathbf{r}}{dt^2} = \frac{d^{*2}\mathbf{r}}{dt^2} + \boldsymbol{\omega} \times (\boldsymbol{\omega} \times \mathbf{r}) + 2\boldsymbol{\omega} \times \frac{d^*\mathbf{r}}{dt} + \frac{d\boldsymbol{\omega}}{dt} \times \mathbf{r}. \tag{7-34}$$

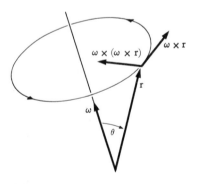

Fig. 7–4. Centripetal acceleration.

Formula (7–34) is called *Coriolis' Theorem.* The first term on the right is the acceleration relative to the starred system. The second term is called the *centripetal acceleration* of a point in rotation about an axis (*centripetal* means "toward the center"). Using the notation in Fig. 7–4, we readily verify that $\boldsymbol{\omega} \times (\boldsymbol{\omega} \times \mathbf{r})$ points directly toward and perpendicular to the axis of rotation, and that its magnitude is

$$|\omega \times (\omega \times r)| = \omega^2 r \sin \theta$$
$$= \frac{v^2}{r \sin \theta}, \tag{7–35}$$

where $v = \omega r \sin \theta$ is the speed of circular motion and $(r \sin \theta)$ is the distance from the axis. The third term is present only when the point r is moving in the starred system, and is called the *coriolis acceleration*. The last term vanishes for a constant angular velocity of rotation about a fixed axis.

If we suppose that Newton's law of motion (7–7) holds in the unstarred coordinate system, we shall have in the starred system:

$$m\frac{d^{*2}r}{dt^2} + m\omega \times (\omega \times r) + 2m\omega \times \frac{d^*r}{dt} + m\frac{d\omega}{dt} \times r = F. \tag{7–36}$$

Transposing the second, third, and fourth terms to the right side, we obtain an equation of motion similar in form to Newton's equation of motion:

$$m\frac{d^{*2}r}{dt^2} = F - m\omega \times (\omega \times r) - 2m\omega \times \frac{d^*r}{dt} - m\frac{d\omega}{dt} \times r. \tag{7–37}$$

The second term on the right is called the *centrifugal force* (*centrifugal* means "away from the center"); the third term is called the *coriolis force*. The last term has no special name, and appears only for the case of non-uniform rotation. If we introduce the fictitious centrifugal and coriolis forces, the laws of motion relative to a rotating coordinate system are the same as for fixed coordinates. A great deal of confusion has arisen regarding the term "centrifugal force." This force is not a real force, at least in classical mechanics, and is not present if we refer to a fixed coordinate system in space. We can, however, treat a rotating coordinate system as if it were fixed by introducing the centrifugal and coriolis forces. Thus a particle moving in a circle has no centrifugal force acting on it, but only a force toward the center which produces its centripetal acceleration. However, if we consider a coordinate system rotating with the particle, in this system the particle is at rest, and the force toward the center is balanced by the centrifugal force. It is very often useful to adopt a rotating coordinate system. In studying the action of a cream separator, for example, it is far more convenient to choose a coordinate system in which the liquid is at rest, and use the laws of diffusion to study the diffusion of cream toward the axis under the action of the centrifugal force field, than to try to study the motion from the point of view of a fixed observer watching the whirling liquid.

We can treat coordinate systems in simultaneous translation and rotation relative to each other by using Eq. (7–1) to represent the relation between the coordinate vectors r and r^* relative to origins O, O^* not necessarily coincident. In the derivation of Eqs. (7–32), no assumption was made about the origin of the starred coordinates, and therefore Eqs. (7–22) and (7–23) may still be used to express the time derivatives of any vector with respect to the unstarred coordinate system in terms of its time derivatives with respect to the starred system.   Replacing $dr*/dt$, d^2r*/dt in Eqs. (7–5) and (7–6) by their expressions in terms of the starred derivatives relative to the starred system as given by Eqs. (7–33) and (7–34), we obtain for the position, velocity, and acceleration of a point with respect to coordinate systems in relative translation and rotation:

$$\mathbf{r} = \mathbf{r^*} + \mathbf{h}, \tag{7–38}$$

$$\frac{d\mathbf{r}}{dt} = \frac{d^*\mathbf{r^*}}{dt} + \boldsymbol{\omega} \times \mathbf{r^*} + \frac{d\mathbf{h}}{dt}, \tag{7–39}$$

$$\frac{d^2\mathbf{r}}{dt^2} = \frac{d^{*2}\mathbf{r^*}}{dt^2} + \boldsymbol{\omega} \times (\boldsymbol{\omega} \times \mathbf{r^*}) + 2\boldsymbol{\omega} \times \frac{d^*\mathbf{r^*}}{dt} + \frac{d\boldsymbol{\omega}}{dt} \times \mathbf{r^*} + \frac{d^2\mathbf{h}}{dt^2}. \tag{7–40}$$

7–3 Laws of motion on the rotating earth.   We write the equation of motion, relative to a coordinate system fixed in space, for a particle of mass m subject to a gravitational force $m\mathbf{g}$ and any other nongravitational forces $\mathbf{F}$:

$$m \frac{d^2\mathbf{r}}{dt^2} = \mathbf{F} + m\mathbf{g}. \tag{7–41}$$

Now if we refer the motion of the particle to a coordinate system at rest relative to the earth, which rotates with constant angular velocity $\boldsymbol{\omega}$, and if we measure the position vector $\mathbf{r}$ from the center of the earth, we have, by Eq. (7–34):

$$m \frac{d^2\mathbf{r}}{dt^2} = F + m\mathbf{g}$$

$$= m \frac{d^{*2}\mathbf{r}}{dt^2} + m\boldsymbol{\omega} \times (\boldsymbol{\omega} \times \mathbf{r}) + 2m\boldsymbol{\omega} \times \frac{d^*\mathbf{r}}{dt}, \tag{7–42}$$

which can be rearranged in the form

$$m \frac{d^{*2}\mathbf{r}}{dt^2} = \mathbf{F} + m[\mathbf{g} - \boldsymbol{\omega} \times (\boldsymbol{\omega} \times \mathbf{r})] - 2m\boldsymbol{\omega} \times \frac{d^*\mathbf{r}}{dt}. \tag{7–43}$$

This equation has the same form as Newton's equation of motion.   We have combined the gravitational and centrifugal force terms because both are proportional to the mass of the particle and both depend only on the position of the particle; in their mechanical effects these two forces are indistinguishable.   We may define the effective gravitational acceleration $\mathbf{g}_e$ at any point on the earth's surface by:

$$\mathbf{g}_e(\mathbf{r}) = \mathbf{g}(\mathbf{r}) - \boldsymbol{\omega} \times (\boldsymbol{\omega} \times \mathbf{r}). \tag{7–44}$$

The gravitational force which we measure experimentally on a body of mass m at rest* on the earth's surface is $m\mathbf{g}_e$. Since $-\boldsymbol{\omega} \times (\boldsymbol{\omega} \times \mathbf{r})$ points radially outward from the earth's axis, $\mathbf{g}_e$ at every point north of the equator will point slightly to the south of the earth's center, as can be seen from Fig. 7-5. A body released near the earth's surface will begin to fall in the direction of $\mathbf{g}_e$, the direction determined by a plumb line is that of $\mathbf{g}_e$, and a liquid will come to equilibrium with its surface

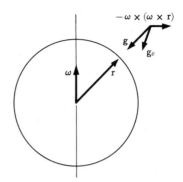

FIG. 7-5. Effective acceleration of gravity on the rotating earth.

perpendicular to $\mathbf{g}_e$. This is why the earth has settled into equilibrium in the form of an oblate ellipsoid, flattened at the poles. The degree of flattening is just such as to make the earth's surface at every point perpendicular to $\mathbf{g}_e$ (ignoring local irregularities).

Equation (7–43) can now be written

$$m\frac{d^{*2}\mathbf{r}}{dt^2} = \mathbf{F} + m\mathbf{g}_e - 2m\boldsymbol{\omega} \times \frac{d^*\mathbf{r}}{dt}. \qquad (7\text{–}45)$$

The velocity and acceleration which appear in this equation are unaffected if we relocate our origin of coordinates at any convenient point at the surface of the earth; hence this equation applies to the motion of a particle of mass m at the surface of the earth relative to a local coordinate system at rest on the earth's surface. The only unfamiliar term is the coriolis force which acts on a moving particle. The reader can convince himself by a few calculations that this force is comparatively small at ordinary velocities $d^*\mathbf{r}/dt$. It will be instructive to try working out the direction of the coriolis force for various directions of motion at various places on the earth's surface. The coriolis force is of major importance in the motion of large air masses, and is responsible for the fact that in the northern hemisphere tornados and cyclones circle in the direction south to east to north to west. In the northern hemisphere, the coriolis force acts to deflect a moving object toward the right. As the winds blow toward a low pressure area, they are deflected to the right, so that they circle the low pressure area in a counterclockwise direction. An air mass circling in this way will have a low pressure on its left, and a higher pressure on its right. This is just what is needed to balance the coriolis force urging it to the right. An air mass can move steadily in one direction only if there is a high pressure to the right of it to balance the coriolis force. Conversely,

---

* A body in motion is subject also to the coriolis force.

a pressure gradient over the surface of the earth tends to develop winds moving at right angles to it.   The prevailing westerly winds in the northern temperate zone indicate that the atmospheric pressure toward the equator is greater than toward the poles, at least near the earth's surface.   The easterly trade winds in the equatorial zone are due to the fact that any air mass moving toward the equator will acquire a velocity toward the west due to the coriolis force acting on it.   The trade winds are maintained by high pressure areas on either side of the equatorial zone.

7–4 The Foucault pendulum.   An interesting application of the theory of rotating coordinate systems is the problem of the Foucault pendulum. The Foucault pendulum has a bob hanging from a string arranged to swing freely in any vertical plane.   The pendulum is started swinging in a definite vertical plane and it is observed that the plane of swinging gradually precesses about the vertical axis during a period of several hours.   The bob must be made heavy, the string very long, and the support nearly frictionless, in order that the pendulum can continue to swing freely for long periods of time.   If we choose the origin of coordinates directly below the point of support, at the point of equilibrium of the pendulum bob of mass m, then the vector $\mathbf{r}$ will be nearly horizontal, for small amplitudes of oscillation of the pendulum.   In the northern hemisphere, $\boldsymbol{\omega}$ points in the general direction indicated in Fig. 7–6, relative to the vertical.   Writing $\mathbf{T}$ for the tension in the string, we have as the equation of motion of the bob, according to Eq. (7–45):

$$m \frac{d^{*2}\mathbf{r}}{dt^2} = \mathbf{T} + m\mathbf{g}_e - 2m\boldsymbol{\omega} \times \frac{d^*\mathbf{r}}{dt}.$$ (7–46)

If the coriolis force were not present, this would be the equation for a simple pendulum on a nonrotating earth.   The coriolis force is very small, less than 0.1% of the gravitational force if the velocity is 5 mi/hr or less, and its vertical component is therefore negligible in comparison with the gravitational force.   (It is the vertical force which determines the magnitude of the tension in the string.) However, the horizontal component of the coriolis force is perpendicular to the velocity $d^*\mathbf{r}/dt$, and as there are no other forces in this direction when the pendulum swings to and fro, it can change the nature of the motion.   Any force with a horizontal

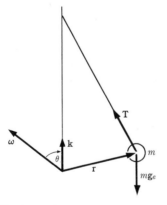

Fig. 7–6.   The Foucault pendulum.

component perpendicular to $d^*\mathbf{r}/dt$ will make it impossible for the pendulum to continue to swing in a fixed vertical plane.   In order to solve the problem including the coriolis term, we use the experimental result as a clue, and try to find a new coordinate system rotating about the vertical axis through the point of support at such an angular velocity that in this system the coriolis terms, or at least their horizontal components, are missing.   Let us introduce a new coordinate system rotating about the vertical axis with constant angular velocity $\mathbf{k}\Omega$, where $\mathbf{k}$ is a vertical unit vector.   We shall call this precessing coordinate system the primed coordinate system, and denote the time derivative with respect to this system by d'/dt.   Then we shall have, by Eqs. (7–33) and (7–34):

$$\frac{d^*\mathbf{r}}{dt} = \frac{d'\mathbf{r}}{dt} + \Omega\mathbf{k} \times \mathbf{r}, \tag{7–47}$$

$$\frac{d^{*2}\mathbf{r}}{dt^2} = \frac{d'^2\mathbf{r}}{dt^2} + \Omega^2\mathbf{k} \times (\mathbf{k} \times \mathbf{r}) + 2\Omega\mathbf{k} \times \frac{d'\mathbf{r}}{dt}. \tag{7–48}$$

Equation (7–46) becomes

$$m\frac{d'^2\mathbf{r}}{dt^2} = \mathbf{T} + m\mathbf{g}_e - 2m\boldsymbol{\omega} \times \left(\frac{d'\mathbf{r}}{dt} + \Omega\mathbf{k} \times \mathbf{r}\right) - m\Omega^2\mathbf{k} \times (\mathbf{k} \times \mathbf{r}) - 2m\Omega\mathbf{k} \times \frac{d'\mathbf{r}}{dt}$$

$$= \mathbf{T} + m\mathbf{g}_e - 2m\Omega\boldsymbol{\omega} \times (\mathbf{k} \times \mathbf{r}) - m\Omega^2\mathbf{k} \times (\mathbf{k} \times \mathbf{r}) - 2m(\boldsymbol{\omega} + \mathbf{k}\Omega) \times \frac{d'\mathbf{r}}{dt}. \tag{7–49}$$

We expand the triple products by means of Eq. (3–35):

$$m\frac{d'^2\mathbf{r}}{dt^2} = \mathbf{T} + m\mathbf{g}_e - m(2\Omega\boldsymbol{\omega} \cdot \mathbf{r} + \Omega^2\mathbf{k} \cdot \mathbf{r})\mathbf{k}$$
$$+ m(2\Omega\mathbf{k} \cdot \boldsymbol{\omega} + \Omega^2)\mathbf{r} - 2m(\boldsymbol{\omega} + \mathbf{k}\Omega) \times \frac{d'\mathbf{r}}{dt}. \tag{7–50}$$

Every vector on the right side of Eq. (7–50) lies in the vertical plane containing the pendulum, except the last term.   Since, for small oscillations, $d'\mathbf{r}/dt$ is practically horizontal, we can make the last term lie in this vertical plane also by making $(\boldsymbol{\omega} + \mathbf{k}\Omega)$ horizontal.   We therefore require that

$$\mathbf{k} \cdot (\boldsymbol{\omega} + \mathbf{k}\Omega) = 0. \tag{7–51}$$

This determines Ω:

$$\Omega = -\omega \cos\theta, \tag{7–52}$$

where ω is the angular velocity of the rotating earth, Ω is the angular velocity of the precessing coordinate system relative to the earth, and θ is the angle between the vertical and the earth's axis, as indicated in Fig. 7–6. The vertical is along the direction of $-\mathbf{g}_e$, and since this is very nearly the same as the direction of $-\mathbf{g}$ (see Fig. 7–5), θ will be practically equal to the colatitude, that is, the angle between $\mathbf{r}$ and $\boldsymbol{\omega}$ in Fig. 7–5.   For small oscillations, if Ω is determined by Eq. (7–52), the cross product in the last term of Eq. (7–50) is vertical.   Since all terms on the right of Eq. (7–50) now lie in a vertical plane containing the pendulum, the acceleration $d'^2\mathbf{r}/dt^2$ of the bob in the precessing system is always toward the vertical axis, and if the pendulum is initially swinging to and fro, it will continue to swing to and fro in the same vertical plane in the precessing coordinate system. Relative to the earth, the plane of the motion precesses with angular velocity Ω of magnitude and sense given by Eq. (7–52). In the northern hemisphere, the precession is clockwise looking down.

Since the last three terms on the right in Eq. (7–50) are much smaller than the first two, the actual motion in the precessing coordinate system is practically the same as for a pendulum on a nonrotating earth. Even at large amplitudes, where the velocity $d'\mathbf{r}/dt$ has a vertical component, careful study will show that the last term in Eq. (7–50), when Ω is chosen according to Eq. (7–52), does not cause any additional precession relative to the precessing coordinate system, but merely causes the bob to swing in an arc which passes slightly east of the vertical through the point of support. At the equator, Ω is zero, and the Foucault pendulum does not precess; by thinking about it a moment, perhaps you can see physically why this is so. At the north or south pole, $\Omega = \pm \omega$, and the pendulum merely swings in a fixed vertical plane in space while the earth turns beneath it.

Note that we have been able to give a fairly complete discussion of the Foucault pendulum, by using Coriolis' Theorem twice, without actually solving the equations of motion at all.

7–5 Larmor's Theorem. The coriolis force in Eq. (7–37) is of the same form as the magnetic force acting on a charged particle (Eq. 3–281), in that both are given by the cross product of the velocity of the particle with a vector representing a force field. Indeed, in the general theory of relativity, the coriolis forces on a particle in a rotating system can be regarded as due to the relative motion of other masses in the universe in a way somewhat analogous to the magnetic force acting on a charged particle which is due to the relative motion of other charges. The similarity in form of the two forces suggests that the effect of a magnetic field on a system of charged particles may be cancelled by introducing a suitable rotating coordinate system. This idea leads to Larmor's Theorem, which we state first, and then prove:

LARMOR'S THEOREM. *If a system of charged particles, all having the same ratio q/m of charge to mass, acted on by their mutual (central) forces, and by a central force toward a common center, is subject in addition to a weak uniform magnetic field $\mathbf{B}$, its possible motions will be the same as the motions it could perform without the magnetic field, superposed upon a slow precession of the entire system about the center of force with angular velocity*

$$\omega = -\frac{q}{2mc}\mathbf{B}. \qquad (7\text{–}53)$$

The definition of a *weak* magnetic field will appear as the proof is developed. We shall assume that all the particles have the same charge q and the same mass m, although it will be apparent that the only thing that needs to be assumed is that the ratio q/m is constant. Practically the only important applications of Larmor's Theorem are to the behavior of an atom in a magnetic field. The particles here are electrons of mass m, charge $q = -e$, acted upon by their mutual electrostatic repulsions and by the electrostatic attraction of the nucleus.

Let the central force acting on the kth particle be $\mathbf{F}_k^c$, and let the sum of the forces due to the other particles be $\mathbf{F}_k^i$. Then the equations of motion of the system of particles, in the absence of a magnetic field, are

$$m\frac{d^2\mathbf{r}_k}{dt^2} = \mathbf{F}_k^c + \mathbf{F}_k^i, \quad k = 1, \ldots, N, \tag{7-54}$$

where N is the total number of particles. The force $\mathbf{F}_k^c$ depends only on the distance of particle k from the center of force, which we shall take as origin, and the forces $\mathbf{F}_k^i$ depend only on the distances of the particles from one another. When the magnetic field is applied, the equations of motion become, by Eq. (3–281):

$$m\frac{d^2\mathbf{r}_k}{dt^2} = \mathbf{F}_k^c + \mathbf{F}_k^i + \frac{q}{c}\frac{d\mathbf{r}_k}{dt} \times \mathbf{B}, \quad k = 1, \ldots, N. \tag{7-55}$$

In order to eliminate the last term, we introduce a starred coordinate system with the same origin, rotating about this origin with angular velocity $\boldsymbol{\omega}$. Making use of Eqs. (7–33) and (7–34), we can write the equations of motion in the starred coordinate system:

$$m\frac{d^{*2}\mathbf{r}_k}{dt^2} = \mathbf{F}_k^c + \mathbf{F}_k^i - m\boldsymbol{\omega} \times (\boldsymbol{\omega} \times \mathbf{r}_k) + \frac{q}{c}(\boldsymbol{\omega} \times \mathbf{r}_k) \times \mathbf{B} + \frac{d^*\mathbf{r}_k}{dt}$$
$$\times \left(\frac{q\mathbf{B}}{c} + 2m\boldsymbol{\omega}\right). \tag{7-56}$$

We can make the last term vanish by setting

$$\boldsymbol{\omega} = -\frac{q}{2mc}\mathbf{B}. \tag{7-57}$$

Equation (7–56) then becomes

$$m\frac{d^{*2}\mathbf{r}_k}{dt^2} = \mathbf{F}_k^c + \mathbf{F}_k^i + \frac{q^2}{4mc^2}\mathbf{B} \times (\mathbf{B} \times \mathbf{r}_k), \quad k = 1, \ldots, N. \tag{7-58}$$

The forces $\mathbf{F}_k^c$ and $\mathbf{F}_k^i$ depend only on the distances of the particles from the origin and on their distances from one another, and these distances will be the same in the starred and unstarred coordinate systems. Therefore, if we neglect the last term, Eqs. (7–58) have exactly the same form in terms of starred coordinates as Eqs. (7–54) have in unstarred coordinates. Consequently, their solutions will then be the same, and the motions of the system expressed in starred coordinates will be the same as the motions of the system expressed in unstarred coordinates in the absence of a magnetic field. This is Larmor's Theorem.

The condition that the magnetic field be weak means that the last term in Eq. (7–58) must be negligible in comparison with the first two terms. Notice that the term we are neglecting is proportional to B^2, whereas the term in Eq. (7–55) which we have eliminated is proportional to B. Hence, for sufficiently weak fields, the former may be negligible even though the latter is not. The last term in Eq. (7–58) may be written in the form

$$\frac{q^2}{4mc^2} \mathbf{B} \times (\mathbf{B} \times \mathbf{r}_k) = m\boldsymbol{\omega} \times (\boldsymbol{\omega} \times \mathbf{r}_k). \tag{7–59}$$

Another way of formulating the condition for a weak magnetic field is to say that the Larmor frequency ω, given by Eq. (7–57), must be small compared with the frequencies of the motion in the absence of a magnetic field.

The reader who has understood clearly the above derivation should be able to answer the following two questions. The cyclotron frequency, given by Eq. (3–299), for the motion of a charged particle in a magnetic field is twice the Larmor frequency, given by Eq. (7–57). Why does not Larmor's Theorem apply to the charged particles in a cyclotron? Equation (7–58) can be derived without any assumption as to the origin of coordinates in the starred system. Why is it necessary that the axis of rotation of the starred coordinate system pass through the center of force of the system of particles?

PROBLEMS

1. (a) Solve the problem of the freely falling body by introducing a translating coordinate system with an acceleration **g**. Set up and solve the equations of motion in this accelerated coordinate system and transform the result back to a coordinate system fixed relative to the earth. (Neglect the earth's rotation.) (b) In the same accelerated coordinate system, set up the equations of motion for a falling body subject to an air resistance proportional to its velocity (relative to the fixed air).

2. Derive a formula for $d^3\mathbf{A}/dt^3$ in terms of starred derivatives relative to a rotating coordinate system.

3. Westerly winds blow from west to east in the northern hemisphere with an average speed v. If the density of the air is ρ, what pressure gradient is required to maintain a steady flow of air from west to east with this speed? Make reasonable estimates of v and ρ, and estimate the pressure gradient in lb-in^{-2}-mile^{-1}.

4. A mass m of a perfect gas of molecular weight M, at temperature T, is placed in a cylinder of radius a, height h, and whirled rapidly with an angular velocity ω about the axis of the cylinder. By introducing a coordinate system rotating with the gas, and applying the laws of static equilibrium, assuming that all other body forces are negligible compared with the centrifugal force, show that

$$p = \frac{RT}{M}\, \rho_0 \exp\left(\frac{M\omega^2 r^2}{2RT}\right),$$

where p is the pressure, r is the distance from the axis, and

$$\rho_0 = \frac{mM\omega^2}{2\pi hRT\left[\exp\left(\dfrac{M\omega^2 a^2}{2RT}\right) - 1\right]}.$$

5. A gyroscope consists of a wheel of radius r, all of whose mass is located on the rim. The gyroscope is rotating with angular velocity $\dot\theta$ about its axis, which is fixed relative to the earth's surface. We choose a coordinate system at rest relative to the earth whose z-axis coincides with the gyroscope axis and whose origin lies at the center of the wheel. The angular velocity $\boldsymbol{\omega}$ of the earth lies in the xz-plane, making an angle α with the gyroscope axis.

Find the x-, y-, and z-components of the torque $\mathbf{N}$ about the origin, due to the coriolis force in the xyz-coordinate system, acting on a mass m on the rim of the gyroscope wheel whose polar coordinates in the xy-plane are r,θ. Use this result to show that the total coriolis torque on the gyroscope, if the wheel has a mass M, is

$$\mathbf{N} = \mathbf{j}Mr^2\omega\dot\theta \sin\alpha.$$

This equation is the basis for the operation of the gyrocompass.

6. A ball of mass m rolls without friction over a horizontal plane at the surface of the earth. Show that in the northern hemisphere it rolls in a clockwise sense around a circle of radius

$$r = \frac{v}{2\omega \cos\theta},$$

where v is the speed of the ball, ω the angular velocity of the earth, and θ the co-latitude.

7. A particle moves in the xy-plane under the action of a force

$$F = -kr,$$

directed toward the origin. Find its possible motions by introducing a coordinate system rotating about the z-axis with angular velocity ω chosen so that the centrifugal force just cancels the force F, and solving the equations of motion in this coordinate system. Describe the resulting motions, and show that your result agrees with that of problem 27, Chapter 3.

CHAPTER 8

INTRODUCTION TO THE MECHANICS OF CONTINUOUS MEDIA

In this chapter, we begin the study of the mechanics of continuous media, solids, fluids, strings, etc. In such problems, the number of particles is so large that it is not practical to study the motion of individual particles, and we instead regard matter as continuously distributed in space and characterized by its density. We are interested primarily in gaining an understanding of the concepts and methods of treatment which are useful, rather than in developing in detail methods of solving practical problems. In the first four sections, we shall treat the vibrating string, using concepts which are a direct generalization of particle mechanics. In the remainder of the chapter, the mechanics of fluids will be developed in a way less directly related to particle mechanics.

8–1 The equation of motion for the vibrating string. In this section, we shall study the motion of a string of length l, stretched horizontally and fastened at each end, and set into vibration. In order to simplify the problem, we assume the string vibrates only in a vertical plane, and that the amplitude of vibration is small enough so that each point on the string moves only vertically, and so that the tension in the string does not change appreciably during the vibration.

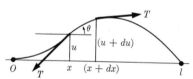

FIG. 8–1. The vibrating string.

We shall designate a point on the string by giving its horizontal distance x from the left-hand end (Fig. 8–1). The distance the point x has moved from the horizontal straight line representing the equilibrium position of the string will be designated by $u(x)$. Thus any position of the entire string is to be specified by specifying the function $u(x)$ for $0 \leq x \leq l$. This is precisely analogous, in the case of a system of N particles, to specifying the coordinates x_i, y_i, z_i, for $i = 1, \ldots, N$. In the case of the string, x is not a coordinate, but plays the same role as the subscript i; it designates a point on the string. Our idealized continuous string has infinitely many points, corresponding to the infinitely many values of x between 0 and l. For a given point x, it is $u(x)$ that plays the role of a coordinate locating that point, in analogy with the coordinates x_i, y_i, z_i of particle i. Just as a motion of the system of particles is to be described by functions $x_i(t), y_i(t), z_i(t)$, locating each particle at every instant of time, so a motion of the string is to be described by a function $u(x,t)$, locating each point x on the string at every instant of time.

In order to obtain an equation of motion for the string, we consider a segment of string of length dx between x and $x + dx$. If the density of the string per unit length is σ, then the mass of this segment is $\sigma \, dx$. The velocity of the string at any point is $\partial u/\partial t$, and its slope is $\partial u/\partial x$. The vertical component of tension exerted from right to left across any point in the string is

$$T_u = T \sin \theta, \qquad (8\text{-}1)$$

where θ is the angle between the string and the horizontal (Fig. 8–1). We are assuming that θ is very small and, in this case,

$$T \sin \theta \doteq T \tan \theta = T \frac{\partial u}{\partial x}. \qquad (8\text{-}2)$$

The net upward force dF due to the tension, on the segment dx of string, is the difference in the vertical component T_u between the two ends of the segment:

$$dF = [T_u]_{x+dx} - [T_u]_x$$
$$\doteq \frac{\partial}{\partial x}\left(T \frac{\partial u}{\partial x}\right) dx. \qquad (8\text{-}3)$$

If we do not limit ourselves to very small slopes $\partial u/\partial x$, then a segment of string may also have a net horizontal component of force due to tension, and the segment will move horizontally as well as vertically, a possibility we wish to exclude. If there is, in addition, a vertical force f per unit length, acting along the string, the equation of motion of the segment dx will be

$$\sigma \, dx \, \frac{\partial^2 u}{\partial t^2} = \frac{\partial}{\partial x}\left(T \frac{\partial u}{\partial x}\right) dx + f \, dx. \qquad (8\text{-}4)$$

For a horizontal string acted on by no horizontal forces except at its ends, and for small amplitudes of vibration, the tension is constant, and Eq. (8–4) can be rewritten:

$$\sigma \frac{\partial^2 u}{\partial t^2} = T \frac{\partial^2 u}{\partial x^2} + f. \qquad (8\text{-}5)$$

The force f may be the gravitational force acting on the string, which is usually negligible unless the tension is very small. The force f may also represent an external force applied to the string to set it into vibration. We shall consider only the case $f = 0$, and we rewrite Eq. (8–5) in the form

$$\frac{\partial^2 u}{\partial x^2} - \frac{1}{c^2} \frac{\partial^2 u}{\partial t^2} = 0, \qquad (8\text{-}6)$$

where

$$c = \left(\frac{T}{\sigma}\right)^{\frac{1}{2}}. \qquad (8\text{-}7)$$

The constant c has the dimensions of a velocity, and we shall see in Section 8–3 that it is the velocity with which a wave travels along the string.

Equation (8–6) is a partial differential equation for the function $u(x,t)$; it is the mathematical expression of Newton's law of motion applied to the vibrating string. We shall want to find solutions $u(x,t)$ to Eq. (8–6), for any given initial position $u_0(x)$ of the string, and any given initial velocity $v_0(x)$ of each point along the string. If we take the initial instant at $t = 0$, this means that we want a solution $u(x,t)$ which satisfies the initial conditions:

$$u(x,0) = u_0(x),$$
$$\left[\frac{\partial u}{\partial t}\right]_{t=0} = v_0(x). \tag{8–8}$$

The solution must also satisfy the *boundary conditions:*

$$u(0,t) = u(l,t) = 0, \tag{8–9}$$

which express the fact that the string is tied at its ends. From the nature of the physical problem, we expect that there should be just one solution $u(x,t)$ of Eq. (8–6) which satisfies Eqs. (8–8) and (8–9), and this solution will represent the motion of the string with the given initial conditions. It is therefore reasonable to expect that the mathematical theory of partial differential equations will lead to the same conclusion regarding the number of solutions of Eq. (8–6), and indeed it does.

8–2 Normal modes of vibration for the vibrating string. We shall first try to find some solutions of Eq. (8–6) which satisfy the boundary conditions (8–9), without regard to the initial conditions (8–8). This is analogous to our treatment of the harmonic oscillator, in which we first looked for solutions of a certain type and later adjusted these solutions to fit the initial conditions of the problem. The method of finding solutions which we shall use is called the method of *separation of variables.* It is one of the few general methods so far devised for solving partial differential equations, and many important equations can be solved by this method. Unfortunately, it does not always work. In principle, any partial differential equation can be solved by numerical methods, but the labor involved in doing so is often prohibitive, even for the modern large-scale automatic computing machines.

The method of separation of variables consists in looking for solutions of the form

$$u(x,t) = X(x)\Theta(t), \tag{8–10}$$

that is, u is to be a product of a function X of x and a function Θ of t. The derivatives of u will then be

$$\frac{\partial^2 u}{\partial x^2} = \Theta \frac{d^2 X}{dx^2}, \qquad \frac{\partial^2 u}{\partial t^2} = X \frac{d^2 \Theta}{dt^2}. \tag{8–11}$$

If these expressions are substituted in Eq. (8–6), and if we divide through by ΘX, then Eq. (8–6) can be rewritten:

$$\frac{c^2}{X}\frac{d^2X}{dx^2} = \frac{1}{\Theta}\frac{d^2\Theta}{dt^2}. \tag{8–12}$$

The left member of this equation is a function only of x, and the right member is a function only of t.   If we hold t fixed and vary x, the right member remains constant, and the left member must therefore be independent of x.   Similarly, the right member must actually be independent of t. We may set both members equal to a constant.   It is clear on physical grounds that this constant must be negative, for the right member of Eq. (8–12) is the acceleration of the string divided by the displacement, and the acceleration must be opposite to the displacement or the string will not return to its equilibrium position.   We shall call the constant $-\omega^2$:

$$\frac{1}{\Theta}\frac{d^2\Theta}{dt^2} = -\omega^2, \quad \frac{c^2}{X}\frac{d^2X}{dx^2} = -\omega^2. \tag{8–13}$$

The first of these equations can be rewritten as

$$\frac{d^2\Theta}{dt^2} + \omega^2\Theta = 0, \tag{8–14}$$

which we recognize as the equation of the harmonic oscillator, whose general solution, in the form most suitable for our present purpose, is

$$\Theta = A\cos\omega t + B\sin\omega t, \tag{8–15}$$

where A and B are arbitrary constants.   The second of Eqs. (8–13) has a similar form:

$$\frac{d^2X}{dx^2} + \frac{\omega^2}{c^2}X = 0, \tag{8–16}$$

and has a similar solution:

$$X = C\cos\frac{\omega x}{c} + D\sin\frac{\omega x}{c}. \tag{8–17}$$

The boundary condition (8–9) can hold for all times t only if X satisfies the conditions

$$X(0) = C = 0,$$
$$X(l) = C\cos\frac{\omega l}{c} + D\sin\frac{\omega l}{c} = 0. \tag{8–18}$$

The first of these equations determines C, and the second then requires that

$$\sin\frac{\omega l}{c} = 0. \tag{8–19}$$

This will hold only if ω has one of the values

$$\omega_n = \frac{n\pi c}{l}, \quad n = 1,2,3,\ldots . \tag{8-20}$$

Had we taken the separation constant in Eqs. (8–13) as positive, we would have obtained exponential solutions in place of Eq. (8–17), and it would have been impossible to satisfy the boundary conditions (8–18).

The frequencies $\nu_n = \omega_n/2\pi$ given by Eq. (8–20) are called the *normal frequencies of vibration* of the string. For a given n, we obtain a solution by substituting Eqs. (8–15) and (8–17) in Eq. (8–10), and making use of Eqs. (8–18), (8–20):

$$u(x,t) = A \sin \frac{n\pi x}{l} \cos \frac{n\pi ct}{l} + B \sin \frac{n\pi x}{l} \sin \frac{n\pi ct}{l}, \tag{8-21}$$

where we have set $D = 1$. This is called a *normal mode of vibration* of the string, and is entirely analogous to the normal modes of vibration which we found in Section 4–10 for coupled harmonic oscillators. Each point on the string vibrates at the same frequency ω_n with an amplitude which varies sinusoidally along the string. Instead of two coupled oscillators, we have an infinite number of oscillating points, and instead of two normal modes of vibration, we have an infinite number.

The initial position and velocity at $t = 0$ of the nth normal mode of vibration as given by Eq. (8–21) are

$$u_0(x) = A \sin \frac{n\pi x}{l},$$

$$v_0(x) = \frac{n\pi cB}{l} \sin \frac{n\pi x}{l}. \tag{8-22}$$

Only for these very special types of initial conditions will the string vibrate in one of its normal modes. However, we can build up more general solutions by adding solutions; for the vibrating string, like the harmonic oscillator, satisfies a principle of superposition. Let $u_1(x,t)$ and $u_2(x,t)$ be any two solutions of Eq. (8–6) which satisfy the boundary conditions (8–9). Then the function

$$u(x,t) = u_1(x,t) + u_2(x,t)$$

also satisfies the equation of motion and the boundary conditions. This is readily verified simply by substituting $u(x,t)$ in Eqs. (8–6) and (8–9), and making use of the fact that $u_1(x,t)$ and $u_2(x,t)$ satisfy these equations. A more general solution of Eqs. (8–6) and (8–9) is therefore to be obtained by adding solutions of the type (8–21), using different constants A and B for each normal frequency:

$$u(x,t) = \sum_{n=0}^{\infty} \left\{ A_n \sin \frac{n\pi x}{l} \cos \frac{n\pi ct}{l} + B_n \sin \frac{n\pi x}{l} \sin \frac{n\pi ct}{l} \right\}. \tag{8-23}$$

The initial position and velocity for this solution are

$$u_0(x) = \sum_{n=0}^{\infty} A_n \sin \frac{n\pi x}{l},$$

$$v_0(x) = \sum_{n=0}^{\infty} \frac{n\pi c B_n}{l} \sin \frac{n\pi x}{l}.$$

(8–24)

Whether or not Eq. (8–23) gives a general solution to our problem depends on whether, with suitable choices of the infinite set of constants A_n, B_n, we can make the functions $u_0(x)$ and $v_0(x)$ correspond to any possible initial position and velocity for the string. Our intuition is not very clear on this point, although it is clear that we now have a great variety of possible functions $u_0(x)$ and $v_0(x)$. The answer is provided by the Fourier series theorem, which states that any continuous function $u_0(x)$ for $(0 < x < l)$, which satisfies the boundary conditions (8–9), can be represented by the sum on the right in Eq. (8–24), if the constants A_n are properly chosen.* Similarly, with the proper choice of the constants B_n, any continuous function $v_0(x)$ for $(0 < x < l)$ can be represented.† The expressions for A_n and B_n are, in this case,

$$A_n = \frac{2}{l} \int_0^l u_0(x) \sin \frac{n\pi x}{l}\, dx,$$

$$B_n = \frac{2}{n\pi c} \int_0^l v_0(x) \sin \frac{n\pi x}{l}\, dx.$$

(8–25)

The most general motion of the vibrating string is therefore a superposition of normal modes of vibration at the fundamental frequency $\nu_1 = c/2l$ and its harmonics $\nu_n = nc/2l$.

8–3 Wave propagation along a string. Equations (8–14) and (8–16) have also the complex solutions

$$\Theta = A e^{\pm i\omega t},$$ (8–26)

$$X = e^{\pm i(\omega/c)x}.$$ (8–27)

Hence Eq. (8–6) has complex solutions of the form

$$u(x,t) = A e^{\pm i(\omega/c)(x \pm ct)}.$$ (8–28)

---

* R. V. Churchill, *Fourier Series and Boundary Value Problems.* New York: McGraw-Hill, 1941. (Pages 57–70.) Even functions with a finite number of discontinuities can be represented by Fourier series, but this point is not of great interest in the present application.

† The Fourier series theorem was quoted in Section 2–11 in a slightly different form. The connection between Eqs. (8–24) and (2–205) is to be made by replacing t by x and T by $2l$ in Eq. (2–205). Both sine and cosine terms are then needed to represent an arbitrary function $u_0(x)$ in the interval $(0 < x < 2l)$, but only sine terms are needed if we want to represent $u_0(x)$ only in the interval $(0 < x < l)$. [Cosine terms alone would also do for this interval, but sine terms are appropriate if $u_0(x)$ vanishes at $x = 0$ and $x = l$.]

By taking the real part, or by adding complex conjugates and dividing by 2, we obtain the real solutions

$$u(x,t) = A \cos \frac{\omega}{c} (x - ct), \qquad (8\text{–}29)$$

$$u(x,t) = A \cos \frac{\omega}{c} (x + ct). \qquad (8\text{–}30)$$

By taking imaginary parts, or by subtracting complex conjugates and dividing by $2i$, we could obtain similar solutions with cosines replaced by sines. These solutions do not satisfy the boundary conditions (8–9), but they are of considerable interest in that they represent waves traveling down the string, as we now show.

A fixed point x on the string will oscillate harmonically in time, according to the solution (8–29) or (8–30), with amplitude A and angular frequency ω. At any given instant t, the string will be in the form of a sinusoidal curve with amplitude A and *wavelength* λ (distance between successive maxima):

$$\lambda = \frac{2\pi c}{\omega}. \qquad (8\text{–}31)$$

We now show that this pattern moves along the string with velocity c, to the right in solution (8–29), and to the left in solution (8–30). Let

$$\xi = x - ct, \qquad (8\text{–}32)$$

so that Eq. (8–29) becomes

$$u = A \cos \frac{\omega \xi}{c}, \qquad (8\text{–}33)$$

where ξ is called the *phase* of the wave represented by the function u. For a fixed value of ξ, u has a fixed value. Let us consider a short time interval dt and find the increment dx required to maintain a constant value of ξ:

$$d\xi = dx - c\, dt = 0. \qquad (8\text{–}34)$$

Now if dx and dt have the ratio given by Eq. (8–34),

$$\frac{dx}{dt} = c, \qquad (8\text{–}35)$$

then the value of u at the point $x + dx$ at time $t + dt$ will be the same as its value at the point x at time t. Consequently, the pattern moves along the string with velocity c given by Eq. (8–7). The constant c is the *phase velocity* of the wave. Similarly, the velocity dx/dt for solution (8–30) is $-c$.

It is often convenient to introduce the *angular wave number* k defined by the equation

$$|k| = \frac{\omega}{c} = \frac{2\pi}{\lambda}, \qquad (8\text{–}36)$$

where k is taken as positive for a wave traveling to the right, and negative for a wave traveling to the left. Then both solutions (8–29) and (8–30) can be written in the symmetrical form

$$u = A \cos (kx - \omega t). \qquad (8\text{--}37)$$

The angular wave number k is measured in radians per centimeter, just as the angular frequency ω is measured in radians per second. The expression for u in Eq. (8–37) is the real part of the complex function

$$u = A e^{i(kx-\omega t)}. \qquad (8\text{--}38)$$

This form is often used in the study of wave motion.

The possibility of superposing solutions of the form (8–29) and (8–30) with various amplitudes and frequencies, together with the Fourier series theorem, suggests a more general solution of the form

$$u(x,t) = f(x - ct) + g(x + ct), \qquad (8\text{--}39)$$

where $f(\xi)$ and $g(\eta)$ are arbitrary functions of the variables $\xi = x - ct$, and $\eta = x + ct$. Equation (8–39) represents a wave of arbitrary shape traveling to the right with velocity c, and another traveling to the left. We can readily verify that Eq. (8–39) gives a solution of Eq. (8–6) by calculating the derivatives of u:

$$\frac{\partial u}{\partial x} = \frac{df}{d\xi}\frac{\partial \xi}{\partial x} + \frac{dg}{d\eta}\frac{\partial \eta}{\partial x} = \frac{df}{d\xi} + \frac{dg}{d\eta},$$

$$\frac{\partial^2 u}{\partial x^2} = \frac{d^2 f}{d\xi^2} + \frac{d^2 g}{d\eta^2},$$

$$\frac{\partial u}{\partial t} = \frac{df}{d\xi}\frac{\partial \xi}{\partial t} + \frac{dg}{d\eta}\frac{\partial \eta}{\partial t} = -c\frac{df}{d\xi} + c\frac{dg}{d\eta},$$

$$\frac{\partial^2 u}{\partial t^2} = c^2 \frac{d^2 f}{d\xi^2} + c^2 \frac{d^2 g}{d\eta^2}.$$

When these expressions are substituted in Eq. (8–6), it is satisfied identically, no matter what the functions $f(\xi)$ and $g(\eta)$ may be, provided, of course, that they have second derivatives. Equation (8–39) is, in fact, the most general solution of the equation (8–6); this follows from the theory of partial differential equations, according to which the general solution of a second order partial differential equation contains two arbitrary functions. We can prove this without resorting to the theory of partial differential equations by assuming the string to be of infinite length, so that there are no boundary conditions to concern us, and by supposing that the initial position and velocity of all points on the string are given by the functions $u_0(x), v_0(x)$. If the solution (8–39) is to meet these initial conditions, we must have, at $t = 0$:

$$u(x,0) = f(x) + g(x) = u_0(x), \qquad (8\text{--}40)$$

$$\left[\frac{\partial u}{\partial t}\right]_{t=0} = \left[-c\frac{df}{d\xi} + c\frac{dg}{d\eta}\right]_{t=0} = v_0(x). \tag{8-41}$$

At $t = 0$, $\xi = \eta = x$, so that Eq. (8-41) can be rewritten:

$$\frac{d}{dx}\left[-f(x) + g(x)\right] = \frac{v_0(x)}{c}, \tag{8-42}$$

which can be integrated to give

$$-f(x) + g(x) = \frac{1}{c}\int_0^x v_0(x)\,dx + C. \tag{8-43}$$

By adding and subtracting Eqs. (8-40) and (8-43), we obtain the functions f and g:

$$f(x) = \tfrac{1}{2}\left\{u_0(x) - \frac{1}{c}\int_0^x v_0(x)\,dx - C\right\},$$
$$g(x) = \tfrac{1}{2}\left\{u_0(x) + \frac{1}{c}\int_0^x v_0(x)\,dx + C\right\}. \tag{8-44}$$

The constant C can be omitted, since it will cancel out in $u = f + g$, and we can replace x by ξ and η respectively in these equations:

$$f(\xi) = \tfrac{1}{2}\left\{u_0(\xi) - \frac{1}{c}\int_0^\xi v_0(\xi)\,d\xi\right\},$$
$$g(\eta) = \tfrac{1}{2}\left\{u_0(\eta) + \frac{1}{c}\int_0^\eta v_0(\eta)\,d\eta\right\}. \tag{8-45}$$

This gives a solution to Eq. (8-6) for any initial position and velocity of the string.

Associated with a wave

$$u = f(x - ct), \tag{8-46}$$

there is a flow of energy down the string, as we show by computing the power delivered from left to right across any point x on the string. The power P is the product of the upward velocity of the point x and the upward force [Eq. (8-2)] exerted by the left half of the string on the right half across the point x:

$$P = -T\frac{\partial u}{\partial x}\frac{\partial u}{\partial t}. \tag{8-47}$$

If u is given by Eq. (8-46), this is

$$P = cT\left(\frac{df}{d\xi}\right)^2, \tag{8-48}$$

which is always positive, indicating that the power flow is always from left to right for the wave (8-46). For a wave traveling to the left, P will be negative, indicating a flow of power from right to left. For a sinusoidal wave given by Eq. (8-37), the power is

$$P = k\omega T A^2 \sin^2 (kx - \omega t), \tag{8-49}$$

or, averaged over a cycle,

$$\langle P \rangle_{\text{av}} = \tfrac{1}{2} k\omega T A^2. \tag{8-50}$$

We now consider a string tied at $x = 0$ and extending to the left from $x = 0$ to $x = -\infty$. The solution (8-39) must now satisfy the boundary condition

$$u(0,t) = f(-ct) + g(ct) = 0, \tag{8-51}$$

or

$$f(-\xi) = -g(\xi), \tag{8-52}$$

for all values of ξ. The initial values $u_0(x)$ and $v_0(x)$ will now be given only for negative values of x, and Eqs. (8-45) will define $f(\xi)$ and $g(\eta)$ only for negative values of ξ and η. The values of $f(\xi)$ and $g(\eta)$ for positive values of ξ and η can then be found from Eq. (8-52):

$$f(\xi) = -g(-\xi), \quad g(\eta) = -f(-\eta). \tag{8-53}$$

Let us consider a wave represented by $f(x - ct)$ traveling toward the end $x = 0$. A particular phase ξ_0, for which the wave amplitude is $f(\xi_0)$, will at time t_0 be at the point

$$x_0 = \xi_0 + ct_0. \tag{8-54}$$

Let us suppose that ξ_0 and t_0 are so chosen that x_0 is negative. At a later time $t_0 + \tau$, the phase ξ_0 will be at the point

$$x_1 = \xi_0 + ct_0 + c\tau = x_0 + c\tau. \tag{8-55}$$

At $\tau = -x_0/c$, $x_1 = 0$ and the phase ξ_0 reaches the end of the string. At later times x_1 will be positive, and $f(x_1 - ct)$ will have no physical meaning, since the string does not extend to positive values of x. Now consider the phase η_0, of the leftward traveling wave $g(x + ct)$, defined by

$$\eta_0 = x + ct = -\xi_0. \tag{8-56}$$

The amplitude of the leftward wave $g(\eta_0)$ for the phase η_0 is related to the amplitude of the rightward wave $f(\xi_0)$ for the corresponding phase ξ_0 by Eq. (8-53):

$$g(\eta_0) = -f(\xi_0). \tag{8-57}$$

At time $t_0 + \tau$, the phase η_0 will be at the point

$$x_2 = \eta_0 - ct_0 - c\tau = -x_0 - c\tau. \tag{8-58}$$

If $\tau > -x_0/c$, x_2 is negative and $g(\eta_0)$ represents a wave of equal and opposite amplitude to $f(\xi_0)$, traveling to the left. Thus the wave $f(x - ct)$ is reflected out of phase at $x = 0$ and becomes an equal and opposite wave

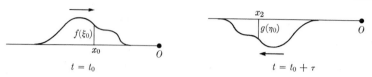

FIG. 8–2.   A wave reflected at $x = 0$.

traveling to the left.   (See Fig. 8–2.)   The total distance traveled by the wave during the time τ, from $x = x_0$ to $x = 0$ and back to $x = x_2$ is, by Eq. (8–58),

$$-x_0 - x_2 = c\tau, \qquad (8\text{–}59)$$

as it should be.

The solution (8–39) can also be fitted to a string of finite length fastened at $x = 0$ and $x = l$.   In this case, the initial position and velocity $u_0(x)$ and $v_0(x)$ are given only for $(0 \leq x \leq l)$.   The functions $f(\xi)$ and $g(\eta)$ are then defined by Eq. (8–45) only for $(0 \leq \xi \leq l, 0 \leq \eta \leq l)$.   If we define $f(\xi)$ and $g(\eta)$ for negative values of ξ and η by Eq. (8–53), in terms of their values for positive ξ and η, then the boundary condition (8–51) will be satisfied at $x = 0$.   By an argument similar to that which led to Eq. (8–53), we can show that the boundary condition (8–9) for $x = l$ will be satisfied if, for all values of ξ and η,

$$\begin{aligned} f(\xi + l) &= -g(l - \xi), \\ g(\eta + l) &= -f(l - \eta). \end{aligned} \qquad (8\text{–}60)$$

By means of Eqs. (8–53) and (8–60), we can find $f(\xi)$ and $g(\eta)$ for all values of ξ and η, once their values are given [by Eqs. (8–45)] for $0 \leq \xi \leq l, 0 \leq \eta \leq l$.   Thus we find a solution for the vibrating string of length l in terms of waves traveling in opposite directions and continuously being reflected at $x = 0$ and $x = l$.   The solution is equivalent to the solution given by Eqs. (8–23) and (8–25) in terms of standing sinusoidal waves.

8–4 The string as a limiting case of a system of particles.   In the first three sections of this chapter, we have considered an idealized string characterized by a continuously distributed mass with density σ and tension T.   An actual string is made up of particles (atoms and molecules); our treatment of it as continuous is valid because of the enormously large number of particles in the string.   A treatment of an actual string which takes into account the individual atoms would be hopelessly difficult, but we shall consider in this section an idealized model of a string made up of a finite number of particles, each of mass m.   Figure 8–3 shows this idealized string, in which an attractive force T acts between adjacent particles along the line joining

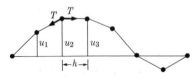

FIG. 8–3.   A string made up of particles.

them. The interparticle forces are such that in equilibrium the string is horizontal, with the particles equally spaced a distance h apart. The string is of length $(N + 1)h$, with $N + 2$ particles, the two end particles being fastened at the x-axis. The N particles which are free to move are numbered $1, 2, \ldots, N$, and the upward displacement of particle j from the horizontal axis will be called u_j. It will be assumed that the particles move only vertically and that only small vibrations are considered, so that the slope of the string is always small. Then the equations of motion of this system of particles are

$$m \frac{d^2 u_j}{dt^2} = T \frac{u_{j+1} - u_j}{h} - T \frac{u_j - u_{j-1}}{h}, \quad j = 1, \ldots, N, \qquad (8\text{-}61)$$

where the expression on the right represents the vertical components of the forces T between particle j and the two adjacent particles, and we are supposing that the forces T are equal between all pairs of particles. Now let us assume that the number N of particles is very large, and that the displacement of the string is such that at any time t, a smooth curve $u(x,t)$ can be drawn through the particles, so that

$$u(jh,t) = u_j(t). \qquad (8\text{-}62)$$

We can then represent the system of particles approximately as a continuous string of tension T, and of linear density

$$\sigma = \frac{m}{h}. \qquad (8\text{-}63)$$

The equations of motion (8-61) can be written in the form

$$\frac{d^2 u_j}{dt^2} = \frac{T}{\sigma} \frac{1}{h} \left(\frac{u_{j+1} - u_j}{h} - \frac{u_j - u_{j-1}}{h} \right). \qquad (8\text{-}64)$$

Now if the particles are sufficiently close together, we shall have, approximately,

$$\frac{u_{j+1} - u_j}{h} \doteq \left[\frac{\partial u}{\partial x} \right]_{x=(j+\frac{1}{2})h}, \qquad (8\text{-}65)$$

$$\frac{u_j - u_{j-1}}{h} \doteq \left[\frac{\partial u}{\partial x} \right]_{x=(j-\frac{1}{2})h},$$

and hence

$$\frac{1}{h} \left(\frac{u_{j+1} - u_j}{h} - \frac{u_j - u_{j-1}}{h} \right) \doteq \left[\frac{\partial^2 u}{\partial x^2} \right]_{x=jh}. \qquad (8\text{-}66)$$

The function $u(x,t)$ therefore, when h is very small, satisfies the equation

$$\frac{\partial^2 u}{\partial t^2} = \frac{T}{\sigma} \frac{\partial^2 u}{\partial x^2}, \qquad (8\text{-}67)$$

which is the same as Eq. (8-6) for the continuous string.

The solutions of Eqs. (8–61) when N is large will be expected to approximate the solutions of Eq. (8–6). If we were unable to solve Eq. (8–6) otherwise, one method of solving it numerically would be to carry out the above process in reverse, so as to reduce the partial differential equation (8–67) to the set of ordinary differential equations (8–61), which could then be solved by numerical methods. The solutions of Eqs. (8–61) are of some interest in their own right. Let us rewrite these equations in the form

$$m\frac{d^2u_j}{dt^2} + \frac{2T}{h}u_j - \frac{T}{h}(u_{j+1} + u_{j-1}) = 0, \quad j = 1, \ldots, N. \qquad (8\text{–}68)$$

These are the equations for a set of harmonic oscillators, each coupled to the two adjacent oscillators. We are led, either by our method of treatment of the coupled oscillator problem or by considering our results for the continuous string, to try a solution of the form

$$u_j = a_j e^{\pm i\omega t}. \qquad (8\text{–}69)$$

If we substitute this trial solution in Eqs. (8–68), the factor $e^{\pm i\omega t}$ cancels out, and we get a set of algebraic equations:

$$\left(\frac{2T}{h} - m\omega^2\right)a_j - \frac{T}{h}a_{j+1} - \frac{T}{h}a_{j-1} = 0, \quad j = 1, \ldots, N. \qquad (8\text{–}70)$$

This is a set of linear difference equations which could be solved for a_{j+1} in terms of a_j and a_{j-1}. Since $a_0 = 0$, if a_1 is given we can find the values of the remaining constants a_j by successive applications of these equations. A neater method of solution is to notice the analogy between the linear difference equations (8–70) and the linear differential equation (8–16), and to try the solution

$$a_j = A e^{ipj}, \quad j = 1, \ldots, N. \qquad (8\text{–}71)$$

When this is substituted in Eqs. (8–70), we get, after canceling the factor Ae^{ipj}:

$$\left(\frac{2T}{h} - m\omega^2\right) - \frac{T}{h}(e^{ip} + e^{-ip}) = 0, \qquad (8\text{–}72)$$

or

$$\cos p = 1 - \frac{mh\omega^2}{2T}. \qquad (8\text{–}73)$$

If ω is less than

$$\omega_c = \left(\frac{4T}{mh}\right)^{\frac{1}{2}}, \qquad (8\text{–}74)$$

there will be real solutions for p. Let a solution be given by

$$p = kh, \quad 0 \le kh \le \pi. \qquad (8\text{–}75)$$

Then another solution is

$$p = -kh. \qquad (8\text{–}76)$$

All other solutions for p differ from these by multiples of 2π, and in view of the form of Eq. (8–71), they lead to the same values of a_j, so we can restrict our attention to values of p given by Eqs. (8–75) and (8–76).

If we substitute Eq. (8–71) in Eq. (8–69), making use of Eq. (8–75), we have a solution of Eqs. (8–68) in the form

$$u_j = Ae^{\pm i(kjh - \omega t)}. \tag{8–77}$$

Since the horizontal distance of particle j from the left end of the string is

$$x_j = jh, \tag{8–78}$$

we see that the solution (8–77) corresponds to our previous solution (8–38) for the continuous string, and represents traveling sinusoidal waves. By combining the two complex conjugate solutions (8–77) and using Eq. (8–78), we obtain the real solution

$$u_j = A \cos(kx_j - \omega t), \tag{8–79}$$

which corresponds to Eq. (8–37). We thus have sinusoidal waves which may travel in either direction with the velocity [Eq. (8–36)]

$$c = \frac{\omega}{k} = \frac{h\omega}{|p|}, \tag{8–80}$$

where p is given by Eq. (8–73). If $\omega \ll \omega_c$ [Eq. (8–74)], then p will be nearly zero, and we can expand $\cos p$ in Eq. (8–73) in a power series:

$$1 - \frac{p^2}{2} \doteq 1 - \frac{mh\omega^2}{2T},$$

$$|p| \doteq \omega \left(\frac{mh}{T}\right)^{\frac{1}{2}}, \tag{8–81}$$

and

$$c \doteq \left(\frac{hT}{m}\right)^{\frac{1}{2}}, \tag{8–82}$$

which agrees with Eq. (8–7) for the continuous string, in view of Eq. (8–63). However, for larger values of ω, the velocity c is smaller than for the continuous string, and approaches

$$c = \frac{h\omega_c}{\pi} = \frac{2}{\pi}\left(\frac{hT}{m}\right)^{\frac{1}{2}} \tag{8–83}$$

as $\omega \to \omega_c$. ($\omega_c = \infty$ for the continuous string for which $mh = \sigma h^2 = 0$.) Since the phase velocity given by Eq. (8–80) depends upon the frequency, we cannot superpose sinusoidal solutions to obtain a general solution of the form (8–39). If a wave of other than sinusoidal shape travels along the string, the sinusoidal components into which it may be resolved travel with different velocities, and consequently the shape of the wave changes as it moves along. This phenomenon is called *dispersion*.

When $\omega > \omega_c$, Eq. (8-73) has only complex solutions for p, of the form

$$p = \pi \pm i\gamma. \tag{8-84}$$

These lead to solutions u_j of the form

$$u_j = (-1)^j A e^{\pm \gamma j} \cos \omega t. \tag{8-85}$$

There is then no wave propagation, but only an exponential decline in amplitude of oscillation to the right or to the left from any point which may be set in oscillation. The minimum wavelength [Eq. (8-36)] which is allowed by Eq. (8-75) is

$$\lambda_c = \frac{2\pi}{k_c} = 2h. \tag{8-86}$$

It is evident that a wave of shorter wavelength than this would have no meaning, since there would not be enough particles in a distance less than λ_c to define the wavelength. The wavelength λ_c corresponds to the frequency ω_c, for which

$$u_j = A e^{ij\pi} e^{\pm i\omega_c t} = (-1)^j A e^{\pm i\omega_c t}. \tag{8-87}$$

Adjacent particles simply oscillate out of phase with amplitude A.

We can build up solutions which satisfy the boundary conditions

$$u_0 = u_{N+1} = 0 \tag{8-88}$$

by adding and subtracting solutions of the form (8-77). We can, by suitably combining solutions of the form (8-77), obtain the solutions

$$u_j = A \sin pj \cos \omega t + B \sin pj \sin \omega t + C \cos pj \cos \omega t + D \cos pj \sin \omega t. \tag{8-89}$$

In order to satisfy the conditions (8-88), we must set

$$C = D = 0,$$
$$p = \frac{n\pi}{N+1}, \quad n = 1, 2, \ldots, N, \tag{8-90}$$

where the limitation $n \leq N$ arises from the limitation on p in Eq. (8-75). The normal frequencies of vibration are now given by Eq. (8-73):

$$\omega_n = \left[\frac{2T}{mh}\left(1 - \cos\frac{n\pi}{N+1}\right)\right]^{\frac{1}{2}}, \quad n = 1, 2, \ldots, N. \tag{8-91}$$

If $n \ll N$, we can expand the cosine in a power series, to obtain

$$\omega_n \doteq \left[\frac{n^2\pi^2 T}{mh(N+1)^2}\right]^{\frac{1}{2}}$$
$$= \frac{n\pi}{l}\left(\frac{T}{\sigma}\right)^{\frac{1}{2}}, \quad [l = (N+1)h], \tag{8-92}$$

which agrees with Eq. (8-20) for the continuous string.

A physical model which approximates fairly closely the string of particles treated in this section can be constructed by hanging weights m at intervals h along a stretched string. The mass m of each weight must be large in comparison with that of a length h of the string.

8–5 General remarks on the propagation of waves. If we designate by F the upward component of force due to tension, exerted from left to right across any point in a stretched string, and by v the upward velocity of any point on the string, then, by Eq. (8–2), we have

$$F = -T \frac{\partial u}{\partial x}, \qquad (8\text{–}93)$$

$$v = \frac{\partial u}{\partial t}. \qquad (8\text{–}94)$$

By Eq. (8–4), if there is no other force on the string, we have

$$\frac{\partial v}{\partial t} = -\frac{1}{\sigma}\frac{\partial F}{\partial x}, \qquad (8\text{–}95)$$

and by differentiating Eq. (8–93) with respect to t, assuming T is constant in time, we obtain

$$\frac{\partial F}{\partial t} = -T \frac{\partial v}{\partial x}. \qquad (8\text{–}96)$$

Equations (8–95) and (8–96) are easily understood physically. The acceleration of the string will be proportional to the difference in the upward force F at the ends of a small segment of string. Likewise, since F is proportional to the slope, the time rate of change of F will be proportional to the difference in upward velocities of the ends of a small segment of the string. The power delivered from left to right across any point in the string is

$$P = Fv. \qquad (8\text{–}97)$$

Equations (8–95) and (8–96) are typical of all types of wave propagation which occur in physics. There are always two quantities, in this case F and v, such that the time rate of change of either is proportional to the space derivative of the other. Whenever equations of the form (8–95) and (8–96) hold, a wave equation of the form (8–6) can be derived for either of the two quantities. For example, if we differentiate Eq. (8–95) with respect to t, and Eq. (8–96) with respect to x, assuming σ, T to be constant, we obtain

$$\frac{\partial^2 F}{\partial x \, \partial t} = -T \frac{\partial^2 v}{\partial x^2} = -\sigma \frac{\partial^2 v}{\partial t^2},$$

or

$$\frac{\partial^2 v}{\partial x^2} - \frac{1}{c^2}\frac{\partial^2 v}{\partial t^2} = 0, \qquad (8\text{–}98)$$

where

$$c = \left(\frac{T}{\sigma}\right)^{\frac{1}{2}}. \tag{8–99}$$

Similarly, we can show that

$$\frac{\partial^2 F}{\partial x^2} - \frac{1}{c^2} \frac{\partial^2 F}{\partial t^2} = 0. \tag{8–100}$$

Usually one of these two quantities can be chosen so as to be analogous to a force (F), and the other to the corresponding velocity (v), and then the power transmitted will be given by an equation like Eq. (8–97). Likewise, all other quantities associated with the wave motion satisfy a wave equation, as, for example, u, which satisfies Eq. (8–6).

As a further example, the equations for a plane sound wave traveling in the x-direction, which will be derived in Section 8–10, can be written in the form

$$\frac{\partial v}{\partial t} = -\frac{1}{\rho} \frac{\partial p'}{\partial x}, \quad \frac{\partial p'}{\partial t} = -B \frac{\partial v}{\partial x}, \tag{8–101}$$

where p' is the excess pressure (above atmospheric), v is the velocity, in the x-direction, of the air at any point, and where ρ is the density and B the bulk modulus.   The physical meaning of these equations is clear almost without further discussion of the motion of gases.   Both p' and v satisfy wave equations, easily derived from Eqs. (8–101):

$$\frac{\partial^2 p'}{\partial x^2} - \frac{1}{c^2} \frac{\partial^2 p'}{\partial t^2} = 0, \quad \frac{\partial^2 v}{\partial x^2} - \frac{1}{c^2} \frac{\partial^2 v}{\partial t^2} = 0, \tag{8–102}$$

where

$$c = \left(\frac{B}{\rho}\right)^{\frac{1}{2}}, \tag{8–103}$$

and the power transmitted in the x-direction per unit area is

$$P = p'v. \tag{8–104}$$

In the case of a plane electromagnetic wave traveling in the x-direction and linearly polarized in the y-direction, the analogous equations can be shown to be (gaussian units)

$$\frac{\partial B_z}{\partial t} = -c \frac{\partial E_y}{\partial x}, \quad \frac{\partial E_y}{\partial t} = -c \frac{\partial B_z}{\partial x}, \tag{8–105}$$

where E_y and B_z are the y- and z-components of electric and magnetic field intensities, and c is the speed of light.   The components E_y and B_z satisfy wave equations with wave velocity c, and the power transmitted in the x-direction per unit area is

$$P = \frac{E_y B_z}{4\pi c}. \tag{8–106}$$

As a final example, on a two-wire electrical transmission line, the voltage E across the line and the current i through the line satisfy the equations

$$\frac{\partial E}{\partial t} = -\frac{1}{C}\frac{\partial i}{\partial x}, \qquad \frac{\partial i}{\partial t} = -\frac{1}{L}\frac{\partial E}{\partial x}, \qquad (8\text{--}107)$$

where C is the shunt capacitance per unit length, and L is the series inductance per unit length. Again we can derive wave equations for i and E with the wave velocity

$$c = \left(\frac{1}{LC}\right)^{\frac{1}{2}}, \qquad (8\text{--}108)$$

and again the power transmitted in the x-direction is

$$P = Ei. \qquad (8\text{--}109)$$

Thus the study of wave propagation in a string is applicable to a wide variety of physical problems, many of them of greater practical and theoretical importance than the string itself. In many cases, our discussion of the string as made up of a number of discrete particles is also of interest. The electrical transmission line, for example, can be considered a limiting case of a series of low-pass filters. An electrical network made up of series inductances and shunt capacitances can be described by a set of equations of the same form as our Eqs. (8–61), with analogous results. In the case of sound waves, we are led by analogy to expect that at very high frequencies, when the wavelength becomes comparable to the distance between molecules, the wave velocity will begin to depend on the frequency, and that there will be a limiting frequency above which no wave propagation is possible.

8-6 Kinematics of moving fluids. In this section, we shall develop the kinematic concepts useful in studying the motion of continuously distributed matter, with particular reference to moving fluids. One way of describing the motion of a fluid would be to attempt to follow the motion of each individual point in the fluid, by assigning coordinates x,y,z to each fluid particle and specifying these as functions of the time. We may, for example, specify a given fluid particle by its coordinates, x_0,y_0,z_0, at an initial instant $t = t_0$. We can then describe the motion of the fluid by means of functions $x(x_0,y_0,z_0,t), y(x_0,y_0,z_0,t), z(x_0,y_0,z_0,t)$ which determine the coordinates x,y,z at time t of the fluid particle which was at x_0,y_0,z_0 at time t_0. This would be an immediate generalization of the concepts of particle mechanics, and of the preceding treatment of the vibrating string. This program leads to the treatment of fluid mechanics due to Lagrange. A more convenient treatment for most purposes, due to Euler, is to abandon the attempt to specify the history of each fluid particle, and to specify instead the density and velocity of the fluid at each point in space at each instant of time. This is the method which we shall follow here. We describe the motion of the fluid by specifying the density $\rho(x,y,z,t)$ and the vector velocity $\mathbf{v}(x,y,z,t)$, at the point x,y,z at the time t. We thus focus our attention on what is happening at a particular point in space at a particular time, rather than on what is happening to a particular fluid particle.

Any quantity which is used in describing the state of the fluid, for example the pressure p, will be a function $[p(x,y,z,t)]$ of the space coordinates x,y,z and of the time t, that is, it will have a definite value at each point in space and at each instant of time. Although the mode of description we have adopted focuses attention on a point in space rather than on a fluid particle, we shall not be able to avoid following the fluid particles themselves, at least for short time intervals dt. For it is to the particles, and not to the space points, that the laws of mechanics apply. We shall be interested, therefore, in two time rates of change for any quantity, say p. The rate at which the pressure is changing with time at a fixed point in space will be the partial derivative with respect to time $(\partial p/\partial t)$; it is itself a function of x, y, z, and t. The rate at which the pressure is changing with respect to a point moving along with the fluid will be the total derivative

$$\frac{dp}{dt} = \frac{\partial p}{\partial t} + \frac{\partial p}{\partial x}\frac{dx}{dt} + \frac{\partial p}{\partial y}\frac{dy}{dt} + \frac{\partial p}{\partial z}\frac{dz}{dt}, \tag{8-110}$$

where dx/dt, dy/dt, dz/dt are the components of the fluid velocity $\mathbf{v}$. The change in pressure, dp, occurring during a time dt, at the position of a moving fluid particle which moves from x,y,z to $x + dx$, $y + dy$, $z + dz$ during this time, will be

$$dp = p(x + dx, y + dy, z + dz, t + dt) - p(x,y,z,t)$$
$$\doteq \frac{\partial p}{\partial x}\,dx + \frac{\partial p}{\partial y}\,dy + \frac{\partial p}{\partial z}\,dz + \frac{\partial p}{\partial t}\,dt,$$

and if $dt \to 0$, this leads to Eq. (8–110). We can also write Eq. (8–110) in the forms:

$$\frac{dp}{dt} = \frac{\partial p}{\partial t} + v_x\frac{\partial p}{\partial x} + v_y\frac{\partial p}{\partial y} + v_z\frac{\partial p}{\partial z} \tag{8-111}$$

and

$$\frac{dp}{dt} = \frac{\partial p}{\partial t} + \mathbf{v}\cdot\boldsymbol{\nabla}p, \tag{8-112}$$

where the second expression is a shorthand for the first, in accordance with the conventions for using the symbol $\boldsymbol{\nabla}$. The total derivative dp/dt is also a function of x, y, z, and t. A similar relation holds between partial and total derivatives of any quantity, and we may write, symbolically,

$$\frac{d}{dt} = \frac{\partial}{\partial t} + \mathbf{v}\cdot\boldsymbol{\nabla}, \tag{8-113}$$

where total and partial derivatives have the meaning defined above.

Let us consider now a small volume δV of fluid, and we shall agree that δV always designates a volume element which moves with the fluid, so that it always contains the same fluid particles. In general, the volume δV will then change with time, and we wish to calculate this rate of change. Let us assume that δV is in the form of a rectangular box of dimensions $\delta x, \delta y, \delta z$ (Fig. 8–4):

$$\delta V = \delta x \, \delta y \, \delta z. \quad (8\text{–}114)$$

The x-component of fluid velocity v_x may be different at the left and right faces of the box. If so, δx will change with time at a rate equal to the difference between these two velocities:

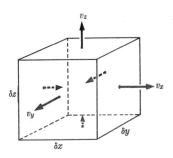

FIG. 8–4. A moving, expanding element of fluid.

$$\frac{d}{dt} \delta x = \frac{\partial v_x}{\partial x} \delta x,$$

and, similarly,

$$\frac{d}{dt} \delta y = \frac{\partial v_y}{\partial y} \delta y, \quad (8\text{–}115)$$

$$\frac{d}{dt} \delta z = \frac{\partial v_z}{\partial z} \delta z.$$

The time rate of change of δV is then

$$\frac{d}{dt} \delta V = \delta y \, \delta z \frac{d}{dt} \delta x + \delta x \, \delta z \frac{d}{dt} \delta y + \delta x \, \delta y \frac{d}{dt} \delta z$$

$$= \left(\frac{\partial v_x}{\partial x} + \frac{\partial v_y}{\partial y} + \frac{\partial v_z}{\partial z} \right) \delta x \, \delta y \, \delta z,$$

and finally,

$$\frac{d}{dt} \delta V = \nabla \cdot \mathbf{v} \, \delta V. \quad (8\text{–}116)$$

This derivation is not very rigorous, but it gives an insight into the meaning of the divergence $\nabla \cdot \mathbf{v}$. The derivation can be made rigorous by keeping careful track of quantities that were neglected here, like the dependence of v_x upon y and z, and showing that we arrive at Eq. (8–116) in the limit as $\delta V \to 0$. However, there is an easier way to give a more rigorous proof of Eq. (8–116). Let us consider a volume V of fluid which is composed of a number of elements δV:

$$V = \sum \delta V. \quad (8\text{–}117)$$

If we sum the left side of Eq. (8–116), we have

$$\sum \frac{d}{dt} \delta V = \frac{d}{dt} \sum \delta V = \frac{dV}{dt}. \quad (8\text{–}118)$$

The summation sign here really represents an integration, since we mean to pass to the limit $\delta V \to 0$, but the algebraic steps in Eq. (8–118) would look rather unfamiliar if the integral sign were used. Now let us sum the right side of Eq. (8–116), this time passing to the limit and using the integral sign, in order that we may apply Gauss' divergence theorem [Eq. (3–115)]:

$$\sum \boldsymbol{\nabla} \cdot \mathbf{v}\, \delta V = \int\!\!\int\!\!\int_V \boldsymbol{\nabla} \cdot \mathbf{v}\, dV$$

$$= \int\!\!\int_S \mathbf{n} \cdot \mathbf{v}\, dS, \qquad (8\text{–}119)$$

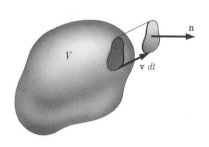

where S is the surface bounding the volume V, and $\mathbf{n}$ is the outward normal unit vector. Since $\mathbf{n} \cdot \mathbf{v}$ is the outward component of velocity of the surface element dS, the volume added to V by the motion of dS in a time dt will be $\mathbf{n} \cdot \mathbf{v}\, dt\, dS$ (Fig. 8–5), and hence the last line in Eq. (8–119) is the proper expression for the rate of increase in volume:

Fig. 8–5. Increase of volume due to motion of surface.

$$\frac{dV}{dt} = \int\!\!\int_S \mathbf{n} \cdot \mathbf{v}\, dS. \quad (8\text{–}120)$$

Therefore Eq. (8–116) must be the correct expression for the rate of increase of a volume element, since it gives the correct expression for the rate of increase of any volume V when summed over V. Note that the proof is independent of the shape of δV. We have incidentally derived an expression for the time rate of change of a volume V of moving fluid:

$$\frac{dV}{dt} = \int\!\!\int\!\!\int_V \boldsymbol{\nabla} \cdot \mathbf{v}\, dV. \qquad (8\text{–}121)$$

If the fluid is incompressible, then the volume of every element of fluid must remain constant:

$$\frac{d}{dt}\, \delta V = 0, \qquad (8\text{–}122)$$

and consequently, by Eq. (8–116),

$$\boldsymbol{\nabla} \cdot \mathbf{v} = 0. \qquad (8\text{–}123)$$

No fluid is absolutely incompressible, but for many purposes liquids may be regarded as practically so and, as we shall see, even the compressibility of gases may often be neglected.

Now the mass of an element of fluid is

$$\delta m = \rho \, \delta V, \qquad (8\text{--}124)$$

and this will remain constant even though the volume and density may not:

$$\frac{d}{dt} \delta m = \frac{d}{dt} (\rho \, \delta V) = 0. \qquad (8\text{--}125)$$

Let us carry out the differentiation, making use of Eq. (8–116):

$$\delta V \frac{d\rho}{dt} + \rho \frac{d \, \delta V}{dt} = \delta V \frac{d\rho}{dt} + \rho \nabla \cdot \mathbf{v} \, \delta V = 0,$$

or, when δV is divided out,

$$\frac{d\rho}{dt} + \rho \nabla \cdot \mathbf{v} = 0. \qquad (8\text{--}126)$$

By utilizing Eq. (8–113), we can rewrite this in terms of the partial derivatives referred to a fixed point in space:

$$\frac{\partial \rho}{\partial t} + \mathbf{v} \cdot \nabla \rho + \rho \nabla \cdot \mathbf{v} = 0.$$

The last two terms can be combined, using the properties of ∇ as a symbol of differentiation:

$$\frac{\partial \rho}{\partial t} + \nabla \cdot (\rho \mathbf{v}) = 0. \qquad (8\text{--}127)$$

This is the *equation of continuity* for the motion of continuous matter. It states essentially that matter is nowhere created or destroyed; the mass δm in any volume δV moving with the fluid remains constant.

––––––––––––

We shall make frequent use in the remainder of this chapter of the properties of the symbol ∇, which were described briefly in Section 3–6. The operator ∇ has the algebraic properties of a vector and, in addition, when a product is involved, it behaves like a differentiation symbol. The simplest way to perform this sort of manipulation, when ∇ operates on a product, is first to write a sum of products in each of which only one factor is to be differentiated. The factor to be differentiated may be indicated by underlining it. Then each term may be manipulated according to the rules of vector algebra, except that the underlined factor must be kept behind the ∇ symbol. When the underlined factor is the only one behind the ∇ symbol, or when all other factors are separated out by parentheses, the underline may be omitted, as there is no ambiguity as to what factor is to be differentiated by the components of ∇. As an example, the relation between Eqs. (8–126) and (8–127) is made clear by the following computation:

$$\boldsymbol{\nabla} \cdot (\rho\mathbf{v}) = \boldsymbol{\nabla} \cdot (\rho\mathbf{v}) + \boldsymbol{\nabla} \cdot (\rho\underline{\mathbf{v}})$$
$$= (\boldsymbol{\nabla}\underline{\rho}) \cdot \mathbf{v} + \rho\boldsymbol{\nabla} \cdot \underline{\mathbf{v}}$$
$$= (\boldsymbol{\nabla}\rho) \cdot \mathbf{v} + \rho\boldsymbol{\nabla} \cdot \mathbf{v}$$
$$= \mathbf{v} \cdot \boldsymbol{\nabla}\rho + \rho\boldsymbol{\nabla} \cdot \mathbf{v}. \qquad (8\text{-}128)$$

Any formulas arrived at in this way can always be verified by writing out both sides in terms of components, and the reader should do this a few times to convince himself. However, it is usually far less work to make use of the properties of the $\boldsymbol{\nabla}$ symbol.

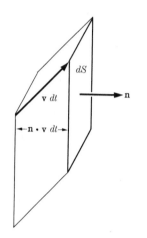

FIG. 8–6. Flow of fluid through a surface element.

We now wish to calculate the rate of flow of mass through a surface S fixed in space. Let dS be an element of surface, and let $\mathbf{n}$ be a unit vector normal to dS. If we construct a cylinder by moving dS through a distance $v\,dt$ in the direction of $-\mathbf{v}$, then in a time dt all the matter in this cylinder will pass through the surface dS (Fig. 8–6). The amount of mass in this cylinder is

$$\rho\mathbf{n} \cdot \mathbf{v}\,dt\,dS,$$

where $\mathbf{n} \cdot \mathbf{v}\,dt$ is the altitude perpendicular to the face dS. The rate of flow of mass through a surface S is therefore

$$\frac{dm}{dt} = \int\!\!\int_S \rho\mathbf{n} \cdot \mathbf{v}\,dS = \int\!\!\int_S \mathbf{n} \cdot (\rho\mathbf{v})\,dS. \qquad (8\text{-}129)$$

If $\mathbf{n} \cdot \mathbf{v}$ is positive, the mass flow across S is in the direction of $\mathbf{n}$; if $\mathbf{n} \cdot \mathbf{v}$ is negative, the mass flow is in the reverse direction. We see that $\rho\mathbf{v}$, the momentum density, is also the mass current, in the sense that its component in any direction gives the rate of mass flow per unit area in that direction. We can now give a further interpretation of Eq. (8–127) by integrating it over a fixed volume V bounded by a surface S with outward normal $\mathbf{n}$:

$$\int\!\!\int\!\!\int_V \frac{\partial\rho}{\partial t}\,dV + \int\!\!\int\!\!\int_V \boldsymbol{\nabla} \cdot (\rho\mathbf{v})\,dV = 0. \qquad (8\text{-}130)$$

Since the volume V here is a fixed volume, we can take the time differentiation outside the integral in the first term. If we apply Gauss' divergence theorem to the second integral, we can rewrite this equation:

$$\frac{d}{dt} \int\!\!\int\!\!\int_V \rho\,dV = -\int\!\!\int_S \mathbf{n} \cdot (\rho\mathbf{v})\,dS. \qquad (8\text{-}131)$$

This equation states that the rate of increase of mass inside the fixed volume V is equal to the negative of the rate of flow of mass outward across the surface. This result emphasizes the physical interpretation of each term in Eq. (8–127). In particular, the second term evidently represents the rate of flow of mass away from any point. Conversely, by starting with the self-evident equation (8–131) and working backwards, we have an independent derivation of Eq. (8–127).

Equations analogous to Eqs. (8–126), (8–127), (8–129), and (8–131) apply to the density, velocity, and rate of flow of any physical quantity. An equation of the form (8–127) applies, for example, to the flow of electric charge, if ρ is the charge density and $\rho\mathbf{v}$ the electric current density.

The curl of the velocity $\nabla \times \mathbf{v}$ is a concept which is useful in describing fluid flow. To understand its meaning, we compute the integral of the normal component of curl $\mathbf{v}$ across a surface S bounded by a curve C. By Stokes' Theorem (3–117), this is

$$\int\!\!\int_S \mathbf{n} \cdot (\nabla \times \mathbf{v})\, dS = \int_C \mathbf{v} \cdot d\mathbf{r}, \qquad (8\text{–}132)$$

where the line integral is taken around C in the positive sense relative to the normal $\mathbf{n}$, as previously defined. If the curve C surrounds a vortex in the fluid, so that $\mathbf{v}$ is parallel to $d\mathbf{r}$ around C (Fig. 8–7), then the line integral on the right is positive and measures, in a sense, the rate at which the fluid is whirling around the vortex. Thus $\nabla \times \mathbf{v}$ is a sort of measure of the rate of rotation of the fluid per unit area; hence the name curl $\mathbf{v}$. Curl $\mathbf{v}$ has a nonzero value in the neighborhood of a vortex in the fluid. Curl $\mathbf{v}$ may also be nonzero, however, in regions where there is no vortex, that is, where the fluid does not actually circle a point, provided there is a transverse velocity gradient. Figure 8–7 illustrates the two cases. In each case, the line integral of $\mathbf{v}$ counterclockwise around the circle C will have a positive value. If the curl of $\mathbf{v}$ is zero everywhere in a moving fluid, the flow is said to be *irrotational*. Irrotational flow is important chiefly because it presents fairly simple mathematical problems. If at any point $\nabla \times \mathbf{v} = 0$, then an element of fluid at that point will have no net angular velocity about that point, although its shape and size may be changing.

We arrive at a more precise meaning of curl $\mathbf{v}$ by introducing a coordinate system rotating with angular velocity $\boldsymbol{\omega}$. If $\mathbf{v}'$ designates the velocity of the fluid relative to the rotating system, then by Eq. (7–33),

$$\mathbf{v} = \mathbf{v}' + \boldsymbol{\omega} \times \mathbf{r},$$

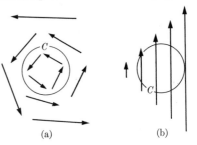

Fig. 8–7. Meaning of nonzero curl $\mathbf{v}$. (a) A vortex. (b) A transverse velocity gradient.

where $\mathbf{r}$ is a vector from the axis of rotation (whose location does not matter in this discussion) to a point in the fluid. Curl $\mathbf{v}$ is now

$$
\begin{aligned}
\nabla \times \mathbf{v} &= \nabla \times \mathbf{v}' + \nabla \times (\boldsymbol{\omega} \times \mathbf{r}) \\
&= \nabla \times \mathbf{v}' + \omega \nabla \cdot \mathbf{r} - \boldsymbol{\omega} \cdot \nabla \mathbf{r} \\
&= \nabla \times \mathbf{v}' + 3\omega - \omega \\
&= \nabla \times \mathbf{v}' + 2\omega,
\end{aligned}
$$

where the second line follows from Eq. (3–35) for the triple cross product, and the third line by direct calculation of the components in the second and third terms. If we set

$$\boldsymbol{\omega} = \tfrac{1}{2}\nabla \times \mathbf{v}, \tag{8–133}$$

then

$$\nabla \times \mathbf{v}' = 0. \tag{8–134}$$

Thus if $\nabla \times \mathbf{v} \neq 0$ at a point P, then in a coordinate system rotating with angular velocity $\boldsymbol{\omega} = \tfrac{1}{2}\nabla \times \mathbf{v}$, the fluid flow is irrotational at the point P. We may therefore interpret $\tfrac{1}{2}\nabla \times \mathbf{v}$ as the angular velocity of the fluid near any point. If $\nabla \times \mathbf{v}$ is constant, then it is possible to introduce a rotating coordinate system in which the flow is irrotational at every point.

8–7 Equations of motion for an ideal fluid. For the remainder of this chapter, except in the last section, we shall consider the motion of an ideal fluid, that is, one in which there are no shearing stresses, even when the fluid is in motion. The stress within an ideal fluid consists in a pressure p alone. This is a much greater restriction in the case of moving fluids than in the case of fluids in equilibrium (Section 5–11). A fluid, by definition, supports no shearing stress when in equilibrium, but all fluids have some viscosity and therefore there are always some shearing stresses between layers of fluid in relative motion. An ideal fluid would have no viscosity, and our results for ideal fluids will therefore apply only when the viscosity is negligible.

Let us suppose that, in addition to the pressure, the fluid is acted on by a body force of density $\mathbf{f}$ per unit volume, so that the body force acting on

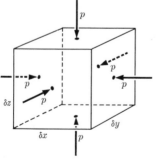

FIG. 8–8. Force on a volume element due to pressure.

a volume element δV of fluid is $\mathbf{f}\,\delta V$. We need, then, to calculate the force density due to pressure. Let us consider a volume element $\delta V = \delta x\,\delta y\,\delta z$ in the form of a rectangular box (Fig. 8–8). The force due to pressure on the left face of the box is $p\,\delta y\,\delta z$, and acts in the x-direction. The force due to pressure on the right face of the box is also $p\,\delta y\,\delta z$, and acts in the opposite direction. Hence the net x-component of force δF_x on the box depends upon the difference in pressure between the left and right faces of the box:

$$\delta F_x = \left(-\frac{\partial p}{\partial x} \delta x \right) \delta y\, \delta z. \qquad (8\text{–}135)$$

A similar expression may be derived for the components of force in the y- and z-directions. The total force on the fluid in the box due to pressure is then

$$\delta \mathbf{F} = \left(-\mathbf{i}\frac{\partial p}{\partial x} - \mathbf{j}\frac{\partial p}{\partial y} - \mathbf{k}\frac{\partial p}{\partial z} \right) \delta V$$
$$= -\nabla p\, \delta V. \qquad (8\text{–}136)$$

The force density per unit volume due to pressure is therefore $-\nabla p$. This result was also obtained in Section 5–11 [Eq. (5–172)].

We can now write the equation of motion for a volume element δV of fluid:

$$\rho\, \delta V \frac{d\mathbf{v}}{dt} = \mathbf{f}\, \delta V - \nabla p\, \delta V. \qquad (8\text{–}137)$$

This equation is usually written in the form

$$\rho\, \frac{d\mathbf{v}}{dt} + \nabla p = \mathbf{f}. \qquad (8\text{–}138)$$

By making use of the relation (8–113), we may rewrite this in terms of derivatives at a fixed point:

$$\frac{\partial \mathbf{v}}{\partial t} + \mathbf{v} \cdot \nabla \mathbf{v} + \frac{1}{\rho} \nabla p = \frac{\mathbf{f}}{\rho}, \qquad (8\text{–}139)$$

where $\mathbf{f}/\rho$ is the body force per unit mass. This is Euler's equation of motion for a moving fluid.

If the density ρ depends only on the pressure p, we shall call the fluid *homogeneous*. This definition does not imply that the density is uniform. An incompressible fluid is homogeneous if its density is uniform. A compressible fluid of uniform chemical composition and uniform temperature throughout is homogeneous. When a fluid expands or contracts under the influence of pressure changes, work is done by or on the fluid, and part of this work may appear in the form of heat. If the changes in density occur sufficiently slowly so that there is adequate time for heat flow to maintain the temperature uniform throughout the fluid, the fluid may be considered homogeneous within the meaning of our definition. The relation between density and pressure is then determined by the equation of state of the fluid or by its isothermal bulk modulus (Section 5–11). In some cases, changes in density occur so rapidly that there is no time for any appreciable flow of heat. In such cases the fluid may also be considered homogeneous, and the adiabatic relation between density and pressure or the adiabatic bulk modulus should be used. In cases between these two extremes, the density will depend not only on pressure, but also on temperature, which, in turn, depends upon the rate of heat flow between parts of the fluid at different temperatures.

In a homogeneous fluid, there are four unknown functions to be determined at each point in space and time, the three components of velocity $\mathbf{v}$, and the pressure p. We have, correspondingly, four differential equations to solve, the three components of the vector equation of motion (8–139), and the equation of continuity (8–127). The only other quantities appearing in these equations are the body force, which is assumed to be given, and the density ρ, which can be expressed as a function of the pressure. Of course, Eqs. (8–139) and (8–127) have a tremendous variety of solutions. In a specific problem we would need to know the conditions at the boundary of the region in which the fluid is moving and the values of the functions $\mathbf{v}$ and p at some initial instant. In the following sections, we shall confine our attention to homogeneous fluids. In the intermediate case mentioned at the end of the last paragraph, where the fluid is inhomogeneous and the density depends on both pressure and temperature, we have an additional unknown function, the temperature, and we will need an additional equation determined by the law of heat flow. We shall not consider this case, although it is a very important one in many engineering problems.

8–8 Conservation laws for fluid motion. Inasmuch as the laws of fluid motion are derived from Newton's laws of motion, we may expect that appropriate generalizations of the conservation laws of momentum, energy, and angular momentum also hold for fluid motion. We have already had an example of a conservation law for fluid motion, namely, the equation of continuity [Eq. (8–127) or (8–131)], which expresses the law of conservation of mass. Mass is conserved also in particle mechanics, but we did not find it necessary to write an equation expressing this fact.

A conservation law in fluid mechanics may be written in many equivalent forms. It will be instructive to study some of these in order to get a clearer idea of the physical meaning of the various mathematical expressions involved. Let ρ be the density of any physical quantity: mass, momentum, energy, or angular momentum. Then the simplest form of the conservation law for this quantity will be equation (8–125), which states that the amount of this quantity in an element δV of fluid remains constant. If the quantity in question is being produced at a rate Q per unit volume, then Eq. (8–125) should be generalized:

$$\frac{d}{dt} (\rho \, \delta V) = Q \, \delta V. \tag{8–140}$$

This is often called a conservation law for the quantity ρ. It states that this quantity is appearing in the fluid at a rate Q per unit volume, or disappearing if Q is negative. In the sense in which we have used the term in Chapter 4, this should not be called a conservation law except when $Q = 0$. By a derivation exactly like that which led to Eq. (8–127), we can rewrite Eq. (8–140) as a partial differential equation:

$$\frac{\partial \rho}{\partial t} + \nabla \cdot (\rho \mathbf{v}) = Q. \tag{8–141}$$

This is probably the most useful form of conservation law. The meaning of the terms in Eq. (8–141) is brought out by integrating each term over a fixed volume V and using Gauss' Theorem,* as in the derivation of Eq. (8–131):

$$\frac{d}{dt} \int\int\int_V \rho \, dV + \int\int_S \mathbf{n} \cdot \mathbf{v}\rho \, dS = \int\int\int_V Q \, dV. \tag{8–142}$$

According to the discussion preceding Eq. (8–129), this equation states that the rate of increase of the quantity within V, plus the rate of flow outward across the boundary S, equals the rate of appearance due to sources within V. Another form of the conservation law which is sometimes useful is obtained by summing equation (8–140) over a volume V moving with the fluid:

$$\sum \frac{d}{dt} (\rho \, \delta V) = \frac{d}{dt} \sum \rho \, \delta V = \sum Q \, \delta V. \tag{8–143}$$

If we pass to the limit $\delta V \to 0$, the summations become integrations:

$$\frac{d}{dt} \int\int\int_V \rho \, dV = \int\int\int_V Q \, dV. \tag{8–144}$$

The surface integral which appears in the left member of Eq. (8–142) does not appear in Eq. (8–144); since the volume V moves with the fluid, there is no flow across its boundary. Since Eqs. (8–140), (8–141), (8–142), and (8–144) are all equivalent, it is sufficient to derive a conservation law in any one of these forms. The others then follow. Usually it is easiest to derive an equation of the form (8–140), starting with the equation of motion in the form (8–138). We can also start with Eq. (8–139) and derive a conservation equation in the form (8–141), but a bit more manipulation is usually required.

In order to derive a conservation law for linear momentum, we first note that the momentum in a volume element δV is $\rho \mathbf{v} \, \delta V$. The momentum density per unit volume is therefore $\rho \mathbf{v}$, and this quantity will play the

---

* If ρ is a vector, as in the case of linear or angular momentum density, then a generalized form of Gauss' Theorem [mentioned in Section 5–11 in connection with Eq. (5–178)] must be used.

role played by ρ in the discussion of the preceding paragraph. In order to obtain an equation analogous to Eq. (8–140), we start with the equation of motion in the form (8–138), which refers to a point moving with the fluid, and multiply through by the volume δV of a small fluid element:

$$\rho \, \delta V \frac{d\mathbf{v}}{dt} + \nabla p \, \delta V = \mathbf{f} \, \delta V. \qquad (8\text{–}145)$$

Since $\rho \, \delta V = \delta m$ is constant, we may include it in the time derivative:

$$\frac{d}{dt} (\rho \mathbf{v} \, \delta V) = (\mathbf{f} - \nabla p) \, \delta V. \qquad (8\text{–}146)$$

The momentum of a fluid element, unlike its mass, is not, in general, constant. This equation states that the time rate of change of momentum of a moving fluid element is equal to the body force plus the force due to pressure acting upon it. The quantity $\mathbf{f} - \nabla p$ here plays the role of Q in the preceding general discussion. Equation (8–146) can be rewritten in any of the forms (8–141), (8–142), and (8–144). For example, we may write it in the form (8–144):

$$\frac{d}{dt} \iiint_V \rho \mathbf{v} \, dV = \iiint_V \mathbf{f} \, dV - \iiint_V \nabla p \, dV. \qquad (8\text{–}147)$$

We can now apply the generalized form of Gauss' Theorem [Eq. (5–178)] to the second term on the right, to obtain

$$\frac{d}{dt} \iiint_V \rho \mathbf{v} \, dV = \iiint_V \mathbf{f} \, dV + \iint_S -\mathbf{n}p \, dS, \qquad (8\text{–}148)$$

where S is the surface bounding V.

This equation states that the time rate of change of the total linear momentum in a volume V of moving fluid is equal to the total external force acting on it. This result is an immediate generalization of the linear momentum theorem (4–7) for a system of particles. The internal forces, in the case of a fluid, are represented by the pressure within the fluid. By the application of Gauss' Theorem, we have eliminated the pressure within the volume V, leaving only the external pressure across the surface of V. It may be asked how we have managed to eliminate the internal forces without making explicit use of Newton's third law, since Eq. (8–138), from which we started, is an expression only of Newton's first two laws. The answer is that the concept of pressure itself contains Newton's third law implicitly, since the force due to pressure exerted from left to right across any surface element is equal and opposite to the force exerted from right to left across the same surface element. Furthermore, the points of application of these two forces are the same, namely, at the surface element. Both forces necessarily have the same line of action, and there is no distinction between the weak and strong forms of Newton's third law. The internal pressures will therefore also be expected to cancel out in the equation for the time rate of change of angular momentum. A similar remark applies to the forces due to any kind of stresses in a fluid or a solid; Newton's third law in strong form is implicitly contained in the concept of stress.

Equations representing the conservation of angular momentum, analogous term by term with Eqs. (8–140) through (8–144), can be derived by taking the cross product of the vector $\mathbf{r}$ with either Eq. (8–138) or (8–139), and suitably manipulating the terms. The vector $\mathbf{r}$ is here the vector from the origin about which moments are to be computed to any point in the moving fluid or in space. This development is left as an exercise. The law of conservation of angular momentum is responsible for the vortices formed when a liquid flows out through a small hole in the bottom of a tank. The only body force here is gravity, which exerts no torque about the hole, and it can be shown that if the pressure is constant, or depends only on vertical depth, there is no net vertical component of torque across any closed surface due to pressure. Therefore the angular momentum of any part of the fluid remains constant. If a fluid element has any angular momentum at all initially, when it is some distance from the hole, its angular velocity will have to increase in inverse proportion to the square of its distance from the hole in order for its angular momentum to remain constant as it approaches the hole.

In order to derive a conservation equation for the energy, we take the dot product of $\mathbf{v}$ with Eq. (8–146), to obtain

$$\frac{d}{dt}\left(\tfrac{1}{2}\rho v^2\, \delta V\right) = \mathbf{v}\cdot(\mathbf{f}-\boldsymbol{\nabla}p)\,\delta V. \tag{8–149}$$

This is the energy theorem in the form (8–140). In place of the density ρ, we have here the kinetic energy density $\tfrac{1}{2}\rho v^2$. The rate of production of kinetic energy per unit volume is

$$Q = \mathbf{v}\cdot(\mathbf{f}-\boldsymbol{\nabla}p). \tag{8–150}$$

In analogy with our procedure in particle mechanics, we shall now try to define additional forms of energy so as to include as much as possible of the right member of Eq. (8–149) under the time derivative on the left. We can see how to rewrite the second term on the right by making use of Eqs. (8–113) and (8–116):

$$\frac{d}{dt}(p\,\delta V) = \frac{dp}{dt}\,\delta V + p\,\frac{d\,\delta V}{dt}$$

$$= \frac{\partial p}{\partial t}\,\delta V + \mathbf{v}\cdot\boldsymbol{\nabla}p\,\delta V + p\boldsymbol{\nabla}\cdot\mathbf{v}\,\delta V, \tag{8–151}$$

so that

$$-\mathbf{v}\cdot\boldsymbol{\nabla}p\,\delta V = -\frac{d}{dt}(p\,\delta V) + \frac{\partial p}{\partial t}\,\delta V + p\boldsymbol{\nabla}\cdot\mathbf{v}\,\delta V. \tag{8–152}$$

Let us now assume that the body force $\mathbf{f}$ is a gravitational force:

$$\mathbf{f} = \rho\mathbf{g} = \rho\nabla\mathcal{G}, \tag{8–153}$$

where $\mathcal{G}$ is the gravitational potential [Eq. (6–16)], i.e., the negative potential energy per unit mass due to gravitation. The first term on the right in Eq. (8–149) is then

$$\mathbf{v} \cdot \mathbf{f}\,\delta V = (\mathbf{v} \cdot \nabla\mathcal{G})\rho\,\delta V = \left(\frac{d\mathcal{G}}{dt} - \frac{\partial\mathcal{G}}{\partial t}\right)\rho\,\delta V$$

$$= \frac{d}{dt}(\rho\mathcal{G}\,\delta V) - \rho\frac{\partial\mathcal{G}}{\partial t}\,\delta V, \tag{8–154}$$

since $\rho\,\delta V = \delta m$ is constant. With the help of Eqs. (8–152) and (8–154), Eq. (8–149) can be rewritten:

$$\frac{d}{dt}\left[(\tfrac{1}{2}\rho v^2 + p - \rho\mathcal{G})\,\delta V\right] = \left(\frac{\partial p}{\partial t} - \rho\frac{\partial\mathcal{G}}{\partial t}\right)\delta V + p\nabla \cdot \mathbf{v}\,\delta V. \tag{8–155}$$

The pressure p here plays the role of a potential energy density whose negative gradient gives the force density due to pressure [Eq. (8–136)]. The time rate of change of kinetic energy plus gravitational potential energy plus potential energy due to pressure is equal to the expression on the right.

Ordinarily, the gravitational field at a fixed point in space will not change with time (except perhaps in applications to motions of gas clouds in astronomical problems). If the pressure at a given point in space is constant also, then the first term on the right vanishes. What is the significance of the second term? For an incompressible fluid, $\nabla \cdot \mathbf{v} = 0$, and the second term would vanish also. We therefore suspect that it represents energy associated with compression and expansion of the fluid element δV. Let us check this hypothesis by calculating the work done in changing the volume of the element δV. The work dW done by the fluid element δV, through the pressure which it exerts on the surrounding fluid when it expands by an amount $d\,\delta V$, is

$$dW = p\,d\,\delta V. \tag{8–156}$$

The rate at which energy is supplied by the expansion of the fluid element is, by Eq. (8–116),

$$\frac{dW}{dt} = p\frac{d\,\delta V}{dt} = p\nabla \cdot \mathbf{v}\,\delta V, \tag{8–157}$$

which is just the last term in Eq. (8–155). So far, all our conservation equations are valid for any problem involving ideal fluids. If we restrict ourselves to homogeneous fluids, that is, fluids whose density depends only on the pressure, we can define a potential energy associated with the expansion and contraction of the fluid element δV. We shall define the potential energy $u\,\delta m$ of the fluid element δV as the negative work done through its pressure on the surrounding fluid when the pressure changes from a standard pressure p_0 to any pressure p.   The potential energy per unit mass u will then be a function of p:

$$u\,\delta m = -\int_{p_0}^{p} pd\,\delta V. \tag{8-158}$$

The volume $\delta V = \delta m/\rho$ is a function of pressure, and we may rewrite this in various forms:

$$u = \int_{p_0}^{p} \frac{p\,d\rho}{\rho^2}$$

$$= \int_{p_0}^{p} \frac{p}{\rho^2} \frac{d\rho}{dp}\,dp \tag{8-159}$$

$$= \int_{p_0}^{p} \frac{p}{\rho B}\,dp,$$

where the last step makes use of the definition of the bulk modulus [Eq. (5–116)].   The time rate of change of u is, by Eqs. (8–158) or (8–159) and (8–116),

$$\frac{d(u\,\delta m)}{dt} = -p\frac{d\,\delta V}{dt} = -p\boldsymbol{\nabla}\cdot\mathbf{v}\,\delta V. \tag{8-160}$$

We can now include the last term on the right in Eq. (8–155) under the time derivative on the left:

$$\frac{d}{dt}\left[(\tfrac{1}{2}\rho v^2 + p - \rho\mathsf{G} + \rho u)\,\delta V\right] = \left(\frac{\partial p}{\partial t} - \rho\frac{\partial \mathsf{G}}{\partial t}\right)\delta V. \tag{8-161}$$

The interpretation of this equation is clear from the preceding discussion. It can be rewritten in any of the forms (8–141), (8–142), and (8–144).

If p and G are constant at any fixed point in space, then the total kinetic plus potential energy of a fluid element remains constant as it moves along. It is convenient to divide by $\delta m = \rho\,\delta V$ in order to eliminate reference to the volume element:

$$\frac{d}{dt}\left(\frac{v^2}{2} + \frac{p}{\rho} - \mathsf{G} + u\right) = \frac{1}{\rho}\frac{\partial p}{\partial t} - \frac{\partial \mathsf{G}}{\partial t}. \tag{8-162}$$

This is Bernoulli's Theorem.   The term $\partial\mathsf{G}/\partial t$ is practically always zero; we have kept it merely to make clear the meaning of the term $(1/\rho)(\partial p/\partial t)$, which plays a similar role and is not always zero.   When both terms on the right are zero, as in the case of steady flow, we have, for a point moving along with the fluid,

$$\frac{v^2}{2} + \frac{p}{\rho} - \mathsf{G} + u = \text{a constant.} \tag{8-163}$$

Other things being equal, that is if u, $\mathcal{G}$, and ρ are constant, the pressure of a moving fluid decreases as the velocity increases. For an incompressible fluid, ρ and u are necessarily constant.

The conservation laws of linear and angular momentum apply not only to ideal fluids, but also, when suitably formulated, to viscous fluids and even to solids, in view of the remarks made above regarding Newton's third law and the concept of stress. The law of conservation of energy will not apply, however, to viscous fluids, since the viscosity is due to an internal friction which results in a loss of kinetic and potential energies, unless conversion of mechanical to heat energy by viscous friction is included in the law.

8–9 Steady flow. By steady flow of a fluid, we mean a motion of the fluid in which all quantities associated with the fluid, velocity, density, pressure, force density, etc., are constant in time at any given point in space. For steady flow, all partial derivatives with respect to time can be set equal to zero. The total time derivative, which designates the time rate of change of a quantity relative to a point moving with the fluid, will not in general be zero, but, by Eq. (8–113), will be

$$\frac{d}{dt} = \mathbf{v} \cdot \boldsymbol{\nabla}. \tag{8–164}$$

The path traced out by any fluid element as it moves along is called a *streamline*. A streamline is a line which is parallel at each point (x,y,z) to the velocity $\mathbf{v}(x,y,z)$ at that point. The entire space within which the fluid is flowing can be filled with streamlines such that through each point there passes one and only one streamline. If we introduce along any streamline a coordinate s which represents the distance measured along the streamline from any fixed point, we can regard any quantity associated with the fluid as a function of s along the streamline. The component of the symbol $\boldsymbol{\nabla}$ along the streamline at any point is d/ds, as we see if we choose a coordinate system whose x-axis is directed along the streamline at that point. Equation (8–164) can therefore be rewritten:

$$\frac{d}{dt} = v \frac{d}{ds}. \tag{8–165}$$

This equation is also evident from the fact that $v = ds/dt$. For example, Eq. (8–162), in the case of steady flow, can be written:

$$\frac{d}{ds}\left(\frac{v^2}{2} + \frac{p}{\rho} - \mathcal{G} + u\right) = 0. \tag{8–166}$$

The quantity in parentheses is therefore constant along a streamline.

The equation of continuity (8–127) in the case of steady flow becomes

$$\boldsymbol{\nabla} \cdot (\rho \mathbf{v}) = 0. \tag{8–167}$$

If we integrate this equation over a
fixed volume V, and apply Gauss'
Theorem, we have

$$\iint_S \mathbf{n} \cdot (\rho\mathbf{v}) \, dS = 0, \quad (8\text{–}168)$$

where S is the closed surface bounding V. This equation simply states
that the total mass flowing out of
any closed surface is zero.

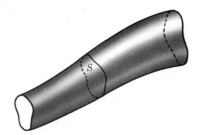

FIG. 8–9. A tube of flow.

If we consider all the streamlines which pass through any (open) surface S, these streamlines form a tube, called a *tube of flow* (Fig. 8–9). The
walls of a tube of flow are everywhere parallel to the streamlines, so that
no fluid enters or leaves it. A surface S which is drawn everywhere perpendicular to the streamlines and through which passes each streamline in
a tube of flow, will be called a *cross section* of the tube. If we apply Eq.
(8–168) to the closed surface bounded by the walls of a tube of flow and
two cross sections S_1 and S_2, then since $\mathbf{n}$ is perpendicular to $\mathbf{v}$ over the
walls of the tube, and $\mathbf{n}$ is parallel or antiparallel to $\mathbf{v}$ over the cross sections,
we have

$$\iint_{S_1} \rho v \, dS - \iint_{S_2} \rho v \, dS = 0, \quad\quad (8\text{–}169)$$

or

$$\iint_S \rho v \, dS = I = \text{a constant}, \quad\quad (8\text{–}170)$$

where S is any cross section along a given tube of flow. The constant I
is called the *fluid current* through the tube.

The energy conservation equation (8–161), when rewritten in the form
(8–141), becomes, in the case of steady flow,

$$\nabla \cdot [(\tfrac{1}{2}\rho v^2 + p - \rho \mathcal{G} + \rho u)\mathbf{v}] = 0. \quad\quad (8\text{–}171)$$

This equation has the same form as Eq. (8–167), and we can conclude in
the same way that the energy current is the same through any cross section S of a tube of flow:

$$\iint_S (\tfrac{1}{2}\rho v^2 + p - \rho \mathcal{G} + \rho u)v \, dS = \text{a constant}. \quad\quad (8\text{–}172)$$

This result is closely related to Eq. (8–166).

___

If the flow is not only steady, but also irrotational, then

$$\nabla \times \mathbf{v} = 0 \quad\quad\quad (8\text{–}173)$$

everywhere. This equation is analogous in form to Eq. (3–189) for a conservative force, and we can proceed as in Section 3–12 to show that if Eq. (8–173) holds, it is possible to define a *velocity potential function* $\phi(x,y,z)$ by the equation

$$\phi(\mathbf{r}) = \int_{\mathbf{r}_s}^{\mathbf{r}} \mathbf{v} \cdot d\mathbf{r}, \tag{8–174}$$

where $\mathbf{r}_s$ is any fixed point. The velocity at any point will then be

$$\mathbf{v} = \boldsymbol{\nabla}\phi. \tag{8–175}$$

Substituting this in Eq. (8–167), we have an equation to be solved for ϕ:

$$\boldsymbol{\nabla} \cdot (\rho\boldsymbol{\nabla}\phi) = 0. \tag{8–176}$$

In the cases usually studied, the fluid can be considered incompressible, and this becomes

$$\nabla^2\phi = 0. \tag{8–177}$$

This equation is identical in form with Laplace's equation (6–35) for the gravitational potential in empty space. Hence the techniques of potential theory may be used to solve problems involving irrotational flow of an incompressible fluid.

8–10 Sound waves. Let us assume a fluid at rest with pressure p_0, density ρ_0, in equilibrium under the action of a body force $\mathbf{f}_0$, constant in time. Equation (8–139) then becomes

$$\frac{1}{\rho_0}\boldsymbol{\nabla}p_0 = \frac{\mathbf{f}_0}{\rho_0}. \tag{8–178}$$

We may note that this equation agrees with Eq. (5–172) deduced in Section 5–11 for a fluid in equilibrium. Let us now suppose that the fluid is subject to a small disturbance, so that the pressure and density at any point become

$$p = p_0 + p', \tag{8–179}$$
$$\rho = \rho_0 + \rho', \tag{8–180}$$

where $p' \ll p$ and $\rho' \ll \rho$. We assume that the resulting velocity $\mathbf{v}$ and its space and time derivatives are everywhere very small. If we substitute Eqs. (8–179) and (8–180) in the equation of motion (8–139), and neglect higher powers than the first of $p', \rho', \mathbf{v}$ and their derivatives, making use of Eq. (8–178), we obtain

$$\frac{\partial \mathbf{v}}{\partial t} = -\frac{1}{\rho_0}\boldsymbol{\nabla}p'. \tag{8–181}$$

Making a similar substitution in Eq. (8–127), we obtain

$$\frac{\partial \rho'}{\partial t} = -\rho_0\boldsymbol{\nabla} \cdot \mathbf{v} - \mathbf{v} \cdot \boldsymbol{\nabla}\rho_0. \tag{8–182}$$

Let us assume that the equilibrium density ρ_0 is uniform, or nearly so, so that $\nabla\rho_0$ is zero or very small, and the second term can be neglected.

The pressure increment p' and density increment ρ' are related by the bulk modulus according to Eq. (5–183):

$$\frac{\rho'}{\rho_0} = \frac{p'}{B}. \qquad (8\text{--}183)$$

This equation may be used to eliminate either ρ' or p' from Eqs. (8–181) and (8–182). Let us eliminate ρ' from Eq. (8–182):

$$\frac{\partial p'}{\partial t} = -B\nabla \cdot \mathbf{v}. \qquad (8\text{--}184)$$

Equations (8–181) and (8–184) are the fundamental differential equations for sound waves. The analogy with the form (8–101) for one-dimensional waves is apparent. Here again we have two quantities, p' and $\mathbf{v}$, such that the time derivative of either is proportional to the space derivatives of the other. In fact, if $\mathbf{v} = \mathbf{i}v_x$ and if v_x and p' are functions of x alone, then Eqs. (8–181) and (8–184) reduce to Eqs. (8–101).

We may proceed, in analogy with the discussion in Section 8–5, to eliminate either $\mathbf{v}$ or p' from these equations. In order to eliminate $\mathbf{v}$, we take the divergence of Eq. (8–181) and interchange the order of differentiation, again assuming ρ_0 nearly uniform:

$$\frac{\partial}{\partial t}\,(\nabla \cdot \mathbf{v}) = -\,\frac{1}{\rho_0}\,\nabla^2 p'. \qquad (8\text{--}185)$$

We now differentiate Eq. (8–184) with respect to t, and substitute from Eq. (8–185):

$$\nabla^2 p' - \frac{1}{c^2}\frac{\partial^2 p'}{\partial t^2} = 0, \qquad (8\text{--}186)$$

where

$$c = \left(\frac{B}{\rho_0}\right)^{\frac{1}{2}}. \qquad (8\text{--}187)$$

This is the three-dimensional wave equation, as we shall show presently. Formula (8–187) for the speed of sound waves was first derived by Isaac Newton, and applies either to liquids or gases. For gases, Newton assumed that the isothermal bulk modulus $B = p$ should be used, but Eq. (8–187) does not then agree with the experimental values for the speed of sound. The sound vibrations are so rapid that they should be treated as adiabatic, and the adiabatic bulk modulus $B = \gamma p$ should be used, where γ is the ratio of specific heat at constant pressure to that at constant volume.*

---

* Millikan, Roller, and Watson, *Mechanics, Molecular Physics, Heat, and Sound.* Boston: Ginn and Co., 1937. (Pages 157, 276.)

Formula (8–187) then agrees with the experimental values of c. If we eliminate p' by a similar process, we obtain a wave equation for $\mathbf{v}$:

$$\nabla^2 \mathbf{v} - \frac{1}{c^2} \frac{\partial^2 \mathbf{v}}{\partial t^2} = \mathbf{0}. \tag{8–188}$$

In order to show that Eq. (8–186) leads to sound waves traveling with speed c, we note first that if p' is a function of x and t alone, Eq. (8–186) becomes

$$\frac{\partial^2 p'}{\partial x^2} - \frac{1}{c^2} \frac{\partial^2 p'}{\partial t^2} = 0. \tag{8–189}$$

This is of the same form as the one-dimensional wave equation (8–6), and therefore has solutions of the form

$$p' = f(x - ct). \tag{8–190}$$

This is called a *plane wave*, for at any time t the phase $x - ct$ and the pressure p' are constant along any plane ($x =$ a constant) parallel to the yz-plane. A plane wave traveling in the direction of the unit vector $\mathbf{n}$ will be given by

$$p' = f(\mathbf{n} \cdot \mathbf{r} - ct), \tag{8–191}$$

where $\mathbf{r}$ is the position vector from the origin to any point in space. To see that this is a wave in the direction $\mathbf{n}$, we rotate the coordinate system until the x-axis lies in this direction, in which case Eq. (8–191) reduces to Eq. (8–190). The planes $f =$ a constant, at any time t, are now perpendicular to $\mathbf{n}$, and travel in the direction of $\mathbf{n}$ with velocity c. We can see from the argument just given that the solution (8–191) must satisfy Eq. (8–186), or we may verify this by direct computation, for any coordinate system:

$$\nabla p' = \frac{dp'}{d\xi} \nabla \xi = \frac{dp'}{d\xi} \mathbf{n}, \tag{8–192}$$

where

$$\xi = \mathbf{n} \cdot \mathbf{r} - ct, \tag{8–193}$$

and, similarly,

$$\nabla^2 p' = \frac{d^2 f}{d\xi^2} \mathbf{n} \cdot \nabla \xi = \frac{d^2 f}{d\xi^2} \mathbf{n} \cdot \mathbf{n} = \frac{d^2 f}{d\xi^2}, \tag{8–194}$$

$$\frac{\partial^2 p'}{\partial t^2} = \frac{d^2 f}{d\xi^2} \left(\frac{\partial \xi}{\partial t} \right)^2 = c^2 \frac{d^2 f}{d\xi^2}, \tag{8–195}$$

so that Eq. (8–186) is satisfied, no matter what the function $f(\xi)$ may be.

Equation (8–188) will also have plane wave solutions:

$$\mathbf{v} = \mathbf{h}(\mathbf{n}' \cdot \mathbf{r} - ct), \tag{8–196}$$

corresponding to waves traveling in the direction $\mathbf{n}'$ with velocity c, where $\mathbf{h}$ is a vector function of $\xi' = \mathbf{n}' \cdot \mathbf{r} - ct$. To any given pressure wave of the form (8–191) will correspond a velocity wave of the form (8–196), related to it by Eqs. (8–181) and (8–182). If we calculate $\partial \mathbf{v}/\partial t$ from Eq.

(8–196), and $\nabla p'$ from Eq. (8–191), and substitute in Eq. (8–181), we will have

$$\frac{d\mathbf{h}}{d\xi'} = \frac{\mathbf{n}}{(B\rho_0)^{\frac{1}{2}}} \frac{df}{d\xi}. \qquad (8\text{–}197)$$

Equation (8–197) must hold at all points $\mathbf{r}$ at all times t. The right member of this equation is a function of ξ and is constant for a constant ξ. Consequently, the left member must be constant when ξ is constant, and must be a function only of ξ, which implies that $\xi' = \xi$ (or at least that ξ' is a function of ξ), and hence $\mathbf{n}' = \mathbf{n}$. This is obvious physically, that the velocity wave must travel in the same direction as the pressure wave. We can now set $\xi' = \xi$, and solve Eq. (8–197) for $\mathbf{h}$:

$$\mathbf{h} = \frac{\mathbf{n}}{(B\rho_0)^{\frac{1}{2}}} f, \qquad (8\text{–}198)$$

where the additive constant is zero, since both p' and $\mathbf{v}$ are zero in a region where there is no disturbance. Equations (8–198), (8–196), and (8–190) imply that for a plane sound wave traveling in the direction $\mathbf{n}$, the pressure increment and velocity are related by the equation

$$\mathbf{v} = \frac{p'}{(B\rho_0)^{\frac{1}{2}}} \mathbf{n}, \qquad (8\text{–}199)$$

where $\mathbf{v}$, of course, is here the velocity of a fluid particle, not that of the wave, which is $c\mathbf{n}$. The velocity of the fluid particles is along the direction of propagation of the sound wave, so that sound waves in a fluid are longitudinal. This is a consequence of the fact that the fluid will not support a shearing stress, and is not true of sound waves in a solid, which may be either longitudinal or transverse.

A plane wave oscillating harmonically in time with angular frequency ω may be written in the form

$$p' = A \cos{(\mathbf{k} \cdot \mathbf{r} - \omega t)} = \text{Re } A e^{i(\mathbf{k} \cdot \mathbf{r} - \omega t)}, \qquad (8\text{–}200)$$

where $\mathbf{k}$, the *wave vector*, is given by

$$\mathbf{k} = \frac{\omega}{c} \mathbf{n}. \qquad (8\text{–}201)$$

If we consider a surface perpendicular to $\mathbf{n}$ which moves back and forth with the fluid as the wave goes by, the work done by the pressure across this surface in the direction of the pressure is, per unit area per unit time,

$$P = pv. \qquad (8\text{–}202)$$

If v oscillates with average value zero, then since $p = p_0 + p'$, where p_0 is constant, the average power is

$$P_{av} = \langle p'v \rangle_{av} = \frac{\langle p'^2 \rangle_{av}}{(\rho_0 B)^{\frac{1}{2}}}, \tag{8-203}$$

where we have made use of Eq. (8–199). This gives the amount of energy per unit area per second traveling in the direction **n**.

The three-dimensional wave equation (8–186) has many other solutions corresponding to waves of various forms whose wave fronts (surfaces of constant phase) are of various shapes, and traveling in various directions. As an example, we consider a spherical wave traveling out from the origin. Since the rate of energy flow is proportional to p'^2 (a small portion of a spherical wave may be considered plane), and we expect that the energy per unit area must fall off inversely as the square of the distance, by the energy conservation law, p' should be inversely proportional to the distance r from the origin. We are therefore led to try a wave of the form

$$p' = \frac{1}{r} f(r - ct). \tag{8-204}$$

This will represent a wave of arbitrary time-dependence, whose wave fronts, $\xi = r - ct =$ a constant, are spheres expanding with the velocity c. It can readily be verified by direct computation, using either rectangular coordinates, or using spherical coordinates with the help of Eq. (3–124), that the solution (8–204) satisfies the wave equation (8–186).

A slight difficulty is encountered with the above development if we attempt to apply to a sound wave the expressions for energy flow and mass flow developed in the two preceding sections. The rate of flow of mass per unit area per second, by Eqs. (8–199), (8–180), and (8–183), is

$$\rho \mathbf{v} = \rho_0 \left(1 + \frac{p'}{B} \right) \frac{p'}{(\rho_0 B)^{\frac{1}{2}}} \, \mathbf{n}.$$

We should expect that $\rho \mathbf{v}$ would be an oscillating quantity whose average value is zero for a sound wave, since there should be no net flow of fluid. If we average the above expression, we have

$$\langle \rho \mathbf{v} \rangle_{av} = \frac{\rho_0^{\frac{1}{2}}}{B^{\frac{3}{2}}} (\langle p'^2 \rangle_{av} + B \langle p' \rangle_{av}) \mathbf{n},$$

so that there is a small net flow of fluid in the direction of the wave, unless

$$\langle p' \rangle_{av} = - \frac{\langle p'^2 \rangle_{av}}{B}. \tag{8-205}$$

If Eq. (8–205) holds, so that there is no net flow of fluid, then it can be shown that, to second order terms in p' and v, the energy current density given by Eq. (8–161) is, on the average, for a sound wave,

$$\langle (\tfrac{1}{2} \rho v^2 + p - \rho \mathcal{G} + \rho u) \mathbf{v} \rangle_{av} = \frac{\langle p'^2 \rangle_{av}}{(\rho_0 B)^{\frac{1}{2}}} \, \mathbf{n}, \tag{8-206}$$

in agreement with Eq. (8–203).

8-11 Normal vibrations of fluid in a rectangular box. The problem of the vibrations of a fluid confined within a rigid box is of interest not only because of its applications to acoustical problems, but also because the methods used can be applied to problems in electromagnetic vibrations, vibrations of elastic solids, wave mechanics, and all phenomena in physics which are described by wave equations. In this section, we consider a fluid confined to a rectangular box of dimensions $L_x L_y L_z$.

We proceed as in the solution of the one-dimensional wave equation in Section 8–2. We first assume a solution of Eq. (8–186) of the form

$$p' = U(x,y,z)\Theta(t). \tag{8-207}$$

Substitution in Eq. (8–186) leads to the equation

$$\frac{1}{U} \nabla^2 U = \frac{1}{c^2 \Theta} \frac{d^2 \Theta}{dt^2}. \tag{8-208}$$

Again we argue that since the left side depends only on x, y, and z, and the right side only on t, both must be equal to a constant, which we shall call $-\omega^2/c^2$:

$$\frac{d^2\Theta}{dt^2} + \omega^2 \Theta = 0, \tag{8-209}$$

$$\nabla^2 U + \frac{\omega^2}{c^2} U = 0. \tag{8-210}$$

The solution of Eq. (8–209) can be written:

$$\Theta = A \cos \omega t + B \sin \omega t, \tag{8-211}$$

or

$$\Theta = Ae^{-i\omega t}, \tag{8-212}$$

where A and B are constant. The form (8–212) leads to traveling waves of the form (8–200). We are concerned here with standing waves, and we therefore choose the form (8–211). In order to solve Eq. (8–210), we again use the method of separation of variables, and assume that

$$U(x,y,z) = X(x) Y(y) Z(z). \tag{8-213}$$

Substitution in Eq. (8–210) leads to the equation

$$\frac{1}{X} \frac{d^2 X}{dx^2} + \frac{1}{Y} \frac{d^2 Y}{dy^2} + \frac{1}{Z} \frac{d^2 Z}{dz^2} = -\frac{\omega^2}{c^2}. \tag{8-214}$$

This can hold for all x,y,z only if each term on the left is constant. We shall call these constants $-k_x^2, -k_y^2, -k_z^2$, so that

$$\frac{d^2 X}{dx^2} + k_x^2 X = 0, \qquad \frac{d^2 Y}{dy^2} + k_y^2 Y = 0, \qquad \frac{d^2 Z}{dz^2} + k_z^2 Z = 0, \tag{8-215}$$

where

$$k_x^2 + k_y^2 + k_z^2 = \frac{\omega^2}{c^2}. \tag{8-216}$$

The solutions of Eqs. (8–215) in which we are interested are

$$X = C_x \cos k_x x + D_x \sin k_x x,$$
$$Y = C_y \cos k_y y + D_y \sin k_y y, \qquad (8\text{–}217)$$
$$Z = C_z \cos k_z z + D_z \sin k_z z.$$

If we choose complex exponential solutions for X, Y, Z, and Θ, we arrive at the traveling wave solution (8–200), where k_x, k_y, k_z are the components of the wave vector $\mathbf{k}$.

We must now determine the appropriate boundary conditions to be applied at the walls of the box, which we shall take to be the six planes $x = 0$, $x = L_x$, $y = 0$, $y = L_y$, $z = 0$, $z = L_z$. The condition is evidently that the component of velocity perpendicular to the wall must vanish at the wall. At the wall $x = 0$, for example, v_x must vanish. According to Eq. (8–181),

$$\frac{\partial v_x}{\partial t} = -\frac{1}{\rho_0} \frac{\partial p'}{\partial x}. \qquad (8\text{–}218)$$

We substitute for p' from Eqs. (8–207), (8–211), (8–213), and (8–217):

$$\frac{\partial v_x}{\partial t} = -\frac{k_x YZ}{\rho_0} (A \cos \omega t + B \sin \omega t)(-C_x \sin k_x x + D_x \cos k_x x). \qquad (8\text{–}219)$$

Integrating, we have

$$v_x = -\frac{k_x YZ}{\omega \rho_0} (A \sin \omega t - B \cos \omega t)(-C_x \sin k_x x + D_x \cos k_x x) \qquad (8\text{–}220)$$

plus a function of x,y,z, which vanishes, since we are looking for oscillating solutions. In order to ensure that v_x vanishes at $x = 0$, we must set $D_x = 0$, i.e., choose the cosine solution for X in Eq. (8–217). This means that the pressure p' must oscillate at maximum amplitude at the wall. This is perhaps obvious physically, and could have been used instead of the condition $v_x = 0$, which, however, seems more self-evident. The velocity component perpendicular to a wall must have a node at the wall, and the pressure must have an antinode. Similarly, the pressure must have an antinode (maximum amplitude of oscillation) at the wall $x = L_x$:

$$\cos k_x L_x = \pm 1, \qquad (8\text{–}221)$$

so that

$$k_x = \frac{l\pi}{L_x}, \quad l = 0,1,2, \ldots \qquad (8\text{–}222)$$

By applying similar considerations to the four remaining walls, we conclude that $D_y = D_z = 0$, and

$$k_y = \frac{m\pi}{L_y}, \quad m = 0,1,2, \ldots,$$
$$k_z = \frac{n\pi}{L_z}, \quad n = 0,1,2, \ldots \qquad (8\text{–}223)$$

For each choice of three integers l,m,n, there is a normal mode of vibration of the fluid in the box. The frequencies of the normal modes of vibration are given by Eqs. (8–216), (8–222), and (8–223):

$$\omega_{lmn} = \pi c \left(\frac{l^2}{L_x^2} + \frac{m^2}{L_y^2} + \frac{n^2}{L_z^2} \right)^{\frac{1}{2}}. \tag{8–224}$$

The three integers l,m,n cannot all be zero, for this gives $\omega = 0$ and does not correspond to a vibration of the fluid. If we combine these results with Eqs. (8–217), (8–213), (8–211), and (8–207), we have for the normal mode of vibration characterized by the numbers l,m,n:

$$p' = (A \cos \omega_{lmn} t + B \sin \omega_{lmn} t) \cos \frac{l\pi x}{L_x} \cos \frac{m\pi y}{L_y} \cos \frac{n\pi z}{L_z}, \tag{8–225}$$

where we have suppressed the superfluous constant $C_x C_y C_z$. The corresponding velocities are

$$v_x = \frac{l\pi}{L_x \rho_0 \omega_{lmn}} (A \sin \omega_{lmn} t - B \cos \omega_{lmn} t) \sin \frac{l\pi x}{L_x} \cos \frac{m\pi y}{L_y} \cos \frac{n\pi z}{L_z},$$

$$v_y = \frac{m\pi}{L_y \rho_0 \omega_{lmn}} (A \sin \omega_{lmn} t - B \cos \omega_{lmn} t) \cos \frac{l\pi x}{L_x} \sin \frac{m\pi y}{L_y} \cos \frac{n\pi z}{L_z}, \tag{8–226}$$

$$v_z = \frac{n\pi}{L_z \rho_0 \omega_{lmn}} (A \sin \omega_{lmn} t - B \cos \omega_{lmn} t) \cos \frac{l\pi x}{L_x} \cos \frac{m\pi y}{L_y} \sin \frac{n\pi z}{L_z}.$$

These four equations give a complete description of the motion of the fluid for a normal mode of vibration. The walls $x = 0$, $x = L_x$, and the $(l - 1)$ equally spaced parallel planes between them are nodes for v_x and antinodes for p', v_y, and v_z. A similar remark applies to nodal planes parallel to the other walls.

It will be observed that the normal frequencies are not, in general, harmonically related to one another, as they were in the case of the vibrating string. If, however, one of the dimensions, say L_z, is much larger than the other two, so that the box becomes a long square pipe, then the lowest frequencies will correspond to the case where $m = n = 0$ and l is a small integer, and these frequencies are harmonically related. Thus, in a pipe, the first few normal frequencies above the lowest will be multiples of the lowest frequency. This explains why it is possible to get musical tones from an organ pipe, as well as from a vibrating string. Our treatment here applies only to a closed organ pipe, and a square one at that. The treatment of a closed circular pipe is not much more difficult than the above treatment and the general nature of the results is similar. The open ended pipe is, however, much more difficult to treat exactly. The difficulty lies in the determination of the boundary condition at the open end; indeed, not the least of the difficulties is in deciding just where the boundary is. As a rough approximation, one may assume that the boundary is a plane surface across the end of the pipe, and that this surface is a pressure node. The results are then similar to those for the closed pipe, except that if one end of a long pipe is closed and one open, the first few frequencies above the lowest are all odd multiples of the lowest.

The general solution of the equations for sound vibrations in a rectangular cavity can be built up, as in the case of the vibrating string, by adding normal mode solutions of the form (8–225) for all normal modes of vibration. The constants A and B for each mode of vibration can again be chosen to fit the initial conditions, which in this case will be a specification of p' and $\partial p'/\partial t$ (or p' and $\mathbf{v}$) at all points in the cavity at some initial instant. We shall not carry out this development here.

For cavities of other simple shapes, for example spheres and cylinders, the method of separation of variables used in the above example works, but in these cases instead of the variables x,y,z, coordinates appropriate to the shape of the boundary surface must be used, for example spherical or cylindrical coordinates. In most cases, except for a few simple shapes, the method of separation of variables cannot be made to work. Approximate methods can be used when the shape is very close to one of the simple shapes whose solution is known. Otherwise the only general methods of solution are numerical methods which usually involve a prohibitive amount of labor. It can be shown, however, that the general features of our results for rectangular cavities hold for all shapes; that is, there are normal modes of vibration with characteristic frequencies, and the most general motion is a superposition of these.

8–12 Sound waves in pipes. A problem of considerable interest is the problem of the propagation of sound waves in pipes. We shall consider a pipe whose axis is in the z-direction, and whose cross section is rectangular, of dimensions $L_x L_y$. This problem is the same as that of the preceding section except that there are no walls perpendicular to the z-axis.

We shall apply the same method of solution, the only difference being that the boundary conditions now apply only at the four walls $x = 0$, $x = L_x$, $y = 0$, $y = L_y$. Consequently, we are restricted in our choice of the functions $X(x)$ and $Y(y)$, just as in the preceding section, by Eqs. (8–217), (8–222), and (8–223). There are no restrictions on our choice of solution of the Z-equation (8–215). Since we are interested in solutions representing the propagation of waves down the pipe, we choose the exponential form of solution for Z:

$$Z = e^{ik_z z}, \tag{8–227}$$

and we choose the complex exponential solution (8–212) for Θ. Our solution for p', then, for a given choice of the integers l,m, is

$$p' = \text{Re } A e^{i(k_z z - \omega t)} \cos \frac{l\pi x}{L_x} \cos \frac{m\pi y}{L_y}$$

$$= A \cos \frac{l\pi x}{L_x} \cos \frac{m\pi y}{L_y} \cos (k_z z - \omega t). \tag{8-228}$$

This represents a harmonic wave, traveling in the z-direction down the pipe, whose amplitude varies over the cross section of the pipe according to the first two cosine factors. Each choice of integers l, m corresponds to what is called a *mode of propagation* for the pipe. (The choice $l = 0$, $m = 0$ is an allowed choice here.) For a given l, m and a given frequency ω, the wave number k_z is determined by Eqs. (8-216), (8-222), and (8-223):

$$k_z = \pm \left[\frac{\omega^2}{c^2} - \left(\frac{l\pi}{L_x} \right)^2 - \left(\frac{m\pi}{L_y} \right)^2 \right]^{\frac{1}{2}}. \tag{8-229}$$

The plus sign corresponds to a wave traveling in the $+z$-direction, and conversely. For $l = m = 0$, this is the same as the relation (8-201) for a wave traveling with velocity c in the z-direction in a fluid filling three-dimensional space. Otherwise, the wave travels with the velocity

$$c_{lm} = \frac{\omega}{|k_z|} = c \left[1 - \left(\frac{l\pi c}{\omega L_x} \right)^2 - \left(\frac{m\pi c}{\omega L_y} \right)^2 \right]^{-\frac{1}{2}}, \tag{8-230}$$

which is greater than c and depends on ω. There is evidently a minimum frequency

$$\omega_{lm} = \left[\left(\frac{l\pi c}{L_x} \right)^2 + \left(\frac{m\pi c}{L_y} \right)^2 \right]^{\frac{1}{2}} \tag{8-231}$$

below which no propagation is possible in the l, m mode; for k_z would be imaginary, and the exponent in Eq. (8-227) would be real, so that instead of wave propagation we would have an exponential decline in amplitude of the wave in the z-direction. Note the similarity of these results to those obtained in Section 8-4 for the discrete string, where, however, there was an upper rather than a lower limit to the frequency. Since c_{lm} depends on ω, we again have the phenomenon of dispersion. A wave of arbitrary shape, which can be resolved into sinusoidally oscillating components of various frequencies ω, will be distorted as it travels along the pipe because each component will have a different velocity. We leave as an exercise the problem of calculating the fluid velocity $\mathbf{v}$, and the power flow, associated with the wave (8-228).

Similar results are obtained for pipes of other than rectangular cross section. Analogous methods and results apply to the problem of the propagation of electromagnetic waves down a wave-guide. This is one reason for our interest in the present problem.

8–13 The Mach number. Suppose we wish to consider two problems in fluid flow having geometrically similar boundaries, but in which the dimensions of the boundaries, or the fluid velocity, density, or compressibility are different. For example, we may wish to investigate the flow of a fluid in two pipes having the same shape but different sizes, or we may be concerned with the flow of a fluid at different velocities through pipes of the same shape, or with the flow of fluids of different densities. We might be concerned with the relation between the behavior of an airplane and the behavior of a scale model, or with the behavior of an airplane at different altitudes, where the density of the air is different. Two such problems involving boundaries of the same shape we shall call *similar* problems. Under what conditions will two similar problems have similar solutions?

In order to make this question more precise, let us assume that for each problem a characteristic distance s_0 is defined which determines the geometrical scale of the problem. In the case of similar pipes, s_0 might be a diameter of the pipe. In the case of an airplane, s_0 might be the wingspan. We then define dimensionless coordinates x', y', z' by the equations

$$x' = x/s_0, \quad y' = y/s_0, \quad z' = z/s_0. \tag{8–232}$$

The boundaries for two similar problems will have identical descriptions in terms of the dimensionless coordinates x', y', z'; only the characteristic distance s_0 will be different. In a similar way, let us choose a characteristic speed v_0 associated with the problem. The speed v_0 might be the average speed of flow of fluid in a pipe, or the speed of the airplane relative to the stationary air at a distance from it, or v_0 might be the maximum speed of any part of the fluid relative to the pipe or the airplane. In any case, we suppose that v_0 is so chosen that the maximum speed of any part of the fluid is not very much larger than v_0. We now define a dimensionless velocity $\mathbf{v}'$, and a dimensionless time coordinate t':

$$\mathbf{v}' = \mathbf{v}/v_0, \tag{8–233}$$
$$t' = v_0 t/s_0. \tag{8–234}$$

We now say that two similar problems have similar solutions if the solutions are identical when expressed in terms of the dimensionless velocity $\mathbf{v}'$ as a function of x', y', z', and t'. The fluid flow pattern will then be the same in both problems, differing only in the distance and time scales determined by s_0 and v_0. We need also to assume a characteristic density ρ_0 and pressure p_0. In the case of the airplane, these would be the density and pressure of the undisturbed atmosphere; in the case of the pipe, they might be the average density and pressure, or the density and pressure at one end of the pipe. We shall define a dimensionless pressure increment p'' as follows:

$$p'' = \frac{p - p_0}{\rho_0 v_0^2}. \tag{8–235}$$

We shall now assume that the changes in density of the fluid are small enough so that we can write

$$\rho = \rho_0 + \frac{d\rho}{dp}\,(p - p_0),\qquad(8\text{–}236)$$

where higher order terms in the Taylor series for ρ have been neglected. By making use of the definition (8–235) for p'', and of the bulk modulus B as given by Eq. (5–183), this can be written

$$\rho = \rho_0(1 + M^2 p''),\qquad(8\text{–}237)$$

where

$$M = v_0 \left(\frac{B}{\rho_0}\right)^{-\frac{1}{2}} = \frac{v_0}{c}.\qquad(8\text{–}238)$$

Here M is the ratio of the characteristic velocity v_0 to the velocity of sound c and is called the *Mach number* for the problem. In a similar way, we can expand $1/\rho$, assuming that $|\rho - \rho_0| \ll \rho_0$:

$$\frac{1}{\rho} = \frac{1}{\rho_0}\,(1 - M^2 p'').\qquad(8\text{–}239)$$

With the help of Eqs. (8–237) and (8–239), we can rewrite the equation of continuity and the equation of motion in terms of the dimensionless variables introduced by Eqs. (8–232) to (8–235). The equation of continuity (8–127), when we divide through by the constant $\rho_0 v_0/s_0$ and collect separately the terms involving M, becomes

$$\boldsymbol{\nabla}' \cdot \mathbf{v}' + M^2 \left[\frac{\partial p''}{\partial t'} + \boldsymbol{\nabla}' \cdot (p''\mathbf{v}')\right] = 0,\qquad(8\text{–}240)$$

where

$$\boldsymbol{\nabla}' = \mathbf{i}\,\frac{\partial}{\partial x'} + \mathbf{j}\,\frac{\partial}{\partial y'} + \mathbf{k}\,\frac{\partial}{\partial z'}.\qquad(8\text{–}241)$$

The equation of motion (8–139), when we divide through by v_0^2/s_0, becomes, in the same way,

$$\frac{\partial \mathbf{v}'}{\partial t'} + \mathbf{v}' \cdot \boldsymbol{\nabla}'\mathbf{v}' + (1 - M^2 p'')\,\boldsymbol{\nabla}'p'' = \frac{s_0}{v_0^2}\,\frac{\mathbf{f}}{\rho}.\qquad(8\text{–}242)$$

Equations (8–240) and (8–242) represent four differential equations to be solved for the four quantities $p', \mathbf{v}'$, subject to given initial and boundary conditions. If the body forces are zero, or if the body forces per unit mass $\mathbf{f}/\rho$ are made proportional to v_0^2/s_0, then the equations for two similar problems become identical if the Mach number M is the same for both. Hence, similar problems will have similar solutions if they have the same Mach number. Results of experiments on scale models in wind tunnels can be extrapolated to full-sized airplanes flying at speeds with corresponding Mach numbers. If the Mach number is much less than one, the terms in M^2 in Eqs. (8–240) and (8–242) can be neglected, and these equations then reduce to the equations for an incompressible fluid, as is obvious either from Eq. (8–240) or (8–237). Therefore at fluid velocities much less than the speed of sound, even air may be treated as an incompressible fluid. On the other hand, at Mach numbers near or greater than one, the compressibility becomes important, even in problems of liquid flow. Note that the Mach number involves only the characteristic velocity v_0, and the velocity of sound, which in turn depends on the characteristic density ρ_0 and the compressibility B. Changes in the distance scale factor s_0 have no effect on the nature of the solution, nor do changes in the characteristic pressure p_0 except insofar as they affect ρ_0 and B.

It must be emphasized that these results are applicable only to ideal fluids, i.e., when viscosity is unimportant, and to problems where the density of the fluid does not differ greatly at any point from the characteristic density ρ_0. The latter condition holds fairly well for liquids, except when there is cavitation (formation of vapor bubbles), and for gases except at very large Mach numbers.

8–14 Viscosity. In many practical applications of the theory of fluid flow, it is not permissible to neglect viscous friction, as has been done in the preceding sections. When adjacent layers of fluid are moving past one another, this motion is resisted by a shearing force which tends to reduce their relative velocity. Let us assume that in a given region the velocity of the fluid is in the x-direction, and that the fluid is flowing in layers parallel to the xz-plane, so that v_x is a function of y only. Let the positive y-axis be directed toward the right. Then if $\partial v_x/\partial y$ is positive, the viscous friction will result in a positive shearing force F_x acting from right to left across an area A parallel to the xz-plane. The *coefficient of viscosity* η is defined as the ratio of the shearing stress to the velocity gradient:

$$\eta = \left(\frac{F_x}{A}\right)\Big/\left(\frac{\partial v_x}{\partial y}\right). \tag{8–243}$$

When the velocity distribution is not of this simple type, the stresses due to viscosity are more complicated.

We shall apply this definition to the important special case of steady flow of a fluid through a pipe of circular cross section, with radius a. We shall assume laminar flow, that is, we shall assume that the fluid flows in layers, as contemplated in the definition above. In this case, the layers are cylinders. The velocity is everywhere parallel to the axis of the pipe, which we take to be the z-axis, and the velocity v_z is a function only of r, the distance from the axis of the pipe. If we consider a cylinder of radius r and of length l, its area will be $A = 2\pi rl$, and according to the definition (8–243), the force exerted across this cylinder by the fluid outside on the fluid inside the cylinder is

$$F_z = \eta(2\pi rl)\frac{dv_z}{dr}. \tag{8–244}$$

Since the fluid within this cylinder is not accelerated, if there is no body force the viscous force must be balanced by a difference in pressure between the two ends of the cylinder:

$$\Delta p(\pi r^2) + F_z = 0, \tag{8-245}$$

where Δp is the difference in pressure between the two ends of the cylinder a distance l apart, and we assume that the pressure is uniform over the cross section of the pipe. Equations (8-244) and (8-245) can be combined to give a differential equation for v_z:

$$\frac{dv_z}{dr} = -\frac{r\,\Delta p}{2\eta l}. \tag{8-246}$$

We integrate outward from the cylinder axis:

$$\int_{v_0}^{v_z} dv_z = -\frac{\Delta p}{2\eta l} \int_0^r r\,dr,$$

$$v_z = v_0 - \frac{r^2\,\Delta p}{4\eta l}, \tag{8-247}$$

where v_0 is the velocity at the axis of the pipe. We shall assume that the fluid velocity is zero at the walls of the pipe:

$$[v_z]_{r=a} = v_0 - \frac{a^2\,\Delta p}{4\eta l} = 0, \tag{8-248}$$

although this assumption is open to question. Then

$$v_0 = \frac{a^2\,\Delta p}{4\eta l}, \tag{8-249}$$

and

$$v_z = \frac{\Delta p}{4\eta l}(a^2 - r^2). \tag{8-250}$$

The total fluid current through the pipe is

$$I = \iint \rho v_z\,dS = 2\pi\rho \int_0^a v_z r\,dr. \tag{8-251}$$

We substitute from Eq. (8-250) and carry out the integration:

$$\frac{I}{\rho} = \frac{\pi a^4\,\Delta p}{8\eta l}. \tag{8-252}$$

This formula is called *Poiseuille's law*. It affords a convenient and simple way of measuring η.

Although a development of the general equations of motion for viscous flow is beyond the scope of this text, we can arrive at a result analogous to that in Section 8-13, taking viscosity into account, without actually setting up the equations for viscous flow. Suppose that we are concerned, as in

Section 8–13, with two similar problems in fluid flow, and let s_0, v_0, p_0, ρ_0 be a characteristic distance, velocity, pressure, and density, which again define the scale in any problem. However, let us suppose that in this case viscosity is to be taken into account, so that the equation of motion (8–139) is augmented by a term corresponding to the force of viscous friction. We do not at present know the precise form of this term, but at any rate it will consist of η multiplied by various derivatives of various velocity components, and divided by ρ [since Eq. (8–139) has already been divided through by ρ]. When we introduce the velocity $\mathbf{v}'$, and the dimensionless coordinates x', y', z', t', as in Section 8–13, and divide the equation of motion by v_0^2 / s_0, we will obtain just Eq. (8–242), augmented by a term involving the coefficient of viscosity. Since all the terms in Eq. (8–242) are dimensionless, the viscosity term will be also, and will consist of derivatives of components of $\mathbf{v}'$ with respect to x', y', z', multiplied by numerical factors and by a dimensionless coefficient consisting of η times some combination of v_0 and s_0, and divided by $\rho = \rho_0(1 + M^2 p'')$ [Eq. (8–237)]. Now the dimensions of η, as determined by Eq. (8–243), are

$$[\eta] = \frac{\text{mass}}{\text{length} \times \text{time}}, \tag{8–253}$$

and the only combination of ρ_0, v_0, and s_0 having these dimensions is $\rho_0 v_0 s_0$. Therefore the viscosity term will be multiplied by the coefficient

$$\frac{1}{R(1 + M^2 p'')}, \tag{8–254}$$

where R is the *Reynolds number*, defined by

$$R = \frac{\rho_0 v_0 s_0}{\eta}. \tag{8–255}$$

We can now conclude that when viscosity is important, two similar problems will have the same equation of motion in dimensionless variables, and hence similar solutions, only if the Reynolds number R, as well as the Mach number M, is the same for both. If the Mach number is very small, then compressibility is unimportant. If the Reynolds number is very large, then viscosity may be neglected. It turns out that there is a critical value of Reynolds number for any given problem, such that the nature of the flow is very different for R larger than this critical value than for smaller values of R. For small Reynolds numbers, the flow is laminar, as the viscosity tends to damp out any vortices which might form. For large Reynolds numbers, the flow tends to be turbulent. This will be the case when the viscosity is small, or the density, velocity, or linear dimensions are large. Note that the Reynolds number depends on s_0, whereas the Mach number does not, so that the distance scale of a problem is important when the effects of viscosity are considered. Viscous effects are more important on a small scale than on a large scale.

It may be noted that the expression (8–255) for the Reynolds number, together with the fact that Eq. (8–139) is divided by v_0^2/s_0 to obtain the dimensionless equation of motion, implies that the viscosity term to be added to Eq. (8–139) has the dimensions of $(\eta v_0)/(\rho_0 s_0^2)$. This, in turn, implies that the viscous force density must be equal to η times a sum of second derivatives of velocity components with respect to x, y, and z. This is perhaps also evident from Eq. (8–243), since in calculating the total force on a fluid element, the differences in stresses on opposite faces of the element will be involved, and hence a second differentiation of velocities relative to x, y, and z will appear in the expression for the force.*

PROBLEMS

1. A stretched string of length l is terminated at the end $x = l$ by a ring of negligible mass which slides without friction on a vertical rod. (a) Show that the boundary condition at this end of the string is

$$\left[\frac{\partial u}{\partial x}\right]_{x=l} = 0.$$

(b) If the end $x = 0$ is tied, find the normal modes of vibration.

2. Find the boundary condition and the normal modes of vibration in problem 1 if the ring at one end has a finite mass m. What is the significance of the limiting cases $m = 0$ and $m = \infty$?

3. The mid-point of a stretched string of length l is pulled a distance $u = l/10$ from its equilibrium position, so that the string forms two legs of an isosceles triangle. The string is then released. Find an expression for its motion by the Fourier series method.

4. A force of linear density

$$f(x,t) = f_0 \sin \frac{n\pi x}{l} \cos \omega t,$$

where n is an integer, is applied along a stretched string of length l. (a) Find the steady state motion of the string. [*Hint:* Assume a similar time and space dependence for $u(x,t)$, and substitute in the equation of motion.] (b) Indicate how one might solve the more general problem of a harmonic applied force

$$f(x,t) = f_0(x) \cos \omega t,$$

where $f_0(x)$ is any function.

5. Assume that the friction of the air around a vibrating string can be represented as a force per unit length proportional to the velocity of the string. Set up the equation of motion for the string, and find the normal modes of vibration if the string is tied at both ends.

6. Discuss the reflection of a wave traveling down a long string terminated by a massless ring, as in problem 1.

7. Find a solution to problem 3 by superposing waves $f(x - ct)$ and $g(x + ct)$ in such a way as to satisfy the initial and boundary conditions. Sketch the appearance of the string at times $t = 0$, $\frac{1}{4}l/c$, $\frac{1}{2}l/c$, and l/c.

---

* For a derivation of the equations of motion of a viscous fluid, see Horace Lamb, *Hydrodynamics*, 6th ed. Cambridge: Cambridge University Press, 1932. (Section 328.)

8. Derive an equation expressing the law of conservation of angular momentum for a fluid in a form analogous to Eq. (8–140). From this, derive equations analogous to Eqs. (8–141), (8–142), and (8–144). Explain the physical meaning of each term in each equation. Show that the internal torques due to pressure can be eliminated from the integrated forms, and derive an equation analogous to Eq. (8–148).

9. Derive directly from Eq. (8–139) an equation expressing the conservation of angular momentum in a form analogous to Eq. (8–141).

10. Derive and interpret the following equation:

$$\frac{d}{dt} \int \int \int_V (\tfrac{1}{2}\rho v^2 - \rho \mathcal{G} - \rho u) \, dV + \int \int_S \mathbf{n} \cdot \mathbf{v} \, (\tfrac{1}{2}\rho v^2 - \rho \mathcal{G} - \rho u) \, dS$$

$$= - \int \int_S (\mathbf{n}p) \cdot \mathbf{v} \, dS - \int \int \int_V \rho \frac{\partial \mathcal{G}}{\partial t} \, dV,$$

where V is a fixed volume bounded by a surface S with normal $\mathbf{n}$.

11. Evaluate the potential energy u per unit mass as a function of p for a perfect gas of molecular weight M at temperature T. For the steady isothermal flow of this gas through a pipe of varying cross section and varying height above the earth, find expressions for the pressure, density, and velocity of the gas as functions of the cross section S of the pipe, the height h, and the pressure p_0 and velocity v_0 at a point in the pipe at height $h = 0$ where the cross section is S_0. Assume p, v, and ρ uniform over the cross section.

12. Work problem 11 for an incompressible fluid of density ρ_0.

13. The function $\phi = a/r$, where a is a constant and r is the distance from a fixed point, satisfies Laplace's equation (8–177), except at $r = 0$, because it has the same form as the gravitational potential of a point mass. If this is a velocity potential, what is the nature of the fluid flow to which it leads?

14. Find the normal modes of vibration of a square organ pipe with one end open and the other closed, on the assumption that the open end is a pressure node.

15. Show that the normal mode of vibration given by Eqs. (8–225) and (8–226) can be represented as a superposition of harmonically oscillating plane waves traveling in appropriately chosen directions with appropriate phase relationships. Show that in the normal vibrations of a fluid in a box, the velocity oscillates 90° out of phase with the pressure at any point. How can this be reconciled with the fact that in a plane wave the velocity and pressure are in phase?

16. Show that the expression (8–228) for a sound wave in a pipe can be represented as a superposition of plane waves traveling with speed c in appropriate directions, and being reflected at the walls. Explain, in terms of this representation, why there is a minimum frequency for any given mode below which a wave cannot propagate through the pipe in this mode.

17. Calculate the fluid velocity $\mathbf{v}$ for the wave given by Eq. (8–228).

18. Calculate the mean rate of power flow through the pipe for the wave given by Eq. (8–228).

19. A fluid of viscosity η flows steadily between two infinite parallel plane walls a distance l apart. The velocity of the fluid is everywhere in the same direction, and depends only on the distance from the walls. The total fluid current between the walls in any unit length measured along the walls perpendicular to the direction of flow, is I. Find the velocity distribution and the pressure gradient parallel to the walls, assuming that the pressure varies only in the direction of flow.

20. Prove that the only combination of ρ_0, v_0, s_0 having the dimensions of viscosity is $\rho_0 v_0 s_0$.

CHAPTER 9

LAGRANGE'S EQUATIONS

9-1 Generalized coordinates. Direct application of Newton's laws to a mechanical system results in a set of equations of motion in terms of the cartesian coordinates of each of the particles of which the system is composed. In many cases, these are not the most convenient coordinates in terms of which to solve the problem or to describe the motion of the system. For example, in the problem of the motion of a single particle acted on by a central force, which we treated in Section 3–13, we found it convenient to introduce polar coordinates in the plane of motion of the particle. The reason was that the force in this case can be expressed more simply in terms of polar coordinates. Again in the two-body problem, treated in Section 4–7, we found it convenient to replace the coordinates r_1, r_2 of the two particles by the coordinate vector $\mathbf{R}$ of the center of mass, and the relative coordinate vector $\mathbf{r}$ which locates particle 1 with respect to particle 2. We had two reasons for this choice of coordinates. First, the mutual forces which the particles exert on each other ordinarily depend on the relative coordinate. Second, in many cases we are interested in a description of the motion of one particle relative to the other, as in the case of planetary motion. In problems involving many particles, it is usually convenient to choose a set of coordinates which includes the coordinates of the center of mass, since the motion of the center of mass is determined by a relatively simple equation (4–18). In Chapter 7, we found the equations of motion of a particle in terms of moving coordinate systems, which are sometimes more convenient to use than the fixed coordinate systems contemplated in Newton's original equations of motion.

We shall include coordinate systems of the sort described above, together with cartesian coordinate systems, under the name *generalized coordinates*. A set of generalized coordinates is any set of coordinates by means of which the positions of the particles in a system may be specified. In a problem requiring generalized coordinates, we may set up Newton's equations of motion in terms of cartesian coordinates, and then change to the generalized coordinates, as in the problems studied in previous chapters. It would be very desirable and convenient, however, to have a general method for setting up equations of motion directly in terms of any convenient set of generalized coordinates. Furthermore it is desirable to have uniform methods of writing down, and perhaps of solving, the equations of motion in terms of any coordinate system. Such a method was invented by Lagrange and is the subject of this chapter.

In each of the cases mentioned in the first paragraph, the number of coordinates in the new system of coordinates introduced to simplify the problem was the same as the number of cartesian coordinates of all the particles involved. We may, for example, replace the two cartesian coordinates x,y of a particle moving in a plane by the two polar coordinates r,θ, or the three space coordinates x,y,z by three spherical or cylindrical coordinates. Or we may replace the six coordinates x_1,y_1,z_1,x_2,y_2,z_2 of a pair of particles by the three coordinates X,Y,Z of the center of mass plus the three coordinates x,y,z of one particle relative to the other. Or we may replace the three coordinates of a particle relative to a fixed system of axes by three coordinates relative to moving axes. (A vector counts as three coordinates.)

In our treatment of the rotation of a rigid body about an axis (Section 5–2), we described the position of the body in terms of the single angular coordinate θ. Here we have a case where we can replace a great many cartesian coordinates, three for each particle in the body, by a single coordinate θ. This is possible because the body is rigid and is allowed to rotate only about a fixed axis. As a result of these two facts, the position of the body is completely determined when we specify the angular position of some reference line in the body. The position of a free rigid body can be specified by six coordinates, three to locate its center of mass, and three to determine its orientation in space. This is a vast simplification compared with the $3N$ cartesian coordinates required to locate its N particles. A rigid body is an example of a system of particles subject to *constraints*, that is, conditions which restrict the possible sets of values of the coordinates. In the case of a rigid body, the constraint is that the distance between any two particles must remain fixed. If the body can rotate only about a fixed axis, then in addition the distance of each particle from the axis is fixed. This is the reason why specifying the value of the single coordinate θ is sufficient to determine the position of each particle in the body. We shall postpone the discussion of systems like this which involve constraints, until Section 9–4. In this section, and the next, we shall set up the theory of generalized coordinates, assuming that there are as many generalized coordinates as cartesian coordinates. We shall then find, in Section 9–4, that this theory applies also to the motion of constrained systems.

When we want to speak about a physical system described by a set of generalized coordinates, without specifying for the moment just what the coordinates are, it is customary to designate each coordinate by the letter q with a numerical subscript. A set of n generalized coordinates would be written as $q_1, q_2, \ldots, q_n$. Thus a particle moving in a plane may be described by two coordinates q_1, q_2, which may in special cases be the cartesian coordinates x,y, or the polar coordinates r,θ, or any other suitable pair of coordinates. A particle moving in space is located by three coordinates, which may be cartesian coordinates x,y,z, or spherical coordinates r,θ,φ, or cylindrical coordinates ρ,z,φ, or, in general, q_1, q_2, q_3.

The configuration of a system of N particles may be specified by the $3N$ cartesian coordinates $x_1, y_1, z_1, x_2, y_2, z_2, \ldots, x_N, y_N, z_N$ of its particles, or by any set of $3N$ generalized coordinates $q_1, q_2, \ldots, q_{3N}$. Since for each configuration of the system, the generalized coordinates must have some definite set of values, the coordinates $q_1, \ldots, q_{3N}$ will be functions of the cartesian coordinates, and possibly also of the time in the case of moving coordinate systems:

$$
\begin{aligned}
q_1 &= q_1(x_1, y_1, z_1, x_2, y_2, \ldots, y_N, z_N; t), \\
q_2 &= q_2(x_1, y_1, \ldots \ldots \ldots \ldots, z_N; t), \\
&\ \vdots
\end{aligned}
\tag{9–1}
$$

$$
q_{3N} = q_{3N}(x_1, y_1, \ldots \ldots \ldots \ldots, z_N; t).
$$

Since the coordinates $q_1, \ldots, q_{3N}$ specify the configuration of the system, it must be possible also to express the cartesian coordinates in terms of the generalized coordinates:

$$
\begin{aligned}
x_1 &= x_1(q_1, q_2, \ldots, q_{3N}; t), \\
y_1 &= y_1(q_1, \ldots \ldots, q_{3N}; t), \\
&\ \vdots
\end{aligned}
\tag{9–2}
$$

$$
z_N = z_N(q_1, \ldots \ldots, q_{3N}; t).
$$

If Eqs. (9–1) are given, they may be solved for $x_1, y_1, \ldots, z_N$ to obtain Eqs. (9–2), and vice versa.

The mathematical condition that this solution be (theoretically) possible is that the Jacobian determinant of Eqs. (9–1) be different from zero at all points, or nearly all points:

$$
\frac{\partial(q_1, \ldots, q_{3N})}{\partial(x_1, y_1, \ldots, z_N)} =
\begin{vmatrix}
\dfrac{\partial q_1}{\partial x_1} & \dfrac{\partial q_2}{\partial x_1} & \cdots & \dfrac{\partial q_{3N}}{\partial x_1} \\[2ex]
\dfrac{\partial q_1}{\partial y_1} & \dfrac{\partial q_2}{\partial y_1} & \cdots & \dfrac{\partial q_{3N}}{\partial y_1} \\[1ex]
\vdots & & & \\[1ex]
\dfrac{\partial q_1}{\partial z_N} & \dfrac{\partial q_2}{\partial z_N} & \cdots & \dfrac{\partial q_{3N}}{\partial z_N}
\end{vmatrix}
\ne 0.
\tag{9–3}
$$

If this inequality does not hold, then Eqs. (9–1) do not define a legitimate set of generalized coordinates. In practically all cases of physical interest, it will be evident from the geometrical definitions of the generalized coordinates whether or not they are a legitimate set of coordinates. Thus we shall not have any occasion to apply the above test to our coordinate systems. [For a derivation of the condition (9–3), see W. F. Osgood, *Advanced Calculus*, New York: Macmillan, 1937. (Page 129.)]

As an example, we have the equations (3–72) and (3–73) connecting the polar coordinates r, θ of a single particle in a plane with its cartesian coordinates x, y. As an example of a moving coordinate system, we consider

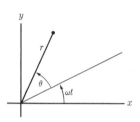

FIG. 9-1. A rotating polar coordinate system.

polar coordinates in which the reference axis from which θ is measured rotates counterclockwise with constant angular velocity ω (Fig. 9-1):

$$r = (x^2 + y^2)^{\frac{1}{2}},$$

$$\theta = \tan^{-1}\frac{y}{x} - \omega t, \qquad (9\text{-}4)$$

and conversely,

$$x = r \cos(\theta + \omega t),$$
$$y = r \sin(\theta + \omega t). \qquad (9\text{-}5)$$

As an example of generalized coordinates for a system of particles, we have the center of mass coordinates X, Y, Z and relative coordinates x, y, z of two particles of masses m_1 and m_2, as defined by Eqs. (4-90) and (4-91), where X, Y, Z are the components of $\mathbf{R}$, and x, y, z are the components of $\mathbf{r}$. Because the transformation equations (4-90) and (4-91) do not contain the time explicitly, we regard this as a fixed coordinate system, even though x, y, z are the coordinates of m_1 referred to a moving origin located on m_2. The rule which defines the coordinates X, Y, Z, x, y, z is the same at all times.

If a system of particles is described by a set of generalized coordinates $q_1, \ldots, q_{3N}$, we shall call the time derivative $\dot{q}_k$, of any coordinate q_k, the *generalized velocity* associated with this coordinate. The generalized velocity associated with a cartesian coordinate x_i is just the corresponding component $\dot{x}_i$ of the velocity of the particle located by that coordinate. The generalized velocity associated with an angular coordinate θ is the corresponding angular velocity $\dot{\theta}$. The velocity associated with the coordinate X in the preceding example is $\dot{X}$, the x-component of velocity of the center of mass. The generalized velocities can be computed in terms of cartesian coordinates and velocities, and conversely, by differentiating Eqs. (9-1) or (9-2) with respect to t according to the rules for differentiating implicit functions. For example, the cartesian velocity components can be expressed in terms of the generalized coordinates and velocities by differentiating Eqs. (9-2):

$$\dot{x}_1 = \sum_{k=1}^{3N} \frac{\partial x_1}{\partial q_k} \dot{q}_k + \frac{\partial x_1}{\partial t},$$
$$\vdots \qquad\qquad\qquad (9\text{-}6)$$
$$\dot{z}_N = \sum_{k=1}^{3N} \frac{\partial z_N}{\partial q_k} \dot{q}_k + \frac{\partial z_N}{\partial t}.$$

As an example, we have, from Eqs. (9-5):

$$\dot{x} = \dot{r} \cos(\theta + \omega t) - r\dot{\theta} \sin(\theta + \omega t) - r\omega \sin(\theta + \omega t),$$
$$\dot{y} = \dot{r} \sin(\theta + \omega t) + r\dot{\theta} \cos(\theta + \omega t) + r\omega \cos(\theta + \omega t). \qquad (9\text{-}7)$$

The kinetic energy of a system of N particles, in terms of cartesian coordinates, is

$$T = \sum_{i=1}^{N} \tfrac{1}{2} m_i (\dot{x}_i^2 + \dot{y}_i^2 + \dot{z}_i^2). \tag{9–8}$$

By substituting from Eqs. (9–6), we obtain the kinetic energy in terms of generalized coordinates. If we rearrange the order of summation, the result is

$$T = \sum_{k=1}^{3N} \sum_{l=1}^{3N} \tfrac{1}{2} A_{kl} \dot{q}_k \dot{q}_l + \sum_{k=1}^{3N} B_k \dot{q}_k + T_0, \tag{9–9}$$

where

$$A_{kl} = \sum_{i=1}^{N} m_i \left(\frac{\partial x_i}{\partial q_k} \frac{\partial x_i}{\partial q_l} + \frac{\partial y_i}{\partial q_k} \frac{\partial y_i}{\partial q_l} + \frac{\partial z_i}{\partial q_k} \frac{\partial z_i}{\partial q_l} \right), \tag{9–10}$$

$$B_k = \sum_{i=1}^{N} m_i \left(\frac{\partial x_i}{\partial q_k} \frac{\partial x_i}{\partial t} + \frac{\partial y_i}{\partial q_k} \frac{\partial y_i}{\partial t} + \frac{\partial z_i}{\partial q_k} \frac{\partial z_i}{\partial t} \right), \tag{9–11}$$

$$T_0 = \sum_{i=1}^{N} \tfrac{1}{2} m_i \left[\left(\frac{\partial x_i}{\partial t} \right)^2 + \left(\frac{\partial y_i}{\partial t} \right)^2 + \left(\frac{\partial z_i}{\partial t} \right)^2 \right]. \tag{9–12}$$

The coefficients A_{kl}, B_k, and T_0 are functions of the coordinates $q_1, \ldots, q_{3N}$, and also of t for a moving coordinate system. If A_{kl} is zero except when $k = l$, the coordinates are said to be *orthogonal*. Coefficients B_k and T_0 are zero when t does not occur explicitly in Eqs. (9–1), i.e., when the generalized coordinate system does not change with time. We see that the kinetic energy, in general, contains three sets of terms:

$$T = T_2 + T_1 + T_0, \tag{9–13}$$

where T_2 contains terms quadratic in the generalized velocities, T_1 contains linear terms, and T_0 is independent of the velocities. The terms T_1 and T_0 appear only in moving coordinate systems; for fixed coordinate systems, the kinetic energy is quadratic in the generalized velocities.

As an example, in plane polar coordinates [Eqs. (3–72)], the kinetic energy is

$$\begin{aligned} T &= \tfrac{1}{2} m (\dot{x}^2 + \dot{y}^2) \\ &= \tfrac{1}{2} (m\dot{r}^2 + mr^2 \dot{\theta}^2), \end{aligned} \tag{9–14}$$

as may be obtained by direct substitution from Eqs. (3–72), or as a special case of Eq. (9–9), where

$$\begin{aligned} \frac{\partial x}{\partial r} &= \cos\theta, & \frac{\partial x}{\partial \theta} &= -r\sin\theta, \\ \frac{\partial y}{\partial r} &= \sin\theta, & \frac{\partial y}{\partial \theta} &= r\cos\theta. \end{aligned} \tag{9–15}$$

If we take the moving coordinate system defined by Eqs. (9–5), we find, by substituting from Eqs. (9–7), or by using Eq. (9–9),

$$T = \tfrac{1}{2}m(\dot{x}^2 + \dot{y}^2)$$
$$= \tfrac{1}{2}(m\dot{r}^2 + mr^2\dot{\theta}^2) + mr^2\omega\dot{\theta} + \tfrac{1}{2}mr^2\omega^2. \tag{9-16}$$

In this case, a term linear in $\dot{\theta}$ and a term independent of $\dot{r}$ and $\dot{\theta}$ appear. The kinetic energy for the two-particle system can also easily be written down in terms of X,Y,Z,x,y,z, defined by Eqs. (4-90) and (4-91).

Instead of finding the kinetic energy first in cartesian coordinates and then translating into generalized coordinates, as in the examples above, it is often quicker to work out the kinetic energy directly in terms of generalized coordinates from a knowledge of their geometrical meaning. It may then be possible to start a problem from the beginning with a suitable set of generalized coordinates without writing out explicitly the transformation equations (9-1) and (9-2) at all. For example, we may obtain Eq. (9-14) immediately from the geometrical meaning of the coordinates r,θ (see Fig. 3-20) by noticing that the linear velocity associated with a change in r is $\dot{r}$ and that associated with a change in θ is $r\dot{\theta}$. Since the directions of the velocities associated with r and θ are perpendicular, the square of the total velocity is

$$v^2 = \dot{r}^2 + r^2\dot{\theta}^2, \tag{9-17}$$

from which Eq. (9-14) follows immediately. Care must be taken in applying this method if the velocities associated with changes of the various coordinates are not perpendicular. For example, let us consider a pair of coordinate axes u,v making an angle α less than 90° with each other, as in Fig. 9-2. Let u and v be the sides of a parallelogram formed by these axes and by lines parallel to the axes through the mass m as shown. Let **a** and **b** be unit vectors in the directions of increasing u and v. Using u and v as coordinates, the velocity of the mass m is

$$\mathbf{v} = \dot{u}\mathbf{a} + \dot{v}\mathbf{b}. \tag{9-18}$$

The kinetic energy is

$$T = \tfrac{1}{2}m\mathbf{v} \cdot \mathbf{v} = \tfrac{1}{2}m\dot{u}^2 + \tfrac{1}{2}m\dot{v}^2$$
$$+ m\dot{u}\dot{v} \cos \alpha. \tag{9-19}$$

This is an example of a set of nonorthogonal coordinates in which a cross product term in the velocities appears in the kinetic energy. The reason for using the term *orthogonal*, which means perpendicular, is clear from this example. When systems of more than one particle are described in terms of generalized coordinates, it is usually safest to write out the kinetic energy first in cartesian coordinates and transform to general-

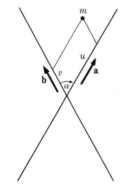

Fig. 9-2. A nonorthogonal coordinate system.

ized coordinates.   However, in some cases, it is possible to write the kinetic
energy directly in general coordinates.   For example, if a rigid body rotates
about an axis, we know that the kinetic energy is $\frac{1}{2}I\omega^2$, where ω is the angular
velocity about that axis and I is the moment of inertia.   Also, we can use
the theorem proved in Section 4–9 that the total kinetic energy of a system
of particles is the kinetic energy associated with the center of mass plus
that associated with the internal coordinates.   [See Eq. (4–127).]   As an
example, the kinetic energy of the two-particle system in terms of the
coordinates $X,Y,Z,\ x,y,z$, defined by Eqs. (4–90) and (4–91) is

$$T = \tfrac{1}{2}M(\dot{X}^2 + \dot{Y}^2 + \dot{Z}^2) + \tfrac{1}{2}\mu(\dot{x}^2 + \dot{y}^2 + \dot{z}^2), \qquad (9\text{--}20)$$

where M and μ are given by Eqs. (4–97) and (4–98).   The result shows
that this is an orthogonal coordinate system.   If the linear velocity of each
particle in a system can be written down directly in terms of the generalized coordinates and velocities, then the kinetic energy can immediately be
written down.

We now note that the components of the linear momentum of particle i,
according to Eq. (9–8), are

$$p_{ix} = m\dot{x}_i = \frac{\partial T}{\partial \dot{x}_i}, \qquad p_{iy} = m\dot{y}_i = \frac{\partial T}{\partial \dot{y}_i}, \qquad p_{iz} = m\dot{z}_i = \frac{\partial T}{\partial \dot{z}_i}. \quad (9\text{--}21)$$

In the case of a particle moving in a plane, the derivatives of T with respect
to $\dot{r}$ and $\dot{\theta}$, as given by Eq. (9–14), are

$$p_r = m\dot{r} = \frac{\partial T}{\partial \dot{r}}, \qquad p_\theta = mr^2\dot{\theta} = \frac{\partial T}{\partial \dot{\theta}}, \qquad (9\text{--}22)$$

where p_r is the component of linear momentum in the direction of increasing r, and p_θ is the angular momentum about the origin.   Similar
results will be found for spherical and cylindrical coordinates in three dimensions.   In fact, it is not hard to show that for any coordinate q_k which
measures the linear displacement of any particle or group of particles in a
given direction, the linear momentum of that particle or group in the given
direction is $\partial T/\partial \dot{q}_k$; and that for any coordinate q_k which measures the angular displacement of a particle or group of particles about an axis, their angu-
lar momentum about that axis is $\partial T/\partial \dot{q}_k$.   This suggests that we define the
generalized momentum p_k associated with the coordinate q_k by*

$$p_k = \frac{\partial T}{\partial \dot{q}_k}. \qquad (9\text{--}23)$$

---

* The kinetic energy T is defined by Eq. (9–9) as a function of $\dot{q}_1, \ldots, \dot{q}_{3N}$;
$q_1, \ldots, q_{3N}$, and perhaps of t.   The derivatives of this function T with respect to
these variables will be denoted by the symbols for partial differentiation.   Since
$q_1, \ldots, q_{3N}; \dot{q}_1, \ldots, \dot{q}_{3N}$ are all functions of the time t for any given motion of the
system, T is also a function of t alone for any given motion.   The derivative of T
with respect to time in this sense will be denoted by d/dt.   The same remarks apply
to any other quantity which may be written as a function of the coordinates and
velocities and perhaps of t, and which is also a function of t alone for any given motion.

If q_k is a distance, p_k is the corresponding linear momentum. If q_k is an angle, p_k is the corresponding angular momentum. In other cases, p_k will have some other corresponding physical significance. According to Eq. (9–9), the generalized momentum p_k is

$$p_k = \sum_{l=1}^{3N} A_{kl}\dot{q}_l + B_k. \tag{9–24}$$

In the case of the coordinates X,Y,Z,x,y,z for the two-particle system, this definition gives

$$\begin{aligned} p_X &= M\dot{X}, & p_Y &= M\dot{Y}, & p_Z &= M\dot{Z}, \\ p_x &= \mu\dot{x}, & p_y &= \mu\dot{y}, & p_z &= \mu\dot{z}, \end{aligned} \tag{9–25}$$

where p_X,p_Y,p_Z are the components of the total linear momentum of the two particles, and p_x,p_y,p_z are the linear momentum components in the equivalent one-dimensional problem in x,y,z to which the two-body problem was reduced in Section 4–7. We shall see in the next section that the analogy between the generalized momenta p_k and the cartesian components of linear momentum can be extended to the equations of motion in generalized coordinates.

If forces $F_{1x},F_{1y},F_{1z}, \ldots, F_{Nz}$ act on the particles, the work done by these forces if the particles move from the positions $x_1,y_1,z_1, \ldots, z_N$ to nearby points $x_1 + \delta x_1,\, y_1 + \delta y_1,\, z_1 + \delta z_1,\, \ldots,\, z_N + \delta z_N$ is

$$\delta W = \sum_{i=1}^{N} (F_{ix}\,\delta x_i + F_{iy}\,\delta y_i + F_{iz}\,\delta z_i). \tag{9–26}$$

The small displacements $\delta x_i, \delta y_i, \delta z_i$ may be expressed in terms of generalized coordinates:

$$\begin{aligned} \delta x_i &= \sum_{k=1}^{3N} \frac{\partial x_i}{\partial q_k}\,\delta q_k, \\ \delta y_i &= \sum_{k=1}^{3N} \frac{\partial y_i}{\partial q_k}\,\delta q_k, \\ \delta z_i &= \sum_{k=1}^{3N} \frac{\partial z_i}{\partial q_k}\,\delta q_k, \end{aligned} \tag{9–27}$$

where $\delta q_1, \ldots, \delta q_{3N}$ are the differences in the generalized coordinates associated with the two sets of positions of the particles. We call this a *virtual displacement* of the system because it is not necessary that it represent any actual motion of the system. It may be any possible motion of the system. In the case of a moving coordinate system, we regard the time as fixed, that is, we specify the changes in position in terms of the coordinate system at a particular time t. If we substitute Eqs. (9–27) in Eq. (9–26), we have, after rearranging terms:

$$\delta W = \sum_{k=1}^{3N} Q_k\,\delta q_k, \tag{9–28}$$

where
$$Q_k = \sum_{i=1}^{N} \left(F_{ix} \frac{\partial x_i}{\partial q_k} + F_{iy} \frac{\partial y_i}{\partial q_k} + F_{iz} \frac{\partial z_i}{\partial q_k} \right). \qquad (9\text{-}29)$$

The coefficients Q_k depend on the forces acting on the particles, on the coordinates $q_1, \ldots, q_{3N}$, and possibly also on the time t. In view of the similarity in form between Eqs. (9–26) and (9–28), it is natural to call the quantity Q_k the *generalized force* associated with the coordinate q_k. We can define the generalized force Q_k directly, without reference to the cartesian coordinate system, as the coefficient which determines the work done in a virtual displacement in which q_k alone changes:

$$\delta W = Q_k \, \delta q_k, \qquad (9\text{-}30)$$

where δW is the work done when the system moves in such a way that q_k increases by δq_k, all other coordinates remaining constant. Notice that the work in Eq. (9–26), and therefore also in Eq. (9–30), is to be computed from the values of the forces for the positions $x_1, \ldots, z_N$, or $q_1, \ldots, q_{3N}$; that is, we do not take account of any change in the forces during the virtual displacement.

If the forces $F_{1x}, \ldots, F_{Nz}$ are derivable from a potential energy $V(x_1, \ldots, z_N)$ [Eqs. (4–32)], then

$$\delta W = -\delta V$$
$$= -\sum_{i=1}^{N} \left(\frac{\partial V}{\partial x_i} \delta x_i + \frac{\partial V}{\partial y_i} \delta y_i + \frac{\partial V}{\partial z_i} \delta z_i \right). \qquad (9\text{-}31)$$

If V is expressed in terms of generalized coordinates, then

$$\delta W = -\delta V$$
$$= -\sum_{k=1}^{3N} \frac{\partial V}{\partial q_k} \delta q_k. \qquad (9\text{-}32)$$

By comparing this with Eq. (9–28), we see that

$$Q_k = - \frac{\partial V}{\partial q_k}, \qquad (9\text{-}33)$$

which shows that in this sense also the definition of Q_k as a generalized force is a natural one. Equation (9–33) may also be verified by direct calculation of $\partial V/\partial q_k$:

$$\frac{\partial V}{\partial q_k} = \sum_{i=1}^{N} \left(\frac{\partial V}{\partial x_i} \frac{\partial x_i}{\partial q_k} + \frac{\partial V}{\partial y_i} \frac{\partial y_i}{\partial q_k} + \frac{\partial V}{\partial z_i} \frac{\partial z_i}{\partial q_k} \right)$$
$$= -\sum_{i=1}^{N} \left(F_{ix} \frac{\partial x_i}{\partial q_k} + F_{iy} \frac{\partial y_i}{\partial q_k} + F_{iz} \frac{\partial z_i}{\partial q_k} \right)$$
$$= -Q_k.$$

As an example, let us calculate the generalized forces associated with the polar coordinates r, θ, for a particle acted on by a force

$$\mathbf{F} = \mathbf{i} F_x + \mathbf{j} F_y = \mathbf{n} F_r + \mathbf{1} F_\theta. \qquad (9\text{-}34)$$

If we use the definition (9–29), we have, using Eqs. (9–15):

$$Q_r = F_x \frac{\partial x}{\partial r} + F_y \frac{\partial y}{\partial r}$$
$$= F_x \cos \theta + F_y \sin \theta$$
$$= F_r,$$

(9–35)

$$Q_\theta = F_x \frac{\partial x}{\partial \theta} + F_y \frac{\partial y}{\partial \theta}$$
$$= -rF_x \sin \theta + rF_y \cos \theta$$
$$= rF_\theta.$$

We see that Q_r is the component of force in the r-direction, and Q_θ is the torque acting to increase θ. It is usually quicker to use the definition (9–30), which enables us to bypass the cartesian coordinates altogether. If we consider a small displacement in which r changes to $r + \delta r$, with θ remaining constant, the work is

$$\delta W = F_r \, \delta r,$$

(9–36)

from which the first of Eqs. (9–35) follows. If we consider a displacement in which r is fixed and θ increases by $\delta \theta$, the work is

$$\delta W = F_\theta r \, \delta \theta,$$

(9–37)

from which the second of Eqs. (9–35) follows. In general, if q_k is a coordinate which measures the distance moved by some part of the mechanical system in a certain fixed direction in space, and if F_k is the component in this direction of the total force acting on this part of the system, then the work done when q_k increases by δq_k, all other coordinates remaining constant, is

$$\delta W = F_k \, \delta q_k.$$

(9–38)

Comparing this with Eq. (9–30), we have

$$Q_k = F_k.$$

(9–39)

In this case, the generalized force Q_k is just the ordinary force F_k. If q_k measures the angular rotation of a certain part of the system about a fixed axis, and if N_k is the total torque about that axis exerted on this part of the system, then the work done when q_k increases by δq_k is

$$\delta W = N_k \, \delta q_k.$$

(9–40)

Comparing this with Eq. (9–30), we have

$$Q_k = N_k.$$

(9–41)

The generalized force Q_k associated with an angular coordinate q_k is the corresponding torque.

9-2 Lagrange's equations. The analogy which led to the definitions of generalized momenta and generalized forces tempts us to suspect that the generalized equations of motion will equate the time rate of change of each momentum p_k to the corresponding force Q_k. To check this suspicion, let us calculate the time rate of change of p_k:

$$\frac{dp_k}{dt} = \frac{d}{dt}\left(\frac{\partial T}{\partial \dot{q}_k}\right). \tag{9-42}$$

We will need to start with Newton's equations of motion in cartesian form:

$$\begin{aligned} m_i \ddot{x}_i &= F_{ix}, \\ m_i \ddot{y}_i &= F_{iy}, \quad [i = 1, \ldots, N] \\ m_i \ddot{z}_i &= F_{iz}. \end{aligned} \tag{9-43}$$

Therefore we express T in cartesian coordinates [Eq. (9-8)]. We then have

$$\frac{\partial T}{\partial \dot{q}_k} = \sum_{i=1}^{N} m_i \left(\dot{x}_i \frac{\partial \dot{x}_i}{\partial \dot{q}_k} + \dot{y}_i \frac{\partial \dot{y}_i}{\partial \dot{q}_k} + \dot{z}_i \frac{\partial \dot{z}_i}{\partial \dot{q}_k} \right), \tag{9-44}$$

where $\dot{x}_1, \dot{y}_1, \ldots, \dot{z}_N$ are given as functions of $q_1, \ldots, q_{3N}; \dot{q}_1, \ldots, \dot{q}_{3N}$; and t by Eqs. (9-6). Since $\partial x_i / \partial q_k$ and $\partial x_i / \partial t$ are functions only of $q_1, \ldots, q_{3N}$, and of t, we have, by differentiating Eqs. (9-6):

$$\begin{aligned} \frac{\partial \dot{x}_i}{\partial \dot{q}_k} &= \frac{\partial x_i}{\partial q_k}, \\ \frac{\partial \dot{y}_i}{\partial \dot{q}_k} &= \frac{\partial y_i}{\partial q_k}, \quad [i = 1, \ldots, N; k = 1, \ldots, 3N] \\ \frac{\partial \dot{z}_i}{\partial \dot{q}_k} &= \frac{\partial z_i}{\partial q_k}. \end{aligned} \tag{9-45}$$

By substituting from Eqs. (9-45) in Eq. (9-44), and differentiating again with respect to t, we obtain

$$\frac{dp_k}{dt} = \sum_{i=1}^{N} m_i \left(\ddot{x}_i \frac{\partial x_i}{\partial q_k} + \ddot{y}_i \frac{\partial y_i}{\partial q_k} + \ddot{z}_i \frac{\partial z_i}{\partial q_k} \right)$$
$$+ \sum_{i=1}^{N} m_i \left(\dot{x}_i \frac{d}{dt}\frac{\partial x_i}{\partial q_k} + \dot{y}_i \frac{d}{dt}\frac{\partial y_i}{\partial q_k} + \dot{z}_i \frac{d}{dt}\frac{\partial z_i}{\partial q_k} \right). \tag{9-46}$$

According to Newton's equations of motion (9-43), and the definition (9-29), the first term in Eq. (9-46) is

$$\sum_{i=1}^{N} m_i \left(\ddot{x}_i \frac{\partial x_i}{\partial q_k} + \ddot{y}_i \frac{\partial y_i}{\partial q_k} + \ddot{z}_i \frac{\partial z_i}{\partial q_k} \right) = \sum_{i=1}^{N} \left(F_{ix} \frac{\partial x_i}{\partial q_k} + F_{iy} \frac{\partial y_i}{\partial q_k} + F_{iz} \frac{\partial z_i}{\partial q_k} \right)$$
$$= Q_k. \tag{9-47}$$

The derivatives appearing in the last term in Eq. (9–46) are calculated as follows:

$$\frac{d}{dt}\frac{\partial x_i}{\partial q_k} = \sum_{l=1}^{3N}\frac{\partial^2 x_i}{\partial q_k\,\partial q_l}\,\dot{q}_l + \frac{\partial^2 x_i}{\partial q_k\,\partial t} = \frac{\partial}{\partial q_k}\left[\sum_{l=1}^{3N}\frac{\partial x_i}{\partial q_l}\,\dot{q}_l + \frac{\partial x_i}{\partial t}\right] = \frac{\partial \dot{x}_i}{\partial q_k}, \quad (9\text{–}48)$$

where we have made use of Eq. (9–6). Similar expressions hold for y and z. Thus the last sum in Eq. (9–46) is

$$\sum_{i=1}^{N} m_i\left(\dot{x}_i\frac{d}{dt}\frac{\partial x_i}{\partial q_k} + \dot{y}_i\frac{d}{dt}\frac{\partial y_i}{\partial q_k} + \dot{z}_i\frac{d}{dt}\frac{\partial z_i}{\partial q_k}\right) = \sum_{i=1}^{N} m_i\left(\dot{x}_i\frac{\partial \dot{x}_i}{\partial q_k} + \dot{y}_i\frac{\partial \dot{y}_i}{\partial q_k} + \dot{z}_i\frac{\partial \dot{z}_i}{\partial q_k}\right)$$

$$= \frac{\partial}{\partial q_k}\sum_{i=1}^{N}\tfrac{1}{2}m_i(\dot{x}_i^2 + \dot{y}_i^2 + \dot{z}_i^2)$$

$$= \frac{\partial T}{\partial q_k}. \quad (9\text{–}49)$$

We have finally:

$$\frac{dp_k}{dt} = Q_k + \frac{\partial T}{\partial q_k}. \quad [k = 1, \ldots, 3N] \quad (9\text{–}50)$$

Our original expectation was not quite correct, in that we must add to the generalized force Q_k another term $\partial T/\partial q_k$ in order to get the rate of change of momentum $\dot{p}_k$. To see its meaning, consider the kinetic energy of a particle in terms of plane polar coordinates, as given by Eq. (9–14). In this case,

$$\frac{\partial T}{\partial r} = mr\dot{\theta}^2, \quad (9\text{–}51)$$

and if we make use of Eqs. (9–22) and (9–35), the equation of motion (9–50) for $q_k = r$ is

$$m\ddot{r} = F_r + mr\dot{\theta}^2. \quad (9\text{–}52)$$

If we compare this with Eq. (3–207), which results from a direct application of Newton's law of motion, we see that the term $\partial T/\partial r$ is part of the mass times acceleration which appears here transposed to the right side of the equation. In fact, $\partial T/\partial r$ is the "centrifugal force" which must be added in order to write the equation of motion for r in the form of Newton's equation for motion in a straight line. Had we been a bit more clever originally, we should have expected that some such term might have to be included. We may call $\partial T/\partial q_k$ a "fictitious force" which appears if the kinetic energy depends on the coordinate q_k. This will be the case when the coordinate system involves "curved" coordinates; that is, if constant generalized velocities $\dot{q}_1, \ldots, \dot{q}_{3N}$ result in curved motions of some parts of the mechanical system. Equations (9–50) are usually written in the form

$$\frac{d}{dt}\left(\frac{\partial T}{\partial \dot{q}_k}\right) - \frac{\partial T}{\partial q_k} = Q_k. \quad [k = 1, \ldots, 3N] \quad (9\text{–}53)$$

If a potential energy exists, so that the forces Q_k are derivable from a potential energy function [Eq. (9–33)], we may introduce the *Lagrangian function*

$$L(q_1, \ldots, q_{3N}; \dot{q}_1, \ldots, \dot{q}_{3N}; t) = T - V, \qquad (9\text{–}54)$$

where T depends on both $q_1, \ldots, q_{3N}$ and $\dot{q}_1, \ldots, \dot{q}_{3N}$, but V depends only on $q_1, \ldots, q_{3N}$ (and possibly t), so that

$$\frac{d}{dt}\frac{\partial L}{\partial \dot{q}_k} = \frac{d}{dt}\frac{\partial T}{\partial \dot{q}_k}, \qquad (9\text{–}55)$$

$$\frac{\partial L}{\partial q_k} = \frac{\partial T}{\partial q_k} - \frac{\partial V}{\partial q_k} = \frac{\partial T}{\partial q_k} + Q_k. \qquad (9\text{–}56)$$

Hence Eqs. (9–53) can be written in this case in the form

$$\frac{d}{dt}\left(\frac{\partial L}{\partial \dot{q}_k}\right) - \frac{\partial L}{\partial q_k} = 0. \quad [k = 1, \ldots, 3N] \qquad (9\text{–}57)$$

In nearly all cases of interest in physics (although not in engineering), the equations of motion can be written in the form (9–57). The most important exception is the case where frictional forces are involved, but such forces do not usually appear in atomic or astronomical problems.

Since Lagrange's equations have been derived from Newton's equations of motion, they do not represent a new physical theory, but merely a different but equivalent way of expressing the same laws of motion. As the example of Eqs. (9–52) and (3–207) illustrates, the equations we get by Lagrange's method can also be obtained by a direct application of Newton's law of motion. However, in complicated cases it is usually easier to work out the kinetic energy and the forces or potential energy in generalized coordinates, and write the equations in Lagrangian form. Particularly in problems involving constraints, as we shall see in Section 9–4, the Lagrangian method is much easier to apply. The chief value of Lagrange's equations is, however, probably a theoretical one. From the manner in which they were derived, it is evident that Lagrange's equations (9–57) or (9–53) hold in the same form in any system of generalized coordinates. The Lagrangian function $L = T - V$ has the same value, for any given set of positions and velocities of the particles, no matter in what coordinate system it may be expressed, but the form of the function L may be different in different coordinate systems. The fact that Lagrange's equations have the same form in all coordinate systems is largely responsible for their theoretical importance. Lagrange's equations represent a uniform way of writing the equations of motion of a system, which is independent of the kind of coordinate system used. They form a starting point for more advanced formulations of mechanics. In developing the general theory of relativity, in which cartesian coordinates may not even exist, Lagrange's equations are particularly important.

9-3 Examples. We first consider a system of particles $m_1, \ldots, m_N$, located by cartesian coordinates, and show that in this case Lagrange's equations become the Newtonian equations of motion. The kinetic energy is

$$T = \sum_{i=1}^{N} \tfrac{1}{2} m_i (\dot{x}_i^2 + \dot{y}_i^2 + \dot{z}_i^2), \qquad (9\text{-}58)$$

and

$$\frac{\partial T}{\partial x_i} = \frac{\partial T}{\partial y_i} = \frac{\partial T}{\partial z_i} = 0, \qquad (9\text{-}59)$$

$$\frac{\partial T}{\partial \dot{x}_i} = m_i \dot{x}_i, \quad \frac{\partial T}{\partial \dot{y}_i} = m_i \dot{y}_i, \quad \frac{\partial T}{\partial \dot{z}_i} = m_i \dot{z}_i. \qquad (9\text{-}60)$$

The generalized force associated with each cartesian coordinate is just the ordinary force, as we see either from Eq. (9-29), or by comparing Eq. (9-28) with Eq. (9-26). Hence the equations of motion (9-53) are

$$\frac{d}{dt}\left(\frac{\partial T}{\partial \dot{x}_i}\right) - \frac{\partial T}{\partial x_i} = m_i \ddot{x}_i = F_{ix},$$

$$\frac{d}{dt}\left(\frac{\partial T}{\partial \dot{y}_i}\right) - \frac{\partial T}{\partial y_i} = m_i \ddot{y}_i = F_{iy}, \qquad [i = 1, \ldots, N] \qquad (9\text{-}61)$$

$$\frac{d}{dt}\left(\frac{\partial T}{\partial \dot{z}_i}\right) - \frac{\partial T}{\partial z_i} = m_i \ddot{z}_i = F_{iz}.$$

For a particle moving in a plane, the kinetic energy in polar coordinates is given by Eq. (9-14), and the forces Q_r and Q_θ by Eqs. (9-35). The Lagrange equations are

$$m\ddot{r} - mr\dot{\theta}^2 = F_r, \qquad (9\text{-}62)$$

$$\frac{d}{dt}(mr^2\dot{\theta}) = rF_\theta. \qquad (9\text{-}63)$$

These equations were obtained in Section 3-13 by elementary methods.

We now consider the rotating coordinate system defined by Eqs. (9-4) or (9-5). The kinetic energy is given by Eq. (9-16), and the generalized forces Q_r and Q_θ will be the same as in the previous example. Lagrange's equations in this case are

$$m\ddot{r} - mr\dot{\theta}^2 - 2m\omega r\dot{\theta} - m\omega^2 r = F_r, \qquad (9\text{-}64)$$

$$\frac{d}{dt}(mr^2\dot{\theta}) + 2m\omega r\dot{r} = rF_\theta. \qquad (9\text{-}65)$$

The reader should verify that the third term on the left in Eq. (9-64) is the negative of the coriolis force in the r-direction due to the rotation of the coordinate system, and that the fourth term is the negative of the centrifugal force. The second term in Eq. (9-65) is the negative of the coriolis torque in the θ-direction. Thus the necessary fictitious forces are automatically included when we write Lagrange's equations in a moving coordinate system. It must be noticed, however, that we use the actual kinetic energy [Eq. (9–16)] with respect to a coordinate system at rest, expressed in terms of the rotating coordinates, and not the kinetic energy as it would appear in the rotating system if we ignored the motion of the coordinate system.

9–4 Systems subject to constraints. One important class of mechanical problems in which Lagrange's equations are particularly useful comprises systems which are subject to constraints.

A rigid body is a good example of a system of particles subject to constraints. A constraint is a restriction on the freedom of motion of a system of particles in the form of a condition which must be satisfied by their coordinates, or by the allowed changes in their coordinates. For example, a very simple hypothetical rigid body would be a pair of particles connected by a rigid weightless rod of length l. These particles are subject to a constraint which requires that they remain a distance l apart. In terms of their cartesian coordinates, the constraint is

$$[(x_2 - x_1)^2 + (y_2 - y_1)^2 + (z_2 - z_1)^2]^{\frac{1}{2}} = l. \qquad (9\text{–}66)$$

If we use the coordinates X, Y, Z of the center of mass and spherical coordinates r, θ, φ to locate particle 2 with respect to particle 1 as origin, the constraint takes the simple form:

$$r = l. \qquad (9\text{–}67)$$

There are thus only five coordinates X, Y, Z, θ, φ left to determine. Each constraint which can be expressed in the form of an equation like (9–66) enables us to eliminate one of the coordinates by choosing coordinates in such a manner that one of them is held constant by the constraint. For a rigid body, the constraints require that the mutual distances of all pairs of particles remain constant. For a body containing N particles, there are $\frac{1}{2}N(N - 1)$ pairs of particles. However, it is not hard to show that it is sufficient to specify the mutual distances of $3N - 6$ pairs, if $N \geq 3$. Hence we can replace the $3N$ cartesian coordinates of the N particles by $3N - 6$ mutual distances, 3 coordinates of the center of mass, and 3 coordinates describing the orientation of the body. Since the $3N - 6$ mutual distances are all constant, the problem is reduced to one of finding the motion in terms of six coordinates. Another example of a system subject to a constraint is that of a bead sliding on a wire. The wire is situated along a certain curve in space, and the constraints require that the position of the bead lie on this curve. Since the coordinates of the points along a space curve satisfy two equations (e.g., the equations of two surfaces which intersect along the curve), there are two constraints, and we can locate the position of the bead by a single coordinate. (Can you suggest a suitable coordinate?) If the wire is moving, we have a moving constraint, and our single coordinate is relative to a moving system of reference. Con-

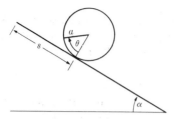
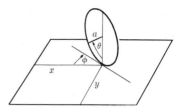

FIG. 9–3. A cylinder rolling down an incline.

FIG. 9–4. A disk rolling on a horizontal plane.

straints which can be expressed in the form of an equation relating the coordinates are called *holonomic*. All the above examples involve holonomic constraints.

Constraints may also be specified by a restriction on the velocities, rather than on the coordinates. For example, a cylinder of radius a, rolling and sliding down an inclined plane, with its axis always horizontal, can be located by two coordinates s and θ, as in Fig. 9–3. The coordinate s measures the distance the cylinder has moved down the plane, and the coordinate θ is the angle that a fixed radius in the cylinder has rotated from the radius to the point of contact with the plane. Now suppose that the cylinder is rolling without slipping. Then the velocities $\dot{s}$ and $\dot{\theta}$ must be related by the equation

$$\dot{s} = a\dot{\theta}, \tag{9–68}$$

which may also be written

$$ds = a\,d\theta. \tag{9–69}$$

This equation can be integrated:

$$s - a\theta = C, \tag{9–70}$$

where C is a constant. This equation is of the same type as Eq. (9–66), and shows that the constraint is holonomic, although it was initially expressed in terms of velocities. If a constraint on the velocities, like Eq. (9–68), can be integrated to give a relation between the coordinates, like Eq. (9–70), then the constraint is holonomic. There are systems, however, in which such equations of constraint cannot be integrated. An example is a disk of radius a rolling on a horizontal table, as in Fig. 9–4. For simplicity, we assume that the disk cannot tip over, and that the diameter which touches the table is always vertical. Four coordinates are required to specify the position of the disk. The coordinates x and y locate the point of contact on the plane; the angle φ determines the orientation of the plane of the disk relative to the x-axis; and the angle θ is the angle between a radius fixed in the disk and the vertical. If we now require that the disk roll without slipping (it can also rotate about the vertical axis), this implies two equations of constraint. The velocity of the point of contact perpendicular to the plane of the disk must be zero:

$$\dot{x} \sin \varphi + \dot{y} \cos \varphi = 0, \tag{9–71}$$

and the velocity parallel to the plane of the disk must be

$$\dot{x} \cos \varphi - \dot{y} \sin \varphi = a\dot{\theta}. \tag{9–72}$$

It is not possible to integrate these equations to get two relations between the coordinates x,y,θ,φ. To see this, we note that by rolling the disk without slipping, and by rotating it about a vertical axis, we can bring the disk to any point x,y, with any angle φ between the plane of the disk and the x-axis, and with any point on the circumference of the disk in contact with the table, i.e., any angle θ. For if the disk is at any point x,y, and the desired point on the circumference is not in contact with the table, we may roll the disk around a circle whose circumference is of proper length, so that when it returns to x,y, the desired point will be in contact with the table. It may then be rotated to the desired angle φ. This shows that the four coordinates x,y,θ,φ are independent of one another, and there cannot be any relation between them. It must therefore be impossible to integrate Eqs. (9–71) and (9–72), and consequently this is an example of a nonholonomic constraint.

The number of independent ways in which a mechanical system can move without violating any constraints which may be imposed is called the number of *degrees of freedom* of the system. To be more precise, the number of degrees of freedom is the number of quantities which must be specified in order to determine the velocities of all particles in the system for any motion which does not violate the constraints. For example, a single particle moving in space has three degrees of freedom, but if it is constrained to move along a certain curve, it has only one. A system of N free particles has $3N$ degrees of freedom, a rigid body has 6 degrees of freedom (three translational and three rotational), and a rigid body constrained to rotate about an axis has one degree of freedom. The disk shown in Fig. 9–4 has four degrees of freedom if it is allowed to slip on the table, because we need then to specify $\dot{x},\dot{y},\dot{\theta},\dot{\varphi}$. But if the disk is required to roll without slipping, there are only two degrees of freedom, because if $\dot{\varphi}$ and any one of the velocities $\dot{x},\dot{y},\dot{\theta}$ are given, the remaining two can be found from Eqs. (9–71) and (9–72). The disk is only free to roll, and to rotate about a vertical axis. For holonomic systems, the number of degrees of freedom is equal to the minimum number of coordinates required to specify the configuration of the system when coordinates held constant by the constraints are eliminated. Nonholonomic constraints occur in some problems in which bodies roll without slipping, but they are not of very great importance in physics. We shall therefore restrict our attention to holonomic systems.

For a holonomic system of N particles subject to c independent constraints, we can express the constraints as c relations which must hold between the $3N$ cartesian coordinates (including possibly the time if the constraints are changing with time):

$$h_1(x_1,y_1, \ldots, z_N; t) = a_1,$$
$$h_2(x_1,y_1, \ldots, z_N; t) = a_2,$$
$$\vdots$$
$$h_c(x_1,y_1, \ldots, z_N; t) = a_c,$$

$\hspace{8cm}$ (9–73)

where $h_1, \ldots, h_c$ are c specified functions. The number of degrees of freedom will be

$$f = 3N - c.$$

$\hspace{8cm}$ (9–74)

As Eqs. (9–73) are independent, we may solve them for c of the $3N$ cartesian coordinates in terms of the other $3N - c$ coordinates and the constants $a_1, \ldots, a_c$. Thus only $3N - c$ coordinates need be specified, and the remainder can be found from Eqs. (9–73) if the constants $a_1, \ldots, a_c$ are known. We may take as generalized coordinates these $3N - c$ cartesian coordinates and the c quantities $a_1, \ldots, a_c$ defined by Eqs. (9–73), and held constant by the constraints. Or we may define $3N - c$ generalized coordinates $q_1, \ldots, q_f$, in any convenient way:

$$q_1 = q_1(x_1,y_1, \ldots, z_N; t),$$
$$q_2 = q_2(x_1,y_1, \ldots, z_N; t),$$
$$\vdots$$
$$q_f = q_f(x_1,y_1, \ldots, z_N; t).$$

$\hspace{8cm}$ (9–75)

Equations (9–73) and (9–75) define a set of $3N$ coordinates $q_1, \ldots, q_f$; $a_1, \ldots, a_c$, and are analogous to Eqs. (9–1). They may be solved for the cartesian coordinates:

$$x_1 = x_1(q_1, \ldots, q_f; a_1, \ldots, a_c; t),$$
$$y_1 = y_1(q_1, \ldots, q_f; a_1, \ldots, a_c; t),$$
$$\vdots$$
$$z_N = z_N(q_1, \ldots, q_f; a_1, \ldots, a_c; t).$$

$\hspace{8cm}$ (9–76)

Now let $Q_1, \ldots, Q_f, Q_{f+1}, \ldots, Q_{f+c}$ be the generalized forces corresponding to the coordinates $q_1, \ldots, q_f; a_1, \ldots, a_c$. We have then a set of Lagrange equations for the constrained coordinates and another for the unconstrained coordinates:

$$\frac{d}{dt}\frac{\partial T}{\partial \dot{q}_k} - \frac{\partial T}{\partial q_k} = Q_k, \quad [k = 1, \ldots, f]$$

$\hspace{8cm}$ (9–77)

$$\frac{d}{dt}\frac{\partial T}{\partial \dot{a}_j} - \frac{\partial T}{\partial a_j} = Q_{f+j}. \quad [j = 1, \ldots, c; c + f = 3N]$$

$\hspace{8cm}$ (9–78)

The importance of this separation of the problem into two groups of equations is that the forces of constraint can be so chosen that they do no work unless the constraints are violated, as we shall show in the next paragraph.

If this is true, then according to the definition (9–30) of the generalized force, the forces of constraint do not contribute to the generalized force Q_k associated with an unconstrained coordinate q_k. Since the values of the constrained coordinates $a_1, \ldots, a_c$ are held constant, we can solve Eqs. (9–77) for the motion of the system in terms of the coordinates $q_1, \ldots, q_f$, treating $a_1, \ldots, a_c$ as given constants, without knowing the forces of constraint. This is a great advantage, for the forces of constraint depend upon how the system is moving, and cannot, in general, be determined until after the motion has been found. All we usually know about the constraining forces is that they have whatever values are required to maintain the constraints. Having solved Eqs. (9–77) for $q_1(t), \ldots, q_f(t)$, we may then, if we wish, substitute these functions in Eqs. (9–78) and calculate the forces of constraint. This may be a matter of considerable interest to the engineer who needs to verify that the constraining members are strong enough to withstand the constraining forces. Lagrange's equations thus reduce the problem of finding the motion of any holonomic system with f degrees of freedom to the problem of solving f second order differential equations (9–77). When we speak of the generalized coordinates, the constrained coordinates $a_1, \ldots, a_c$ may or may not be included, as convenient.

If a bead slides on a frictionless wire, the wire can only exert constraining forces perpendicular to itself, so that no work is done on the bead so long as it stays on the wire.* If there is friction, we can separate the force on the bead into a component perpendicular to the wire which holds the bead on the wire without doing any work, and a frictional component along the wire which does work and will therefore have to be included in the generalized force associated with motion along the wire. If the frictional component depends on the perpendicular component, as it does for dry sliding friction, then we cannot solve Eqs. (9–77) first, independently of Eqs. (9–78), and one great advantage of the Lagrangian method is lost. If two particles are held a fixed distance apart by a rigid rod, then by Newton's third law, the force exerted by the rod on one particle is equal and opposite to that on the other. It was shown in Section 5–1 that no net work is done on the system by the rod so long as the constraint is not violated, that is, so long as the rod is not stretched or compressed. A similar situation will be found in all other cases; the constraints *could* always be maintained by forces which do no work.

---

* If the wire is moving, the force exerted by the wire may do work on the bead, but the virtual displacements in terms of which the generalized forces have been defined are to be imagined as taking place at a fixed instant of time, and for such a displacement which does not violate the constraints, no work is done. Hence even in the case of moving constraints, the constraining forces do not appear in the generalized forces associated with the unconstrained coordinates.

If the forces $Q_1, \ldots, Q_f$ are derivable from a potential energy function, then we can define a Lagrangian function $L(q_1, \ldots, q_f; \dot{q}_1, \ldots, \dot{q}_f)$ which may in some cases depend on t, and which may also depend on the constants $a_1, \ldots, a_c$. The first f Lagrange equations (9–77) can then be written in the form

$$\frac{d}{dt}\frac{\partial L}{\partial \dot{q}_k} - \frac{\partial L}{\partial q_k} = 0. \quad [k = 1, \ldots, f] \tag{9–79}$$

9–5 Examples of systems subject to constraints. A simple mechanical system involving constraints is the Atwood's machine shown in Fig. 9–5. Weights m_1, m_2 are connected by a rope of length l over a fixed pulley. We assume the weights move only vertically, so that we have only one degree of freedom. We take as coordinates the distance x of m_1 below the pulley axle, and l, the length of the rope. The coordinate l is constrained to have a constant value, and could be left out of consideration from the start if we wish only to find the motion. If we also want to find the tension in the string, we must include l as a coordinate. The kinetic energy is

$$T = \tfrac{1}{2}m_1\dot{x}^2 + \tfrac{1}{2}m_2(\dot{l} - \dot{x})^2. \tag{9–80}$$

The only forces acting on m_1 and m_2 are the tension τ in the rope and the force of gravity. The work done when x increases by δx, l remaining constant, is

$$\begin{aligned}\delta W &= (m_1 g - \tau)\,\delta x - (m_2 g - \tau)\,\delta x \\ &= (m_1 - m_2)g\,\delta x = Q_x\,\delta x,\end{aligned} \tag{9–81}$$

so that

$$Q_x = (m_1 - m_2)g. \tag{9–82}$$

Note that Q_x is independent of τ. The work done when l increases by δl, x remaining constant, is

$$\delta W = (m_2 g - \tau)\,\delta l = Q_l\,\delta l, \tag{9–83}$$

so that

$$Q_l = m_2 g - \tau. \tag{9–84}$$

Notice that in order to obtain an equation involving the force of constraint τ, we must consider a motion which violates the constraint. This is also true if we wish to measure a force physically; we must allow at least a small motion in the direction of the force. The Lagrange equations of motion are (since $\dot{l} = \ddot{l} = 0$)

$$\frac{d}{dt}\left(\frac{\partial T}{\partial \dot{x}}\right) - \frac{\partial T}{\partial x} = (m_1 + m_2)\ddot{x} = (m_1 - m_2)g, \tag{9–85}$$

$$\frac{d}{dt}\left(\frac{\partial T}{\partial \dot{l}}\right) - \frac{\partial T}{\partial l} = -m_2\ddot{x} = m_2 g - \tau. \tag{9–86}$$

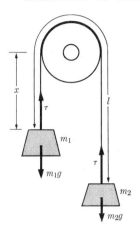

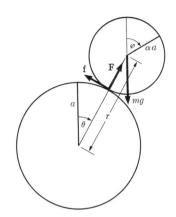

FIG. 9-5. Atwood's machine.

FIG. 9-6. One cylinder rolling on another.

The first equation is to be solved to find the motion:

$$x = x_0 + v_0 t + \tfrac{1}{2} \frac{m_1 - m_2}{m_1 + m_2} g t^2. \qquad (9\text{-}87)$$

The second equation can then be used to find the tension τ necessary to maintain the constraint:

$$\tau = m_2(g + \ddot{x}) = \frac{2m_1 m_2}{m_1 + m_2} g. \qquad (9\text{-}88)$$

In this case the tension is independent of time and can be found from Eqs. (9-85) and (9-86) immediately, although in most cases the constraining forces depend on the motion and can be determined only after the motion is found.   Equations (9-85) and (9-86) have an obvious physical interpretation and could be written down immediately from elementary considerations, as was done in Section 1-7.

A problem of little practical importance, but which is quite instructive, is that in which one cylinder rolls upon another, as shown in Fig. 9-6.   The cylinder of radius a is fixed, and the cylinder of radius αa rolls around it under the action of gravity.   Suppose we are given that the coefficient of static friction between the cylinders is μ, the coefficient of sliding friction is zero,* and that the moving cylinder starts from rest with its center vertically above the center of the fixed cylinder.   We shall assume that the axis of the moving cylinder remains horizontal during the motion.   It is advisable in all problems, and essential in this one, to think carefully about

---

* This implies that the moving cylinder either rolls without slipping, if the static friction is great enough, or slips without any friction at all.   The latter assumption is made to simplify the problem.

the motion before attempting to find the mathematical solution. It is clear that the moving cylinder cannot roll all the way around the fixed cylinder, for the normal force F which is exerted by the fixed cylinder on the moving one can only be directed outward, never inward. Therefore at some point, the moving cylinder will fly off the fixed one. The point at which it flies off is the point at which

$$F = 0. \tag{9-89}$$

Furthermore, the cylinder cannot continue to roll without slipping right up to the point at which it flies off, for the frictional force f which prevents slipping is limited by the condition

$$f \leq \mu F, \tag{9-90}$$

and will certainly become too small to prevent slipping before the point at which Eq. (9-89) holds. The motion therefore is divided into three parts. At first the cylinder rolls without slipping through an angle θ_1 determined by the condition

$$f = \mu F. \tag{9-91}$$

Beyond the angle θ_1, the cylinder slides without friction until it reaches the angle θ_2 determined by Eq. (9-89), after which it leaves the fixed cylinder and falls freely. We may anticipate some mathematical difficulties with the initial part of the motion due to the fact that the initial position of the moving cylinder is one of unstable equilibrium. Physically there is no difficulty, since the slightest disturbance will cause the cylinder to roll down, but mathematically there may be a difficulty which we must watch out for, inasmuch as the needed slight disturbance will not appear in the equations.

Let us find that part of the motion when the moving cylinder rolls without slipping. There is then only one degree of freedom, and we shall specify the position of the cylinder by the angle θ between the vertical and the line connecting the centers of the two cylinders. In order to compute the kinetic energy, we introduce the auxiliary angle φ through which the moving cylinder has rotated about its axis. The condition that the cylinder roll without slipping leads to the equation of constraint:

$$a\dot{\theta} = \alpha a\dot{\varphi}, \tag{9-92}$$

which can be integrated in the form

$$\theta = \alpha\varphi. \tag{9-93}$$

If we were concerned only with the rolling motion, we could now proceed to set up the Lagrange equation for θ, but inasmuch as we need to know the forces of constraint F and f, it is necessary to introduce additional coordinates which are maintained constant by these constraining forces.

The frictional force **f** maintains the constraint (9–93), and an appropriate coordinate is

$$\gamma = \theta - \alpha\varphi. \tag{9-94}$$

So long as the cylinder rolls without slipping, $\gamma = 0$; γ measures the angle of slip around the fixed cylinder. The normal force **F** maintains the distance r between the centers of the cylinders:

$$r = a + \alpha a = (1 + \alpha)a. \tag{9-95}$$

The kinetic energy of the rolling cylinder is the energy associated with the motion of its center of mass plus the rotational energy about the center of mass:

$$T = \tfrac{1}{2}m(\dot{r}^2 + r^2\dot{\theta}^2) + \tfrac{1}{2}I\dot{\varphi}^2. \tag{9-96}$$

After substituting φ from Eq. (9–94), and since $I = \tfrac{1}{2}m\alpha^2 a^2$, for a solid cylinder of radius αa, we have

$$T = \tfrac{1}{2}m\dot{r}^2 + \tfrac{1}{2}m(r^2 + \tfrac{1}{2}a^2)\dot{\theta}^2 - \tfrac{1}{2}ma^2\dot{\theta}\dot{\gamma} + \tfrac{1}{4}ma^2\dot{\gamma}^2. \tag{9-97}$$

The equations of constraint [Eq. (9–95) and $\gamma = 0$] *must not be used* until *after* the equations of motion are written down. The generalized forces are most easily determined with the help of Eq. (9–30); they are*

$$Q_\theta = mgr \sin \theta, \tag{9-98}$$
$$Q_\gamma = -fa, \tag{9-99}$$
$$Q_r = F - mg \cos \theta. \tag{9-100}$$

The Lagrange equations for θ, γ, and r are now

$$m(r^2 + \tfrac{1}{2}a^2)\ddot{\theta} + 2mr\dot{r}\dot{\theta} - \tfrac{1}{2}ma^2\ddot{\gamma} = mgr \sin \theta, \tag{9-101}$$
$$-\tfrac{1}{2}ma^2\ddot{\theta} + \tfrac{1}{2}ma^2\ddot{\gamma} = -fa, \tag{9-102}$$
$$m\ddot{r} - mr\dot{\theta}^2 = F - mg \cos \theta. \tag{9-103}$$

We can now insert the constraints $\gamma = 0$ and $r = (1 + \alpha)a$, so that these equations become

$$[(1 + \alpha)^2 + \tfrac{1}{2}]ma^2\ddot{\theta} = (1 + \alpha)mga \sin \theta, \tag{9-104}$$
$$f = \tfrac{1}{2}ma\ddot{\theta}, \tag{9-105}$$
$$F = mg \cos \theta - (1 + \alpha)ma\dot{\theta}^2. \tag{9-106}$$

Had we ignored the terms involving $\dot{\gamma}$ in the kinetic energy, the θ equation, which determines the motion, would have come out correctly, but the equation for the constraining force **f** would have been missing a term. This happens when the constrained coordinates are not orthogonal to the unconstrained coordinates, since a cross term ($\dot{\gamma}\dot{\theta}$) then appears in the kinetic energy.

---

* The reader will find it an instructive exercise to verify these formulas.

The equation of motion (9–104) can be solved by the energy method. The total energy, so long as the cylinder rolls without slipping, is

$$\frac{(\alpha + 1)^2 + \frac{1}{2}}{2} ma^2\dot{\theta}^2 + (1 + \alpha)mga \cos \theta = E, \qquad (9\text{–}107)$$

and is constant, as can easily be shown from Eq. (9–104), and as we know anyway since the gravitational force is conservative and the forces of constraint do no work. Since the moving cylinder starts from rest at $\theta = 0$,

$$E = (1 + \alpha)mga. \qquad (9\text{–}108)$$

We substitute this in Eq. (9–107) and solve for $\dot{\theta}$:

$$\dot{\theta} = 2\left(\frac{\beta g}{a}\right)^{\frac{1}{2}} \sin \frac{\theta}{2}, \qquad (9\text{–}109)$$

where

$$\beta = \frac{\alpha + 1}{(\alpha + 1)^2 + \frac{1}{2}}. \qquad (9\text{–}110)$$

We can now integrate to find $\theta(t)$:

$$\int_0^\theta \frac{\frac{1}{2}\, d\theta}{\sin \frac{\theta}{2}} = \left(\frac{\beta g}{a}\right)^{\frac{1}{2}} \int_0^t dt, \qquad (9\text{–}111)$$

$$\left[\ln \tan \frac{\theta}{4}\right]_0^\theta = \left(\frac{\beta g}{a}\right)^{\frac{1}{2}} t. \qquad (9\text{–}112)$$

When we substitute the lower limit $\theta = 0$, we run into a difficulty, for $\ln 0 = -\infty$! This is the expected difficulty due to the fact that $\theta = 0$ is a point of equilibrium, albeit unstable. If there is no disturbance whatever, it will take an infinite time for the cylinder to roll off the equilibrium point. Let us suppose, however, that it does roll off due to some slight disturbance, and let us take the time $t = 0$ as the time when the angle θ has some small value θ_0. There is now no difficulty, and we have

$$\tan \frac{\theta}{4} = \left(\tan \frac{\theta_0}{4}\right) \exp\left[\left(\frac{\beta g}{a}\right)^{\frac{1}{2}} t\right]. \qquad (9\text{–}113)$$

As $t \to \infty$, $\theta \to 2\pi$, and the moving cylinder rolls all the way around the fixed one, *if* the constraints continue to hold. The rolling constraint holds, however, only so long as Eq. (9–90) holds. When we substitute from Eqs. (9–105), (9–106), and (9–109), Eq. (9–90) becomes

$$\frac{\beta}{2} mg \sin \theta \leq \mu mg \left[\cos \theta - 2\beta(1 + \alpha)(1 - \cos \theta)\right]. \qquad (9\text{–}114)$$

At $\theta = 0$, this certainly holds, so that the cylinder does initially roll, as we have supposed. At $\theta = \pi/2$, however, it certainly does not hold, since the left member is then positive and the right, negative. The angle θ_1 at which slipping begins is determined by the equation

$$\frac{\beta}{2\mu} \sin \theta_1 = \cos \theta_1 - 2\beta(1 + \alpha)(1 - \cos \theta_1), \qquad (9\text{–}115)$$

whose solution is

$$\tan \frac{\theta_1}{2} = \frac{\left[\frac{\beta^2}{4\mu^2} + 1 + 4\beta(1 + \alpha)\right]^{\frac{1}{2}} - \frac{\beta}{2\mu}}{1 + 4\beta(1 + \alpha)}. \qquad (9\text{–}116)$$

The second part of the motion, during which the moving cylinder slides without friction around the fixed one, can be found by solving Eqs. (9–101) and (9–102) for $\theta(t), \gamma(t)$, with $f = 0$ and with only the single constraint $r = (1 + \alpha)a$, and with initial values $\theta = \theta_1$, $\dot\theta = \dot\theta_1$, determined from Eqs. (9–116) and (9–109). The solution can be found without essential difficulty, and the angle θ_2 at which the moving cylinder leaves the fixed one can then be determined from Eqs. (9–106) and (9–89). These calculations are left to the reader.

9–6 Constants of the motion and ignorable coordinates. We remarked in Chapter 3 that one general method for solving dynamical problems is to look for constants of the motion, that is, functions of the coordinates and velocities which are constant in time. One common case in which such constants can be found arises when the dynamical system is characterized by a Lagrangian function in which some coordinate q_k does not occur explicitly. The corresponding Lagrange equation (9–57) then reduces to

$$\frac{d}{dt}\left(\frac{\partial L}{\partial \dot q_k}\right) = 0. \qquad (9\text{–}117)$$

This equation can be integrated immediately:

$$\frac{\partial L}{\partial \dot q_k} = p_k = \text{a constant}. \qquad (9\text{–}118)$$

Thus, whenever a coordinate q_k does not occur explicitly in the Lagrangian function, the corresponding momentum p_k is a constant of the motion. Such a coordinate q_k is said to be *ignorable*. If q_k is ignorable, we can solve Eq. (9–118) for $\dot q_k$ in terms of the other coordinates and velocities, and of the constant momentum p_k, and substitute in the remaining Lagrange equations to eliminate $\dot q_k$ and reduce by one the number of variables in the problem (q_k was already missing from the equations, since it was assumed ignorable). When the remaining variables have been found, they can be substituted in Eq. (9–118), to give $\dot q_k$ as a function of t; q_k is then obtained by integration. If all but one of the coordinates are ignorable, the problem can thus be reduced to a one-dimensional problem and solved by the energy integral method, if L does not depend on the time t explicitly.

For example, in the case of central forces, the potential energy depends only on the distance r from the origin, so that if we use polar coordinates r,θ in a plane, V is independent of θ. Since T is also independent of θ according to Eq. (9–14) (T depends of course on $\dot\theta$), we will have

$$\frac{\partial L}{\partial \theta} = \frac{\partial}{\partial \theta}(T - V) = 0, \tag{9–119}$$

and hence

$$\frac{\partial L}{\partial \theta} = mr^2\dot\theta = p_\theta = \text{a constant}, \tag{9–120}$$

a result which we obtained in Section 3–13 by a different argument. We see that the constancy of p_θ is a result of the fact that the system is symmetrical about the origin, so that L cannot depend on θ. If a system of particles is acted on by no external forces, then if we displace the whole system in any direction, without changing the velocities and relative positions of the particles, there will be no change in T or V, or in L. If X, Y, and Z are rectangular coordinates of the center of mass, and if the remaining coordinates are relative to the center of mass, so that changing X corresponds to displacing the whole system, then

$$\frac{\partial L}{\partial X} = 0, \tag{9–121}$$

and therefore p_X, the total linear momentum in the x-direction, will be constant, a result we proved in Section 4–1 by a different method.

It is of interest to see how to show from Lagrange's equations that the total energy is a constant of the motion. In order to find an energy integral of the equations of motion in Lagrangian form, it is necessary to know how to express the total energy in terms of the Lagrangian function L. To this end, let us consider a system described in terms of a fixed system of coordinates, so that the kinetic energy T is a homogeneous quadratic function of the coordinate velocities $\dot q_1, \ldots, \dot q_f$ [i.e., $T_1 = T_0 = 0$ in Eq. (9–13)]. By Euler's theorem,* we have

$$\sum_{k=1}^{f} \dot q_k \frac{\partial T}{\partial \dot q_k} = 2T. \tag{9–122}$$

Thus if

$$L = T_2 - V, \tag{9–123}$$

where V is a function of the coordinates $q_1, \ldots, q_f$ alone, then, by Eq. (9–122),

$$\sum_{k=1}^{f} \dot q_k \frac{\partial L}{\partial \dot q_k} - L = T + V = E. \tag{9–124}$$

---

* W. F. Osgood, *Advanced Calculus.* New York: Macmillan, 1937. (Page 121.) The reader unfamiliar with Euler's theorem can readily verify Eq. (9–122) for himself by substituting for $T = T_2$ from Eq. (9–9).

We now consider the time derivative of the left member of Eq. (9–124). For greater generality, we shall at first allow L to depend explicitly on t. In the case we have considered, L does not depend explicitly on t. There are cases, however, when a system is subject to external forces that change with time and that can be derived from a potential V that varies with time. An example would be an atom subject to a varying external electric field. In such cases, the equations of motion can be written in the Lagrangian form (9–57) with the Lagrangian depending explicitly on the time t. In the case of moving coordinate systems also, the Lagrangian may depend on the time even though the forces are conservative. The time derivative of the left member of Eq. (9–124) is

$$\frac{d}{dt}\left(\sum_{k=1}^{f} \dot{q}_k \frac{\partial L}{\partial \dot{q}_k} - L\right) = \sum_{k=1}^{f}\left[\ddot{q}_k \frac{\partial L}{\partial \dot{q}_k} + \dot{q}_k \frac{d}{dt}\left(\frac{\partial L}{\partial \dot{q}_k}\right) - \frac{\partial L}{\partial q_k}\dot{q}_k - \frac{\partial L}{\partial \dot{q}_k}\ddot{q}_k\right] - \frac{\partial L}{\partial t}$$

$$= \sum_{k=1}^{f} \dot{q}_k\left[\frac{d}{dt}\left(\frac{\partial L}{\partial \dot{q}_k}\right) - \frac{\partial L}{\partial q_k}\right] - \frac{\partial L}{\partial t}$$

$$= -\frac{\partial L}{\partial t}. \tag{9–125}$$

If L does not depend explicitly on t, the right side of Eq. (9–125) is zero, and

$$\sum_{k=1}^{f} \dot{q}_k \frac{\partial L}{\partial \dot{q}_k} - L = \text{a constant.} \tag{9–126}$$

When L has the form $(T_2 - V)$, as in a stationary coordinate system, this is the conservation of energy theorem. Regardless of the form of L, Eq. (9–126) represents an integral of Lagrange's equations (9–57), whenever L does not contain t explicitly, but the constant quantity on the left is not always the total energy. Note the analogy between the conservation of generalized momentum p_k when L is independent of q_k, and the conservation of energy when L is independent of t. There are many ways in which the relation between time and energy is analogous to the relation between a coordinate and the corresponding momentum.

9–7 Further examples. The spherical pendulum is a simple pendulum free to swing through the entire solid angle about a point. The pendulum bob is constrained to move on a spherical surface of radius R. We locate the bob by the spherical coordinates θ, φ (Fig. 9–7). We may include the length R of the pendulum as a coordinate if we wish to find the tension in the string, but we omit it here, as we are concerned only with finding the motion. If the bob swings above the horizontal, we will suppose that it still remains on the sphere, which would be true if the string were replaced by a rigid rod. Otherwise the constraint disappears whenever a compressional stress is required to maintain it, since a string will support only a tension and not a compression. The velocity of the bob is

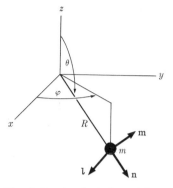

FIG. 9–7. A spherical pendulum.

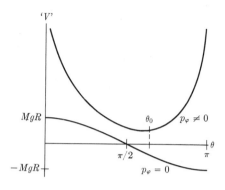

FIG. 9–8. Effective potential 'V' (θ) for spherical pendulum.

$$\mathbf{v} = R\dot{\theta}\mathbf{l} + R \sin \theta \dot{\varphi}\mathbf{m}. \tag{9–127}$$

Hence the kinetic energy is

$$T = \tfrac{1}{2}mv^2 = \tfrac{1}{2}mR^2\dot{\theta}^2 + \tfrac{1}{2}mR^2 \sin^2 \theta\dot{\varphi}^2. \tag{9–128}$$

The potential energy due to gravity, relative to the horizontal plane, is

$$V = mgR \cos \theta. \tag{9–129}$$

Hence the Lagrangian function is

$$L = T - V = \tfrac{1}{2}mR^2\dot{\theta}^2 + \tfrac{1}{2}mR^2 \sin^2 \theta\dot{\varphi}^2 - mgR \cos \theta. \tag{9–130}$$

The Lagrange equations are

$$\frac{d}{dt}(mR^2\dot{\theta}) - mR^2\dot{\varphi}^2 \sin \theta \cos \theta - mgR \sin \theta = 0, \tag{9–131}$$

$$\frac{d}{dt}(mR^2 \sin^2 \theta\dot{\varphi}) = 0. \tag{9–132}$$

The coordinate φ is ignorable, and the second equation can be integrated immediately:

$$mR^2 \sin^2 \theta\dot{\varphi} = p_\varphi = \text{a constant.} \tag{9–133}$$

Also, since

$$\frac{\partial L}{\partial t} = 0, \tag{9–134}$$

the quantity

$$\dot{\theta}\frac{\partial L}{\partial \dot{\theta}} + \dot{\varphi}\frac{\partial L}{\partial \dot{\varphi}} - L = \tfrac{1}{2}mR^2\dot{\theta}^2 + \tfrac{1}{2}mR^2 \sin^2\theta\dot{\varphi}^2 + mgR \cos \theta \tag{9–135}$$

is constant, by Eq. (9–126). We recognize the quantity on the right as the total energy, as it should be, since we are using a fixed coordinate system. Calling this constant E, and substituting for $\dot{\varphi}$ from Eq. (9–133), we have

$$\tfrac{1}{2}mR^2\dot{\theta}^2 + \frac{p_\varphi^2}{2mR^2\sin^2\theta} + mgR\cos\theta = E. \tag{9-136}$$

We may introduce an effective potential 'V'(θ) for the motion:

$$'V'(\theta) = mgR\cos\theta + \frac{p_\varphi^2}{2mR^2\sin^2\theta}, \tag{9-137}$$

so that

$$\tfrac{1}{2}mR^2\dot{\theta}^2 = E - {}'V'(\theta). \tag{9-138}$$

Since the left member cannot be negative, the motion is confined to those values of θ for which 'V'$(\theta) \leq E$. The effective potential 'V'(θ) is plotted in Fig. 9–8. We see that for $p_\varphi = 0$, 'V'(θ) is the potential curve for a simple pendulum, with a minimum at $\theta = \pi$ and a maximum at $\theta = 0$. For $E = -mgR$, the pendulum is at rest at $\theta = \pi$. For $mgR > E > -mgR$, the pendulum oscillates about $\theta = \pi$. For $E > mgR$, the pendulum swings in a circular motion through the top and bottom points $\theta = 0$ and π. When $p_\varphi \neq 0$, the motion is no longer that of a simple pendulum, and 'V'(θ) now has a minimum at a point θ_0 between $\pi/2$ and π, and rises to infinity at $\theta = 0$ and $\theta = \pi$. The larger p_φ, the larger the minimum value of 'V'(θ), and the closer θ_0 is to $\pi/2$. If $E = {}'V'(\theta_0)$, then θ is constant and equal to θ_0, and the pendulum swings in a circle about the vertical axis. As $p_\varphi \to \infty$, the pendulum swings more and more nearly in a horizontal plane. For $E > {}'V'(\theta_0)$, θ oscillates between a maximum and minimum value while the pendulum swings about the vertical axis. The reader should compare these results with his mechanical intuitions or his experience regarding the motion of a spherical pendulum. The solution of Eq. (9–138) for $\theta(t)$ cannot be carried out in terms of elementary functions, but we can treat circular and nearly circular motions very easily. The relation between p_φ and θ_0 for uniform circular motion of the pendulum about the z-axis is

$$\left[\frac{d'V'}{d\theta}\right]_{\theta_0} = -mgR\sin\theta_0 - \frac{p_\varphi^2\cos\theta_0}{mR^2\sin^3\theta_0} = 0. \tag{9-139}$$

It is evident from this equation that $\theta_0 > \pi/2$, and that $\theta_0 \to \pi/2$ as $p_\varphi \to \infty$. By substituting from Eq. (9–133), we obtain a relation between $\dot{\varphi}$ and θ_0 for uniform circular motion:

$$\dot{\varphi}^2 = \frac{g}{R}\frac{1}{(-\cos\theta_0)}. \tag{9-140}$$

The energy for uniform circular motion at an angle θ_0, if we use Eqs. (9–136) and (9–139), and the fact that $\dot{\theta} = 0$, is

$$E_0 = \frac{mgR}{2}\left(\frac{2 - 3\sin^2\theta_0}{\cos\theta_0}\right). \tag{9-141}$$

For an energy slightly larger than E_0, and an angular momentum p_φ given by Eq. (9–139), the angle θ will perform simple harmonic oscillations about the value θ_0. For if we set

$$k = \left[\frac{d^{2\prime}V'}{d\theta^2}\right]_{\theta_0} = \frac{mgR}{-\cos\theta_0}(1 + 3\cos^2\theta_0), \qquad (9\text{–}142)$$

then, for small values of $\theta - \theta_0$, we can expand $'V'(\theta)$ in a Taylor series:

$$'V'(\theta) \doteq E_0 + \tfrac{1}{2}k(\theta - \theta_0)^2. \qquad (9\text{–}143)$$

The energy equation (9–138) now becomes

$$\tfrac{1}{2}mR^2\dot\theta^2 + \tfrac{1}{2}k(\theta - \theta_0)^2 = E - E_0. \qquad (9\text{–}144)$$

This is the energy for a harmonic oscillator with energy $E - E_0$, coordinate $\theta - \theta_0$, mass mR^2, spring constant k. The frequency of oscillation in θ is therefore given by

$$\omega^2 = \frac{k}{mR^2} = \frac{g}{R}\frac{1 + 3\cos^2\theta_0}{-\cos\theta_0}. \qquad (9\text{–}145)$$

This oscillation in θ is superposed upon a circular motion around the z-axis with an angular velocity $\dot\varphi$ given by Eq. (9–133); $\dot\varphi$ will vary slightly as θ oscillates, but will remain very nearly equal to the constant value given by Eq. (9–140). It is of interest to compare $\dot\varphi$ and ω:

$$\frac{\dot\varphi^2}{\omega^2} = \frac{1}{1 + 3\cos^2\theta_0}. \qquad (9\text{–}146)$$

If $\theta_0 > \pi/2$, this ratio is less than 1, so that $\omega > \dot\varphi$, and the pendulum wobbles up and down as it goes around the circle. If ω were less than $\dot\varphi$, the pendulum would spiral up and down. At $\theta_0 = \pi/2$, $\dot\varphi = \omega$, and the pendulum moves in a circle whose plane is tilted slightly from the horizontal; this case occurs only in the limit of very large values of p_φ. It is clear physically that when p_φ is so large that gravity may be neglected, the motion can be a circle in any plane through the origin. Can you show this mathematically? Near $\theta_0 = 0$, $\omega = 2\dot\varphi$, so that θ oscillates twice per revolution and the pendulum bob moves in an ellipse whose center is on the z-axis. This corresponds to the motion of the two-dimensional harmonic oscillator discussed in Section 3–10, with equal frequencies in the two perpendicular directions.

As a last example, we consider a system in which there are moving constraints. A bead of mass m slides without friction on a circular hoop of radius a. The hoop lies in a vertical plane which is constrained to rotate about a vertical diameter with constant angular velocity ω. There is just one degree of freedom, and inasmuch as we are not interested in the forces of constraint, we choose a single coordinate θ which measures the angle around the circle from the bottom of the vertical diameter to the bead (Fig. 9–9). The kinetic energy is then

$$T = \tfrac{1}{2}ma^2\dot\theta^2 + \tfrac{1}{2}ma^2\omega^2\sin^2\theta, \qquad (9\text{–}147)$$

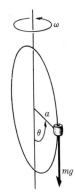

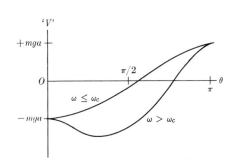

Fig. 9–9. A bead sliding on a rotating hoop.

Fig. 9–10. Effective potential energy for system shown in Fig. 9–9.

and the potential energy is

$$V = -mga \cos \theta. \tag{9–148}$$

The Lagrangian function is

$$L = \tfrac{1}{2}ma^2\dot{\theta}^2 + \tfrac{1}{2}ma^2\omega^2 \sin^2 \theta + mga \cos \theta. \tag{9–149}$$

The Lagrange equation of motion can easily be written out, but this is unnecessary, for we notice that

$$\frac{\partial L}{\partial t} = 0,$$

and therefore, by Eq. (9–126), the quantity

$$\dot{\theta}\frac{\partial L}{\partial \dot{\theta}} - L = \tfrac{1}{2}ma^2\dot{\theta}^2 - \tfrac{1}{2}ma^2\omega^2 \sin^2 \theta - mga \cos \theta = \text{'}E\text{'} \tag{9–150}$$

is constant. The constant 'E' is not the total energy $T + V$, for the middle term has the wrong sign. The total energy is evidently not constant in this case. (What force does the work which produces changes in $T + V$?) We may note, however, that we can interpret Eq. (9–149) as a Lagrangian function in terms of a fixed coordinate system with the middle term regarded as part of an effective potential energy:

$$\text{'}V\text{'}(\theta) = -\tfrac{1}{2}ma^2\omega^2 \sin^2 \theta - mga \cos \theta. \tag{9–151}$$

The energy according to this interpretation is 'E'. The first term in 'V'(θ) is the potential energy associated with the centrifugal force which must be added if we regard the rotating system as fixed. The effective potential is plotted in Fig. 9–10. The shape of the potential curve depends on whether ω is greater or less than a critical angular velocity

$$\omega_c = (g/a)^{\frac{1}{2}}. \tag{9–152}$$

It is left to the reader to show this, and to discuss the nature of the motion of the bead in the two cases.

9–8 Electromagnetic forces and velocity dependent potentials. If the forces acting on a dynamical system depend upon the velocities, it may be possible to find a function $U(q_1, \ldots, q_f; \dot{q}_1, \ldots, \dot{q}_f; t)$ such that

$$Q_k = \frac{d}{dt} \frac{\partial U}{\partial \dot{q}_k} - \frac{\partial U}{\partial q_k}. \quad [k = 1, \ldots, f] \tag{9-153}$$

If such a function U can be found, then we can define a Lagrangian function

$$L = T - U, \tag{9-154}$$

so that the equations of motion (9–53) can be written in the form (9–57):

$$\frac{d}{dt} \frac{\partial L}{\partial \dot{q}_k} - \frac{\partial L}{\partial q_k} = 0. \quad [k = 1, \ldots, f] \tag{9-155}$$

The function U may be called a *velocity dependent potential*. If there are also forces derivable from an ordinary potential energy $V(q_1, \ldots, q_f)$, V may be included in U, since Eq. (9–153) reduces to Eq. (9–33) for those terms which do not contain the velocities. The function U may depend explicitly on the time t. If it does not, and if the coordinate system is a fixed one, then L will be independent of t, and the quantity

$$E = \sum_{k=1}^{f} \dot{q}_k \frac{\partial L}{\partial \dot{q}_k} - L, \tag{9-156}$$

will be a constant of the motion, according to Eq. (9–126). In this case, we may say that the forces are conservative even though they depend on the velocities. It is clear from this result that it cannot be possible to express frictional forces in the form (9–153), for the total energy is not constant when there is friction unless we include heat energy, and heat energy cannot be defined in terms of the coordinates and velocities $q_1, \ldots, q_f$; $\dot{q}_1, \ldots, \dot{q}_f$, and hence cannot be included in Eq. (9–156). It is not hard to show that if the velocity dependent parts of U are linear in the velocities, as they are in all important examples, the energy E defined by Eq. (9–156) is just $T + V$, where V is the ordinary potential energy and contains the terms in U that are independent of the velocities. As an example, a particle of charge q subject to a constant magnetic field $\mathbf{B}$ is acted on by a force (gaussian units)

$$\mathbf{F} = \frac{q}{c} \mathbf{v} \times \mathbf{B}, \tag{9-157}$$

or

$$F_x = \frac{q}{c} (\dot{y} B_z - \dot{z} B_y),$$

$$F_y = \frac{q}{c} (\dot{z} B_x - \dot{x} B_z), \tag{9-158}$$

$$F_z = \frac{q}{c} (\dot{x} B_y - \dot{y} B_x).$$

Equations (9–158) have the form (9–153) if

$$U = \frac{q}{c}\left(z\dot{y}B_x + x\dot{z}B_y + y\dot{x}B_z\right). \tag{9–159}$$

It is, in fact, possible to express the electromagnetic force in the form (9–153) for any electric and magnetic field. The electromagnetic force on a particle of charge q is given by Eq. (3–283);

$$\mathbf{F} = q\mathbf{E} + \frac{q}{c}\mathbf{v} \times \mathbf{B}. \tag{9–160}$$

It is shown in electromagnetic theory* that for any electromagnetic field, it is possible to define a scalar function $\phi(x,y,z,t)$ and a vector function $\mathbf{A}(x,y,z,t)$ such that

$$\mathbf{E} = -\nabla\phi - \frac{1}{c}\frac{\partial\mathbf{A}}{\partial t}, \tag{9–161}$$

$$\mathbf{B} = \nabla \times \mathbf{A}. \tag{9–162}$$

The function ϕ is called the *scalar potential*, and $\mathbf{A}$ is called the *vector potential*. If these expressions are substituted in Eqs. (9–160), we obtain

$$\mathbf{F} = -q\nabla\phi - \frac{q}{c}\frac{\partial\mathbf{A}}{\partial t} + \frac{q}{c}\mathbf{v} \times (\nabla \times \mathbf{A}). \tag{9–163}$$

The last term can be rewritten using formula (3–35) for the triple cross product:

$$\mathbf{F} = -q\nabla\phi - \frac{q}{c}\frac{\partial\mathbf{A}}{\partial t} - \frac{q}{c}\mathbf{v}\cdot\nabla\mathbf{A} + \frac{q}{c}\nabla(\mathbf{v}\cdot\mathbf{A}). \tag{9–164}$$

[The components of $\mathbf{v}$ are $(\dot{x},\dot{y},\dot{z})$ and are independent of x,y,z, so that $\mathbf{v}$ is not differentiated by the operator ∇.] The two middle terms can be combined according to Eq. (8–113):

$$\mathbf{F} = -q\nabla\phi - \frac{q}{c}\frac{d\mathbf{A}}{dt} + \frac{q}{c}\nabla(\mathbf{v}\cdot\mathbf{A}), \tag{9–165}$$

where $d\mathbf{A}/dt$ is the time derivative of $\mathbf{A}$ evaluated at the position of the moving particle. It may now be verified by direct computation that the potential function

$$U = q\phi - \frac{q}{c}\mathbf{v}\cdot\mathbf{A}, \tag{9–166}$$

when substituted in Eqs. (9–153), with $q_1,q_2,q_3 = x,y,z$, yields the components of the force $\mathbf{F}$ given by Eq. (9–165). It is also easy to show that the energy E defined by Eq. (9–156) with $L = T - U$ is

$$E = T + q\phi. \tag{9–167}$$

---

* See, e.g., Slater and Frank, *Electromagnetism*, McGraw-Hill Book Co., New York, 1947. (Page 87.)

If **A** and ϕ are independent of t, then L is independent of t in a fixed coordinate system and the energy E is constant, a result derived by more elementary methods in Section 3–17 [Eq. (3–288)].

When there is a velocity dependent potential, it is customary to define the momentum in terms of the Lagrangian function, rather than in terms of the kinetic energy:

$$p_k = \frac{\partial L}{\partial \dot{q}_k}. \tag{9–168}$$

If the potential is not velocity dependent, then this definition is equivalent to Eq. (9–23). In any case, it is $\partial L/\partial \dot{q}_k$ whose time derivative occurs in the Lagrange equation for q_k, and which is constant if q_k is ignorable. In the case of a particle subject to electromagnetic forces, the momentum components p_x, p_y, p_z will be, by Eqs. (9–168) and (9–166),

$$p_x = m\dot{x} + \frac{q}{c} A_x,$$

$$p_y = m\dot{y} + \frac{q}{c} A_y, \tag{9–169}$$

$$p_z = m\dot{z} + \frac{q}{c} A_z.$$

The second terms play the role of a potential momentum.

It appears that gravitational forces, electromagnetic forces, and indeed all the fundamental forces in physics can be expressed in the form (9–153), for a suitably chosen potential function U. (Frictional forces we do not regard as fundamental in this sense, because they are ultimately reducible to electromagnetic forces between atoms, and hence are in principle also expressible in the form (9–153) if we include all the coordinates of the atoms and molecules of which a physical system is composed.) Therefore the equations of motion of any system of particles can always be expressed in the Lagrangian form (9–155), even when velocity dependent forces are present. It appears that there is something fundamental about the form of Eqs. (9–155). One important property of these equations, as we have already noted, is that they retain the same form if we substitute any new set of coordinates for $q_1, \ldots, q_f$. This can be verified by a straightforward, if somewhat tedious, calculation. Further insight into the fundamental character of the Lagrange equations must await the study of the more advanced formulations of mechanics associated with the name of Hamilton.*

---

* See, e.g., H. Goldstein, *Classical Mechanics*. Cambridge, Mass.: Addison-Wesley, 1950. (Chapter 2.)

PROBLEMS

1. (a) Set up the expression for the kinetic energy of a particle of mass m in terms of plane parabolic coordinates f,h, as defined in problem 11 of Chapter 3. Find the momenta p_f and p_h. (b) Write out the Lagrange equations in these coordinates if the particle is not acted on by any force.

2. (a) Find the forces Q_f and Q_h required to make the particle in problem 1 move along a parabola $f = f_0 =$ a constant, with constant generalized velocity $\dot{h} = \dot{h}_0$, starting from $h = 0$ at $t = 0$. (b) Find the corresponding forces F_x and F_y relative to a cartesian coordinate system.

3. (a) Set up the Lagrange equations of motion in spherical coordinates r,θ,φ, for a particle of mass m subject to a force whose spherical components are F_r, F_θ, F_φ.

(b) Set up Lagrange equations of motion for the same particle in a system of spherical coordinates rotating with angular velocity ω about the z-axis.

(c) Identify the generalized centrifugal and coriolis forces 'Q_r', 'Q_θ', and 'Q_φ' by means of which the equations in the rotating system can be made to take the same form as in the fixed system. Calculate the spherical components 'F_r','F_θ','F_φ' of these centrifugal and coriolis forces, and show that your results agree with the expressions derived in Chapter 7.

4. Masses m and $2m$ are suspended from a string of length l_1 which passes over a pulley. Masses $3m$ and $4m$ are similarly suspended by a string of length l_2 over another pulley. These two pulleys hang from the ends of a string of length l_3 over a third fixed pulley. Set up Lagrange's equations, and find the accelerations and the tensions in the strings.

5. A massless tube is hinged at one end. A uniform rod of mass m, length l, slides freely in it. The axis about which the tube rotates is horizontal, so that the motion is confined to a plane. Choose a suitable set of generalized coordinates, one for each degree of freedom, and set up Lagrange's equations.

6. Set up Lagrange's equations for a uniform door whose axis is slightly out of plumb. What is the period of small vibrations?

7. A double pendulum is formed by suspending a mass m_2 by a string of length l_2 from a mass m_1 which in turn is suspended from a fixed support by a string of length l_1. (a) Choose a suitable set of coordinates, and write the Lagrangian function, assuming the double pendulum swings in a single vertical plane.

(b) Write out Lagrange's equations, and show that they reduce to the equations for a pair of coupled oscillators if the strings remain nearly vertical.

(c) Find the normal frequencies for small vibrations of the double pendulum. Describe the nature of the corresponding vibrations. Find the limiting values of these frequencies when $m_1 \gg m_2$, and when $m_2 \gg m_1$. Show that these limiting values are to be expected on physical grounds by considering the nature of the normal modes of vibration when either mass becomes vanishingly small.

8. A ladder rests against a smooth wall and slides without friction on wall and floor. Set up the equation of motion, assuming that the ladder maintains contact with the wall. If initially the ladder is at rest at an angle α with the floor, at what angle, if any, will it leave the wall?

9. One end of a uniform rod of mass M makes contact with a smooth vertical wall, the other with a smooth horizontal floor. A bead of mass m and negligible dimensions slides on the rod. Choose a suitable set of coordinates, set up the Lagrangian function, and write out the Lagrange equations. The rod moves in a single vertical plane perpendicular to the wall.

10. A ring of mass M rests on a smooth horizontal surface and is pinned at a point on its circumference so that it is free to swing about a vertical axis. A bug of mass m crawls around the ring with constant speed. (a) Set up the equations of motion, taking this as a system with two degrees of freedom, with the force exerted by the bug against the ring to be determined from the condition that he moves with constant speed.

(b) Now set up the equation of motion, taking this as a system with one degree of freedom, the bug being constrained to be at a certain point on the ring at each instant of time. Show that the two formulations of the problem are equivalent.

11. A pendulum bob of mass m is suspended by a string of length l from a point of support. The point of support moves to and fro along a horizontal x-axis according to the equation

$$x = a \cos \omega t.$$

Assume that the pendulum swings only in a vertical plane containing the x-axis. Let the position of the pendulum be described by the angle θ which the string makes with a line vertically downward. (a) Set up the Lagrangian function and write out the Lagrange equation.

(b) Show that for small values of θ, the equation reduces to that of a forced harmonic oscillator, and find the corresponding steady state motion. How does the amplitude of the steady state oscillation depend on m, l, a, and ω?

12. A pendulum bob of mass m is suspended by a string of length l from a car of mass M which moves without friction along a horizontal overhead rail. The pendulum swings in a vertical plane containing the rail. (a) Set up the Lagrange equations. (b) Show that there is an ignorable coordinate, eliminate it, and discuss the nature of the motion by the energy method.

13. Find the tension in the string for the spherical pendulum discussed in Section 9–7, as a function of E, p_φ, and θ. Determine, for a given E and p_φ, the angle θ_1 at which the string will collapse.

14. A particle of mass m slides over the inner surface of an inverted cone of half angle α. The apex of the cone is at the origin, and the axis of the cone extends vertically upward. The only force acting on the particle, other than the force of constraint, is the force of gravity. (a) Set up the equations of motion, using as coordinates the horizontal distance ρ of the particle from the axis, and the angle φ measured in a horizontal circle around the cone. Show that φ is ignorable, and discuss the motion by the method of the effective potential.

(b) For a given radius ρ_0, find the angular velocity $\dot\varphi_0$ of revolution in a horizontal circle, and the angular frequency ω of small oscillations about this circular motion. Show that the small oscillations are a wobbling or an up-and-down spiraling motion, depending on whether the angle α is greater than or less than the angle

$$\alpha_c = \tan^{-1} \frac{1}{\sqrt{2}}.$$

15. A flyball governor for a steam engine is shown in Fig. 9–11. Two balls, each of mass m, are attached by means of four hinged arms, each of length l, to sleeves which slide on a

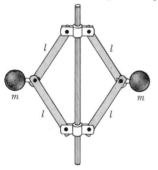

Fig. 9–11. A flyball governor.

vertical rod. The upper sleeve is fastened to the rod; the lower sleeve has mass M and is free to slide up and down the rod as the balls move out from or toward the rod. The rod and ball system rotates with constant angular velocity ω. (a) Set up the equation of motion, neglecting the weight of the arms and rod. Discuss the motion by the energy method. (b) Determine the value of the height z of the lower sleeve above its lowest point as a function of ω for steady rotation of the balls, and find the frequency of small oscillations of z about this steady value.

16. Discuss the motion of the governor described in problem 15 if the shaft is not constrained to rotate at angular velocity ω, but is free to rotate, without any externally applied torque. (a) Find the angular velocity of steady rotation for a given height z of the sleeve. (b) Find the frequency of small vibrations about this steady motion. (c) How does this motion differ from that of problem 15?

17. A rectangular coordinate system with axes x,y,z is rotating with uniform angular velocity ω about the z-axis. A particle of mass m moves under the action of a potential energy $V(x,y,z)$. (a) Set up the Lagrange equations of motion.

(b) Show that these equations can be regarded as the equations of motion of a particle in a fixed coordinate system acted on by the force $-\nabla V$, and by a force derivable from a velocity dependent potential U. Hence find a velocity dependent potential for the centrifugal and coriolis forces. Express U in spherical coordinates $r,\theta,\varphi,\dot{r},\dot{\theta},\dot{\varphi}$, and verify that it gives rise to the forces 'Q_r','Q_θ','Q_φ' found in problem 3.

BIBLIOGRAPHY

BIBLIOGRAPHY

The following is a list, by no means complete, of books related to the subject matter of this text which the reader may find helpful.

ELEMENTARY MECHANICS TEXTS

1. CAMPBELL, J. W., *An Introduction to Mechanics.* New York: Pitman, 1947.
2. MILLIKAN, R. A., ROLLER, D., AND WATSON, E. C., *Mechanics, Molecular Physics, Heat, and Sound.* Boston: Ginn and Co., 1937.

INTERMEDIATE MECHANICS TEXTS

3. LINDSAY, ROBERT BRUCE, *Physical Mechanics,* 2nd ed. New York: D. Van Nostrand, 1950.
4. MACMILLAN, WILLIAM D., *Theoretical Mechanics.* New York: McGraw-Hill. Vol. 1: *Statics and Dynamics of a Particle,* 1927. Vol. 3: *Dynamics of Rigid Bodies,* 1936.
5. OSGOOD, WILLIAM F., *Mechanics.* New York: Macmillan Co., 1937.
6. SCOTT, MERIT, *Mechanics, Statics and Dynamics.* New York: McGraw-Hill, 1949.
7. STEPHENSON, REGINALD J., *Mechanics and Properties of Matter.* New York: John Wiley & Sons, 1952.
8. SYNGE, JOHN L., AND GRIFFITH, BYRON A., *Principles of Mechanics,* 2nd ed. New York: McGraw-Hill, 1949.

ADVANCED MECHANICS TEXTS

9. CORBIN, H. C., AND STEHLE, PHILIP, *Classical Mechanics.* New York: John Wiley & Sons, 1950.
10. GOLDSTEIN, HERBERT, *Classical Mechanics.* Cambridge, Mass.: Addison-Wesley, 1950.
11. LAMB, HORACE, *Hydrodynamics,* 6th ed. Cambridge: Cambridge University Press, 1932.
12. LORD RAYLEIGH, *The Theory of Sound* (2 vols.), 2nd ed. London: Macmillan, 1894–96. (New York: Dover Publications, 1945.)
13. SLATER, JOHN C., AND FRANK, NATHANIEL H., *Mechanics.* New York: McGraw-Hill, 1947.
14. WEBSTER, ARTHUR GORDON, *The Dynamics of Particles and of Rigid, Elastic, and Fluid Bodies.* Leipzig: B. G. Teubner, 1904.
15. WHITTAKER, E. T., *A Treatise on the Analytical Dynamics of Particles and Rigid Bodies,* 4th ed. Cambridge: Cambridge University Press, 1937. (New York: Dover Publications, 1944.)

TEXTS ON ELECTRICITY AND MAGNETISM

16. FOWLER, R. G., *Introduction to Electric Theory.* Cambridge, Mass.: Addison-Wesley, 1953.
17. FRANK, N. H., *Introduction to Electricity and Optics,* 2nd ed. New York: McGraw-Hill, 1950.

18. HARNWELL, GAYLORD P., *Principles of Electricity and Magnetism*, 2nd ed. New York: McGraw-Hill, 1949.

19. PAGE, L., AND ADAMS, N. I., *Principles of Electricity*. New York: D. Van Nostrand, 1931.

20. SLATER, JOHN C., AND FRANK, NATHANIEL H., *Electromagnetism*. New York: McGraw-Hill, 1947.

WORKS ON RELATIVITY AND QUANTUM MECHANICS

21. EINSTEIN, ALBERT, AND INFELD, LEOPOLD, *The Evolution of Physics*. New York: Simon & Schuster, 1938. (An excellent popular account.)

22. BERGMANN, PETER G., *An Introduction to the Theory of Relativity*. New York: Prentice-Hall, 1946.

23. BOHM, DAVID, *Quantum Theory*. New York: Prentice-Hall, 1951.

24. BORN, MAX, *Atomic Physics*, tr. by John Dougall, 4th ed. New York: Hafner, 1946.

25. HEISENBERG, WERNER, *The Physical Principles of the Quantum Theory*, tr. by Carl Eckart and Frank C. Hoyt. Chicago: University of Chicago Press, 1930. (New York: Dover Publications, 1949.)

26. LINDSAY, ROBERT BRUCE, AND MARGENAU, HENRY, *Foundations of Physics*. New York: John Wiley & Sons, 1936.

27. TOLMAN, RICHARD C., *Relativity, Thermodynamics, and Cosmology*. Oxford: Oxford University Press, 1934.

TEXTS AND TREATISES ON MATHEMATICAL TOPICS

28. CHURCHILL, RUEL V., *Fourier Series and Boundary Value Problems*. New York: McGraw-Hill, 1941.

29. COURANT, RICHARD, *Differential and Integral Calculus*, tr. by E. F. McShane. London: Blackie & Son, 1934.

30. HOPF, L., *Introduction to the Differential Equations of Physics*, tr. by Walter Nef. New York: Dover Publications, 1948.

31. JACKSON, DUNHAM. *Fourier Series and Orthogonal Polynomials*. Menasha, Wisconsin: George Banta Publishing Co., 1941.

32. VON KARMAN, T., AND BIOT, M. A., *Mathematical Methods in Engineering*. New York: McGraw-Hill, 1940.

33. KELLOGG, OLIVER D., *Foundations of Potential Theory*. Berlin: J. Springer, 1929.

34. LEIGHTON, WALTER, *An Introduction to the Theory of Differential Equations*. New York: McGraw-Hill, 1952.

35. LEVY, H., AND BAGGOTT, E. A., *Numerical Solutions of Differential Equations*, New York: Dover Publications, 1950.

36. MILNE, W. E., *Numerical Calculus*. Princeton: Princeton University Press, 1949.

37. OSGOOD, WILLIAM F., *Introduction to Calculus*. New York: Macmillan, 1922.

38. OSGOOD, WILLIAM F., *Advanced Calculus*. New York: Macmillan, 1925.

39. OSGOOD, WILLIAM F., AND GRAUSTEIN, WILLIAM C., *Plane and Solid Analytic Geometry*. New York: Macmillan, 1938.

40. PEIRCE, B. O., *Elements of the Theory of the Newtonian Potential Function*, 3rd ed. Boston: Ginn & Co., 1902.

41. PEIRCE, B. O., *A Short Table of Integrals*, 3rd ed. Boston: Ginn & Co., 1929.

42. PHILLIPS, H. B., *Vector Analysis*. New York: John Wiley & Sons, 1933.

43. WHITTAKER, E. T., AND ROBINSON, G., *The Calculus of Observations*. New York: Van Nostrand, 1924.

44. WILLS, A. P., *Vector Analysis, with an Introduction to Tensor Analysis*. New York: Prentice-Hall, 1931.

45. WILSON, EDWIN B., *Advanced Calculus*. Boston: Ginn & Co., 1912.

46. WYLIE, D. R., JR., *Advanced Engineering Mathematics*. New York: McGraw-Hill, 1951.

ANSWERS TO PROBLEMS

ANSWERS TO PROBLEMS

CHAPTER 1

1. 4.06×10^{-42} dyne; 9.22×10^{-3} dyne.

5. (b) $\mu \, mg/(\sin \theta - \mu \cos \theta)$.

7. $t = (v_0/g)[(\sin \theta + \mu \cos \theta)^{-1} + (\sin^2 \theta - \mu^2 \cos^2 \theta)^{-\frac{1}{2}}]$.

9. 2.20×10^{27} tons.

11. 1.4×10^{11} sun masses.

CHAPTER 2

1. (a) $v = v_0 + \dfrac{p_0}{m\pi}\left[\dfrac{\pi}{2} + \tan^{-1}\left(\dfrac{t - t_0}{\delta t}\right)\right],$

$x = \left(v_0 + \dfrac{p_0}{2m}\right)(t - t_0) + \dfrac{p_0(t - t_0)}{m\pi} \tan^{-1}\left(\dfrac{t - t_0}{\delta t}\right)$

$\qquad - \dfrac{p_0 \, \delta t}{2m\pi} \ln\left[1 + \left(\dfrac{t - t_0}{\delta t}\right)^2\right],$ (where $x = 0$ at $t = t_0$).

3. (b) $t_s = m(1 - e^{-\alpha v_0})/(\alpha b)$, $x_s = [m/(\alpha^2 b)][1 - e^{-\alpha v_0} - \alpha v_0 e^{-\alpha v_0}]$.

5. (a) $x^2 = \dfrac{E}{k} + \dfrac{\sqrt{E^2 - ka}}{k} \cos\left(2\sqrt{\dfrac{k}{m}}\, t + \theta_0\right).$

$\quad$ (b) $x \doteq \sqrt{\dfrac{a}{2E}} + \sqrt{\dfrac{2E}{k}}\left|\cos\left(\sqrt{\dfrac{k}{m}}\, t + \theta_0/2\right)\right|,$ (interpret).

9. $x = \dfrac{m}{2b} \ln\left(1 + \dfrac{bv_0^2}{mg}\right) + \dfrac{m}{b} \ln \cos\left[\sqrt{\dfrac{bg}{m}}\,(t_0 - t)\right],$ $(0 < t < t_0)$,

$\quad = \dfrac{m}{2b} \ln\left(1 + \dfrac{bv_0^2}{mg}\right) - \dfrac{m}{b} \ln \cosh\left[\sqrt{\dfrac{bg}{m}}\,(t - t_0)\right],$ $(t > t_0)$,

$\quad$ where $t_0 = \sqrt{\dfrac{m}{bg}} \tan^{-1}\left(\sqrt{\dfrac{b}{mg}}\, v_0\right).$

11. $x = (x_0^{\frac{3}{2}} + t\sqrt{9MG/2})^{\frac{2}{3}}$.

13. (c) $(2b/a)^{\frac{1}{6}}$, $(2\pi/3)(m^3 b^4/4a^7)^{\frac{1}{6}}$.

15. (a) $x = C_1 e^{\gamma_1 t} + C_2 e^{-\gamma_2 t}$, $\gamma_1 = [(k/m) + (b/2m)^2]^{\frac{1}{2}} - (b/2m)$,

$\qquad \gamma_2 = [(k/m) + (b/2m)^2]^{\frac{1}{2}} + (b/2m)$;

$\quad$ (b) $x = A e^{\gamma t} \cos(\omega_1 t + \theta)$, $\gamma = b/2m$, $\omega_1 = [(k/m) - \gamma^2]^{\frac{1}{2}}$.

17. $x = x_0 e^{-\gamma t}[\cos \omega_1 t + (\gamma/\omega_1) \sin \omega_1 t]$,

$x = x_0(1 + \gamma t)e^{-\gamma t}, \; x = x_0(\gamma_1 - \gamma_2)^{-1}(\gamma_1 e^{-\gamma_2 t} - \gamma_2 e^{-\gamma_1 t})$.

19. $B = mv_0(\omega_0^2 - \omega^2)/\omega_0, \; \theta = \pi - (3\pi\omega/2\omega_0)$.

21. $x = (F_0/k) + Ae^{-\gamma t} \cos (\omega_1 t + \theta)$.

23. (a) $x = 0$ if $t < t_0$, $x = (p_0/k \, \delta t)[1 - \cos \omega_0(t - t_0)]$, if $t_0 \leq t \leq t_0 + \delta t$,

       $x = (2p_0/k \, \delta t) \sin (\tfrac{1}{2}\omega_0 \, \delta t) \sin \omega_0(t - t_0 - \tfrac{1}{2} \, \delta t)$, if $t > t_0 + \delta t$.

25. (a) $m\omega_0^2 x = (\tfrac{3}{2}A + \tfrac{1}{34}B)e^{-\omega_0 t/3} \cos (\tfrac{2}{3}\sqrt{2} \, \omega_0 t)$

           $+ (\tfrac{3}{8}\sqrt{2} \, A + \tfrac{37}{136}\sqrt{2} \, B)e^{-\omega_0 t/3} \sin (\tfrac{2}{3}\sqrt{2} \, \omega_0 t)$

           $- \tfrac{3}{2}A \cos \omega_0 t - \tfrac{1}{34}B \cos 3\omega_0 t$

           $- \tfrac{2}{17}B \sin 3\omega_0 t$.

27. $x = \dfrac{F_0[\omega_1 e^{-at} - \omega_1 e^{-\gamma t} \cos \omega_1 t - (\gamma - a)e^{-\gamma t} \sin \omega_1 t]}{m\omega_1[(\gamma - a)^2 + \omega_1^2]}, \; (t \geq 0)$.

CHAPTER 3

11. $\dfrac{\partial f}{\partial f} = -\dfrac{1}{2}\left(\dfrac{h}{f}\right)^{\frac{1}{2}}\dfrac{h}{(f + h)}, \; \dfrac{\partial f}{\partial h} = \dfrac{1}{2}\left(\dfrac{f}{h}\right)^{\frac{1}{2}}\dfrac{h}{f + h}$,

    $\dfrac{\partial h}{\partial f} = \dfrac{1}{2}\left(\dfrac{h}{f}\right)^{\frac{1}{2}}\dfrac{f}{f + h}, \; \dfrac{\partial h}{\partial h} = -\dfrac{1}{2}\left(\dfrac{f}{h}\right)^{\frac{1}{2}}\dfrac{f}{f + h};$

    $\mathbf{t} = (f + h)^{\frac{1}{2}}\left(\dfrac{\dot{f}}{f^{\frac{1}{2}}}\mathbf{f} + \dfrac{\dot{h}}{h^{\frac{1}{2}}}\mathbf{h}\right)$.

15. $\left(\dfrac{1}{\rho}\dfrac{\partial A_z}{\partial \varphi} - \dfrac{\partial A_\varphi}{\partial z}\right)\mathbf{h} + \left(\dfrac{\partial A_\rho}{\partial z} - \dfrac{\partial A_z}{\partial \rho}\right)\mathbf{m} + \left(\dfrac{\partial A_\varphi}{\partial \rho} - \dfrac{1}{\rho}\dfrac{\partial A_\rho}{\partial \varphi} + \dfrac{A_\varphi}{\rho}\right)\mathbf{k}$

19. (a) $\tfrac{1}{2} \sin^{-1}\left(\dfrac{gx_0}{v_0^2}\right)$,

    (b) angle of elevation should be increased by

$$\dfrac{4}{3}\dfrac{bv_0 \cos \alpha_0}{mg}\left(\dfrac{1}{\cot^2 \alpha_0 - 1}\right),$$

    where α_0 is angle of elevation with no air resistance.

21. (a) $5x^4 y^2 - 6xyz^3$; (c) $-\displaystyle\int_{x_s}^{x} F_x \, dx - \int_{y_s}^{y} F_y \, dy - \int_{z_s}^{z} F_z \, dz$.

23. $F_x = ae^2(r_1^{-3} - r_2^{-3}) - xe^2(r_1^{-3} + r_2^{-3}), \; F_y = -ye^2(r_1^{-3} + r_2^{-3})$.

25. $\theta = (k/m)^{\frac{1}{2}}, \; \omega_r = 2(k/m)^{\frac{1}{2}}$.

27. $kr^2 = E + (E^2 - \omega^2 L^2)^{\frac{1}{2}} \cos (2\omega t + 2\alpha_0)$,

    $\tan (\theta - \theta_0) = \left[\dfrac{E - (E^2 - \omega^2 L^2)^{\frac{1}{2}}}{E + (E^2 - \omega^2 L^2)^{\frac{1}{2}}}\right]^{\frac{1}{2}}[\tan (\omega t + \alpha_0) - \tan \alpha_0], \; \omega = (k/m)^{\frac{1}{2}}$.

    (This is Lissajous figure with $\omega_x = \omega_y$.)

29. (a) $F = (1 + \alpha r)Ke^{-\alpha r}/r^2$;

(d) $L^2 = -mKa(1 + \alpha a)e^{-\alpha a}$, $E = (1 - \alpha a)Ke^{-\alpha a}/2a$;

(e) $\tau_c = 2\pi[-K(1 + \alpha a)e^{-\alpha a}/ma^3]^{-\frac{1}{2}}$,

$\tau_r = 2\pi[-K(1 + \alpha a - \alpha^2 a^2)e^{-\alpha a}/ma^3]^{-\frac{1}{2}}$.

[Stable circular motion is not possible if $\alpha a \geq \frac{1}{2}(1 + \sqrt{5})$.]

31. (c) Ellipse precesses $2\pi(1 - \alpha)/\alpha$ radians per revolution, in same direction as $\dot\theta$ if $\alpha < 1$, in opposite direction if $\alpha > 1$, where $\alpha^2 = 1 + (mK'/L^2)$.

33. (b) opposite direction, 1.2×10^{-7} gm m^{-3}.

35. (a) $\dfrac{1}{r^2} = \dfrac{1 - \epsilon^2 \cos^2 \theta}{a^2(1 - \epsilon^2)}$; (b) $F(r) = -4\pi^2 mr/\tau^2$.

37. (c) If $\dot z_0 = \dot\rho_0 = 0$, $\dot\varphi_0 = -(qB/2mc) \pm [(qB/2mc)^2 - (qa/m\rho_0^2)]^{\frac{1}{2}}$.

(d) $\omega_\rho = 2[(qB/2mc)^2 - (qa/2m\rho_0^2)]^{\frac{1}{2}}$.

CHAPTER 4

3. $\cos^{-1}[1 - 0.293m_1^2/(m_1 + m_2)^2]$.

9. $(1 + \gamma)p_{1F} = (p_{1I} - p_{2I}) \cos \vartheta_1 \pm [(\gamma p_{1I} + p_{2I})^2 - (p_{1I} - p_{2I})^2 \sin^2 \vartheta_1]^{\frac{1}{2}}$, $\gamma = m_2/m_1$.

11. $Q = \dfrac{p_1^2}{2m_1}\left[1 - \dfrac{(m_1/m_3) \sin^2 \vartheta_4 + (m_1/m_4) \sin^2 \vartheta_3}{\sin^2 (\vartheta_3 + \vartheta_4)}\right]$.

21. $x_1 = x_2 = Ae^{-\gamma t} \cos (\omega_1 t + \theta)$, $\gamma = b_1/2m_1$, $\omega_1^2 = -\gamma^2 + (k_1' + k_3)/m_1$; and $x_1 = -x_2 = Ae^{-\gamma t} \cos (\omega_2 t + \theta)$, $\omega_2^2 = -\gamma^2 + (k_1' - k_3)/m_1$.

CHAPTER 5

3. $\theta = \theta_0 \cos (k/Ma^2)^{\frac{1}{2}}t$.

5. $\theta = \theta_0 + (N_0/b)t + [\alpha N_0/(I^2\omega_0^3 + b^2\omega_0)][b \sin \omega_0 t - I\omega_0 \cos \omega_0 t]$.

7. $g = [4\pi^2(h + h')/\tau^2][1 + 2h'\delta/(h - h')]$.

9. $x_G = 0$, $y_G = -4a/9\pi$; $I_{Ox} = I_{Oy} = I_{Gy} = 3\pi a^4\sigma/8$, $I_{Oz} = 3\pi a^4\sigma/4$, $I_{Gz} = (9\pi^2 - 32)a^4\sigma/108\pi$, $I_{Gx} = (9\pi^2 - 64)a^4\sigma/216\pi$.

11. 30 yards.

15. (a) $\mathbf{F}_0 = (0, -6 \text{ lb}, -14 \text{ lb})$ at center, $\mathbf{F}_c = (0, -3 \text{ lb}, -8 \text{ lb})$ at any front corner, $-\mathbf{F}_c$ at adjacent rear corner. (x-axis outward, y-axis horizontal to right, z-axis vertical, origin at center of cube.)

(b) $\mathbf{F}_1 = (0, 0, 2 \text{ lb})$ at center, $\mathbf{F}_2 = (0, -6 \text{ lb}, -16 \text{ lb})$ at center of front face. (There are other correct answers.)

(c) $\mathbf{F}_0$ [part (a)] at the point $(65/116 \text{ ft}, 0, 0)$, $\mathbf{N} = (0, 9/58 \text{ lb-ft}, 21/58 \text{ lb-ft})$.

17. (a) $\sinh (wa/C) = \frac{1}{2} wl/C$, $\beta = -(C/w) \cosh (wa/C)$;

(c) $2C \sinh \alpha = W$, $2C \sinh [(wa/C) + \alpha] = W + wl$,
$\beta = -(C/w) \cosh [(wa/C) + \alpha]$,
where $y = \beta + (C/w) \cosh [(wx/C) \pm \alpha]$, ($+$ if $x > 0$, $-$ if $x < 0$).

19. $A = (100W/Y)e^{100wz/Y}$.

21. $-\rho L^4/192Y(b^2 + a^2) - \rho L^2/8n$.

23. $p = p_0 - B \ln [1 - (g\rho_0 d/B)]$, where d is depth; about 2%.

Chapter 6

1. $\mathbf{g} = -(MG/r^2)(\mathbf{r}/r)$, $(r \geq a)$, $= -(MG\mathbf{r}/a^3)$, $(r \leq a)$,
$\mathsf{G} = -(MG/r)$, $(r \geq a)$, $= -(MG/2a^3)(3a^2 - r^2)$, $(r \leq a)$.

5. (a) $T \dfrac{d}{dr}\left(\dfrac{R^2 T r^2}{A^2 p}\dfrac{dp}{dr}\right) = -4\pi r^2 G p$, arbitrary constants determined by

$$M = \int_0^\infty \frac{4\pi A p r^2}{RT}\, dr, \ p \to 0 \text{ as } r \to \infty;$$

(b) $p = \dfrac{M^2 G}{4\pi a^4}\left[\ln\left(\dfrac{r^2 + a^2}{r^2}\right) - \dfrac{a^4}{2(r^2 + a^2)^2} - \dfrac{a^2}{r^2 + a^2}\right]$,

$T = \dfrac{AMGr}{2a^2 R}\left[\dfrac{(r^2 + a^2)^2}{a^4}\ln\left(\dfrac{r^2 + a^2}{r^2}\right) - \dfrac{3}{2} - \dfrac{r^2}{a^2}\right]$.

7. (a) $(MG/r) + (MGa^2/4r^3)(1 - 3\cos^2 \theta)$;
(b) $g_r = -(MG/r^2) - (3MGa^2/4r^4)(1 - 3\cos^2 \theta)$,
$g_\theta = (3MGa^2/4r^4)\sin 2\theta$.

9. (a) $g - g_0 = (MG/a^2)(2 - \sqrt{2})$; (b) $g - g_0 = -(\tfrac{3}{4})(MG/a^2)$.

Chapter 7

1. (b) $m\mathbf{a}^* = -b\mathbf{v}^* - bg\mathbf{t}$.

3. $2\rho\omega v \cos \theta$, $\omega = $ angular velocity of earth's rotation, $\theta = $ colatitude; approximately 0.0003 lb-in^{-2}-mile^{-1}.

7. $\omega = (k/m)^{\frac{1}{2}}$; in rotating system, m moves with angular velocity -2ω in circle of arbitrary radius with arbitrary center.

CHAPTER 8

1. (b) $u = A \sin (n\pi x/2l) \cos (n\pi ct/2l) + B \sin (n\pi x/2l) \sin (n\pi ct/2l)$,
$n = 1,3,5, \ldots$.

3. $u = \dfrac{4l}{5\pi^2} \left(\sin \dfrac{\pi x}{l} \cos \dfrac{\pi ct}{l} - \dfrac{1}{9} \sin \dfrac{3\pi x}{l} \cos \dfrac{3\pi ct}{l} + \dfrac{1}{25} \sin \dfrac{5\pi x}{l} \cos \dfrac{5\pi ct}{l} - \cdots \right).$

5. $u = Ae^{-bt/2\sigma} \sin (n\pi x/l) \cos [([n^2\pi^2 c^2/l^2] - [b^2/2\sigma^2])^{\frac{1}{2}}t + \theta]$, $n = 1,2,3, \ldots$

7. $u = f(x - ct) + g(x + ct)$, where $f(\xi) = g(\xi) =$ function obtained by joining by straight lines the points $f = (-1)^n l/20$, $\xi = (n + \frac{1}{2})l$.

11. $u = (RT/M) \ln (p/p_0)$,
v is a solution of $v_0^2 - v^2 + (2RT/M) \ln (vS/v_0 S_0) = 2gh$,
$p = p_0 v_0 S_0/vS$.

13. $\mathbf{v} = -(a/r^2)\mathbf{n}$.

17. $v_x = -(l\pi A/\omega\rho_0 L_x) \sin (l\pi x/L_x) \cos (m\pi y/L_y) \sin (k_z z - \omega t)$,
$v_y = -(m\pi A/\omega\rho_0 L_y) \cos (l\pi x/L_x) \sin (m\pi y/L_y) \sin (k_z z - \omega t)$,
$v_z = (k_z A/\omega\rho_0) \cos (l\pi x/L_x) \cos (m\pi y/L_y) \cos (k_z z - \omega t)$.

19. $v = (3I/2\rho l^3)(l^2 - 4x^2)$, $dp/dz = 12\eta I/\rho l^3$, where x is distance from plane midway between walls.

CHAPTER 9

1. (a) $T = \frac{1}{2}m (f + h) \left(\dfrac{\dot{f}^2}{f} + \dfrac{\dot{h}^2}{h} \right)$, $p_f = \dfrac{m(f + h)}{f} \dot{f}$,
$p_h = \dfrac{m(f + h)}{h} \dot{h}$.

3. (c) $'Q_r' = 'F_r' = mr\omega^2 \sin^2 \theta + 2mr\omega\dot{\varphi} \sin^2 \theta$,
$'Q_\theta' = r'F_\theta' = mr^2\omega^2 \sin \theta \cos \theta + 2mr^2\omega\dot{\varphi} \sin \theta \cos \theta$,
$'Q_\varphi' = r \sin \theta 'F_\varphi' = -2mr\dot{r}\omega \sin^2 \theta - 2mr^2\omega\dot{\theta} \sin \theta \cos \theta$.

7. $\omega^2 = [2g/\mu(l_1 + l_2)][1 \pm (1 - \mu)^{\frac{1}{2}}]$, $\mu = [m_1/(m_1 + m_2)][4l_1 l_2/(l_1 + l_2)^2]$.

11. (b) $\theta \doteq [a\omega^2/(g - l\omega^2)] \cos \omega t$.

13. $\cos \theta_1 = 2E/3mgR$ if $p_\varphi^2 < \frac{2}{3}mR^2 E - 8E^3/27mg^2$; otherwise the string will not collapse.

15. (b) $z = 2l - 2(m + M)g/(m\omega^2)$,
$\omega_z^2 = (m + M)g \sin^2 \theta/(m + 2M \sin^2 \theta) l \cos \theta$,
where $\cos \theta = 1 - (z/2l)$.

17. (b) $U = -\frac{1}{2}m\omega^2(x^2 + y^2) - m\omega(x\dot{y} - y\dot{x})$
$= -\frac{1}{2}m\omega^2 r^2 \sin^2 \theta - m\omega r^2\dot{\varphi} \sin^2 \theta$.

INDEX OF SYMBOLS

INDEX OF SYMBOLS

The following list is not intended to be complete, but includes important symbols and those which might give rise to ambiguity. In general, standard mathematical symbols, and symbols used in a specialized sense occurring only once, are omitted. To facilitate reference, the page on which the symbol first occurs is listed immediately after the definition of the symbol. When use of a symbol in a particular sense is restricted to one or two sections or chapters, this is indicated by chapter or section numbers in parentheses following the definition.

Scalar quantities are designated in the text by italic letters. Vector quantities are designated by boldface letters beginning in Chapter 3. An italic letter is used for the magnitude of the vector represented by the same letter in boldface. In Chapter 2, roman letters are used for complex quantities whose real parts are represented by the same letters in italics· A dot over a letter indicates differentiation with respect to time.

344

d^*/dt time differentiation relative to starred coordinates, 235

E total energy, 29

E_x electric field component, 24

E_0 amplitude of harmonic electric field intensity, 24 (Chapter 2)

$\mathbf{E}$ electric field intensity, 123

e magnitude of elementary electronic charge, 24

$F, \mathbf{F}$ force, 7, 68

F, F' foci of ellipse, hyperbola, or parabola, 114, 115 (Chapters 3, 4)

F_0 real amplitude of harmonic force F, 47

$\mathbf{F}_0$ complex amplitude of harmonic force F, 48

$\mathbf{F}$ total external force, 136

$\mathbf{F}_k^e$ total external force on particle k, 136

$\mathbf{F}_k^i$ total internal force on particle k, 136

$\mathbf{F}_{l \to k}^i$ force exerted by particle l on particle k, 136

f arbitrary function, 255 (Sections 8–3, 8–10)

f frictional force, 15 (Chapters 1, 9)

f number of degrees of freedom, 316 (Chapter 9)

f parabolic coordinate, 130 (Problems, Chapters 3, 9)

$\mathbf{f}$ body force density, 215 (Chapters 5, 8)

$\mathbf{f}, f$ force per unit length, 206, 249 (Sections 5–9, 8–1)

$\mathbf{f}$ unit vector in f-direction, 130 (Problems, Chapters 3, 9)

G gravitational constant, 10

G center of mass, or center of gravity, 185

$\mathcal{G}$ gravitational potential, 226

$g, \mathbf{g}$ acceleration of gravity, 10, 198

g arbitrary function, 255 (Section 8–3)

$\mathbf{g}$ gravitational field intensity, 225

$\mathbf{g}_e$ effective acceleration of gravity, 240

grad gradient of, 84

h, h' distance from center of mass to axis and to center of oscillation, 185 (Chapter 5)

h parabolic coordinate, 130 (Problems, Chapters 3, 9)

$\mathbf{h}$ arbitrary vector function, 284 (Section 8–10)

$\mathbf{h}$ position vector of O^* relative to O, 232 (Chapter 7)

$\mathbf{h}$ unit vector in h-direction, 130 (Problems, Chapters 3, 9)

$\mathbf{h}$ unit vector radially out from z-axis, 81

I fluid current, 281 (Chapter 8)

I_z moment of inertia about z-axis, 180

i $\sqrt{-1}$, 42

$\mathbf{i}$ unit vector parallel to x-axis, 63

J impulse, 186

$\mathbf{j}$ unit vector parallel to y-axis, 63

K central force constant, 111

k angular wave number, 254 (Chapter 8)

k spring constant, 30

k radius of gyration of beam, 212 (Section 5–10)

k_z radius of gyration about z-axis, 180

k_1', k_2', effective spring constants, 166 (Section 4–10)

k_{12} negative acceleration ratio, 5 (Chapter 1)

k   unit vector parallel to z-axis, 63

k   wave vector, 285 (Section 8–10)

$L, \mathbf{L}$ angular momentum, 90, 91

L Lagrangian function, 311 (Chapter 9)

L length, 213

$L_O, \mathbf{L}_O$ angular momentum about point O, 90, 91

l an integer, 288 (Chapter 8)

l length, 12

l   unit vector in direction of increasing θ, polar coordinates, 78, spherical coordinates, 81

M Mach number, 293 (Sections 8–13, 8–14)

M mass, usually total mass of a body or system of particles, 10

M molecular weight, 218 (Section 5–11)

m an integer, 288 (Chapter 8)

m mass, usually of a particle, 6

m   unit vector in direction of increasing φ, 81

N bending moment, 209 (Section 5–10)

$N, \mathbf{N}$ torque, 90, 91

N total number of particles, 135 (Chapters 4, 9)

$N_O, \mathbf{N}_O$ torque about point O, 71, 72

n an integer, 252 (Chapter 8)

n shear modulus, 204 (Chapter 5)

n   unit vector along radius, in polar coordinates, 78, in spherical coordinates, 81

n   unit vector normal to surface, outward normal from closed surface, 86

O point in space, usually the origin, 78

O' point in space, 185

OO' line through centroid of beam cross section, 210 (Section 5–10)

P, P' points in space, 197

P power, 256 (Chapter 8)

P power per unit area, 285 (Section 8–10)

P_x component of dipole moment per unit volume, 26 (Chapter 2)

P   total linear momentum, 136

p complex coefficient in exponential time dependence (e^{pt}), 41

p generalized momentum, 305 (Chapter 9)

p pressure, 215 (Chapters 5, 8)

$p, \mathbf{p}$ linear momentum, 7, 88

p' excess pressure, 264 (Chapter 8)

Q energy absorbed in inelastic collision, 155 (Chapter 4)

Q generalized force, 306 (Chapter 9)

W work, 66

W weight of beam, 213 (Section 5–10)

W load on beam, 213 (Section 5–10)

w weight per unit length, 206 (Chapter 5)

X function of x in separation of variables, 250 (Chapter 8)

X x-coordinate of center of mass, 138

x rectangular coordinate, 4

x x-component of relative coordinate $\mathbf{r}$, 305 (Chapter 9)

x_s coordinate of standard point, 29

x complex number whose real part is x, 48

x_0 complex amplitude of harmonically oscillating coordinate x, 48

Y function of y in separation of variables, 287 (Chapter 8)

Y y-coordinate of center of mass, 138

Y Young's modulus, 204 (Chapter 5)

y rectangular coordinate, 4

Z function of z in separation of variables, 287 (Chapter 8)

Z z-coordinate of center of mass, 138

z rectangular coordinate, 4

GREEK LETTERS

α angular acceleration, 181 (Section 5–2)

α asymptote angle of hyperbola, 115 (Chapter 3)

β phase angle for forced oscillations, 48 (Chapter 2)

γ damping coefficient, 44

γ ratio of specific heats, 282 (Section 8–10)

γ_1, γ_2 damping coefficients for overdamped oscillator, 46 (Chapter 2)

γ_1, γ_2 damping coefficients for coupled oscillators, 171 (Chapter 4)

δ increment in virtual displacement, 137 (Chapters 4, 9)

δm mass of volume element of fluid, 269 (Chapter 8)

δt small time increment, 53

δV increment in potential energy, 307 (Chapter 9)

δV volume element, 267 (Chapter 8)

Δ increment of, 73

$\Delta\omega^2$ $\omega_1^2 - \omega_2^2$ for coupled oscillators, 167

ϵ eccentricity of ellipse or hyperbola, 114, 115

ϵ dielectric constant, 25 (Chapter 2)

η coefficient of viscosity, 18, 294 (page 18, Section 8–14)

η phase of wave, 255 (Section 8–3)

θ angle between string and horizontal, 207 (Section 5–9, Chapter 8)

OTHER SYMBOLS

INDEX

INDEX

ERRATA

On pages 320–323, the equations listed below should be changed to read as follows:

$$a\dot{\theta} = \alpha a(\dot{\phi} - \dot{\theta}), \tag{9-92}$$

$$(1 + \alpha)\theta = \alpha\phi. \tag{9-93}$$

$$\gamma = \theta - \alpha\phi/(1 + \alpha). \tag{9-94}$$

$$T = \tfrac{1}{2}m\dot{r}^2 + \tfrac{1}{2}m[r^2 + \tfrac{1}{2}a^2(1 + \alpha)^2]\dot{\theta}^2 - \tfrac{1}{2}ma^2(1 + \alpha)^2\dot{\theta}\dot{\gamma}$$
$$+ \tfrac{1}{4}ma^2(1 + \alpha)^2\dot{\gamma}^2. \tag{9-97}$$

$$Q_\gamma = -fa(1 + \alpha), \tag{9-99}$$

$$m[r^2 + \tfrac{1}{2}a^2(1 + \alpha)^2]\ddot{\theta} + 2mr\dot{r}\dot{\theta} - \tfrac{1}{2}ma^2(1 + \alpha)^2\ddot{\gamma} = mgr \sin\theta, \tag{9-101}$$

$$-\tfrac{1}{2}ma^2(1 + \alpha)^2\ddot{\theta} + \tfrac{1}{2}ma^2(1 + \alpha)^2\ddot{\gamma} = -fa(1 + \alpha), \tag{9-102}$$

$$\tfrac{3}{2}(1 + \alpha)^2ma^2\ddot{\theta} = (1 + \alpha)mga \sin\theta, \tag{9-104}$$

$$f = \tfrac{1}{2}(1 + \alpha)ma \ddot{\theta}, \tag{9-105}$$

$$\tfrac{3}{4}(1 + \alpha)^2ma^2\dot{\theta}^2 + (1 + \alpha) mga \cos\theta = E, \tag{9-107}$$

$$\beta = \frac{2}{3(1 + \alpha)} \cdot \tag{9-110}$$

$$\tfrac{1}{3}mg \sin\theta \leq \tfrac{1}{3}\mu mg (7 \cos\theta - 4). \tag{9-114}$$

$$\sin\theta_1 = \mu (7 \cos\theta_1 - 4), \tag{9-115}$$

$$\tan\frac{\theta_1}{2} = \frac{(1 + 33\mu^2)^{1/2} - 1}{11\mu} \cdot \tag{9-116}$$